ENVIRONMENT AND ECOLOGY FOR

PENNSYLVANIA

MEETING THE STANDARDS

GLOBE FEARON
Pearson Learning Group

About the Cover

Rattlesnake Creek is a rocky, mountainous, free-running stream that originates near the local landmark of Turkey Knoll (elevation 2,156 ft), west of Mountainhome, Pennsylvania. Approximately 95 percent of Rattlesnake Creek runs through pristine and protected state game lands in the Pocono Mountains. Rattlesnake Creek flows easterly through Mountainhome and runs into Mill Creek, a tributary of Brodhead Creek. Rattlesnake Creek is designated as an exceptional value (E.V.) stream, the highest water quality designation used in Pennsylvania. This cold-water, wild trout stream is home to both brook and brown trout.

ISBN 0–13–024187–3

Printed in the United States of America

3 4 5 6 7 8 9 10   06 05 04

1-800-321-3106
www.pearsonlearning.com

Reviewers

We thank the following educators, who provided valuable comments and suggestions during the development of this book:

Theresa Alberici, Project WILD Coordinator, Pennsylvania Game Commission

Helen Jean Aresto, Teacher, North Allegheny School District

Matthew Cooper, Teacher, Conestoga Valley High School

Dan Dziubek, Ph.D., Associate Professor, Slippery Rock University

Janis Gadow, Teacher, Northeastern School District

Irene Guthrie, Teacher, North Penn High School

Sonja Hipple, Teacher, George Washington High School

James Hovan, Teacher, Conestoga Valley High School

Robert Kotran, Teacher, William Allen High School

Margaret Manbeck, Teacher, Conrad Weiser High School

Jane Monaghan, Teacher, Roxborough High School, Philadelphia School District

John Obruba, Teacher, Norwin School District

Bill Palonis, Teacher, Carlynton JSHS

Gilbert Pielin, Teacher, North Allegheny School District

Michael Ploskunak, Teacher, South Allegheny MS/HS

David Schulte, Jr., Teacher, Mt. View High School

Dean Steinhart, Ph.D., Environment and Ecology Consultant, Steinhart Associates

Joyce Stubbs, Teacher, Roxborough High School, Philadelphia School District

Susan Sweeney, Teacher, Trinity High School

Courtney Vathis, Teacher, Cumberland Valley High School

Patricia Vathis, Environment and Ecology Education Advisor, Pennsylvania Department of Education

Katherine Verbeke, Teacher, Methacton High School

Lisa Vinkler Dubich, Teacher, Ridgeview Academy Charter School

Ron Yerger, Teacher, Lower Dauphin High School

Edward Rajotte, Associate Professor, Pennsylvania State University

Robert Kotran, Teacher, Allentown School District

Christine Bittinger, Assistant Professor, Harrisburg Area Community College

Science & Technology and Environment & Ecology Classroom Connections

Developed as a resource for improving student learning, this kit provides units, lesson plans, and assessment tools to help schools align curriculum, instruction, and assessment with Pennsylvania's Science & Technology and Environment & Ecology Standards. It also offers an array of Internet resources and materials for use by classroom teachers.

This kit is designed with six components: Program & Resource Connections, Curriculum Integration, Science Connections, Technology Connections, Environment & Ecology Connections, and Learning Accommodations. The CD-ROM, which elaborates on instructional designs, strategies, and assessments by providing additional examples and resources, is included.

Sustaining Penn's Woods

Developed as a resource for improving student knowledge as it pertains to the definition in Chapter 4 of Standards for Environment and Ecology, this kit offers specific content on Pennsylvania forest and land use, developmentally appropriate activities for the content, and assessment strategies for use by classroom teachers.

The kit is designed with five components: Human Influence on Pennsylvania's Forest Resources, Benefits of a Pennsylvania Forest, The Forest Industry in Pennsylvania, Pennsylvania Forest Management, and Reference/Resources. An interactive CD-ROM, which elaborates on the environment and ecology content in the kit, will provide students with a hands-on approach in a variety of learning styles. The kit also contains two videos: one on the hardwood industry in Pennsylvania, and the other on the management of white-tailed deer.

"Conserving for the Future," Renewable and Nonrenewable, Standards Based K–12 Activity Guide

This guide should serve kindergarten through 12th-grade students and teachers on their journey of learning about the value of our natural resources through the use of a thematic approach.

The sequential nature of the standards reflects the essentials of what students should know and be able to do by the end of grades 4, 7, 10, and 12. This curriculum activity guide moves students through this sequencing by having the activities address the needs of the different standard statements at the various levels. Students will be able to build on previous knowledge to become true stewards of Earth.

Table of Contents

Chapter 1

Watersheds and Wetlands

Lesson 1.1
The Blue Planet

From space, Earth resembles a large blue marble. Its many oceans, seas, lakes, and rivers cover nearly three fourths of Earth's surface. As a result, people often refer to Earth as the "Blue Planet." In fact, water is the most common substance on Earth, as well as the most important. Without water, life as we know it could not exist on Earth. About 97 percent of the water on Earth is salt water found in the oceans. The remaining 3 percent is fresh water found in lakes, rivers, streams, and glaciers on Earth's surface; trapped in soil and rocks beneath the surface; and present in Earth's atmosphere.

Water can exist as a solid (ice), a liquid, or a gas (water vapor). These three forms move through the environment via the water cycle—an unending circulation process powered by the sun. Several major processes are involved in Earth's water cycle. *Evaporation* occurs when the heat of the sun changes water on Earth's surface from a liquid to a gas. Most evaporation occurs over Earth's oceans. *Condensation* takes place when water vapor cools enough to return to a liquid state. The clouds in Earth's atmosphere form when water vapor in the air condenses high above Earth's surface. *Precipitation* occurs when liquid or solid water falls from these clouds to Earth.

Transpiration is another key process in Earth's water cycle. *Transpiration* occurs when plants release water vapor from their leaves into the air. In Pennsylvania, about

Figure 1.1 View of Earth as seen by the *Apollo 17* crew as they traveled toward the moon.

1

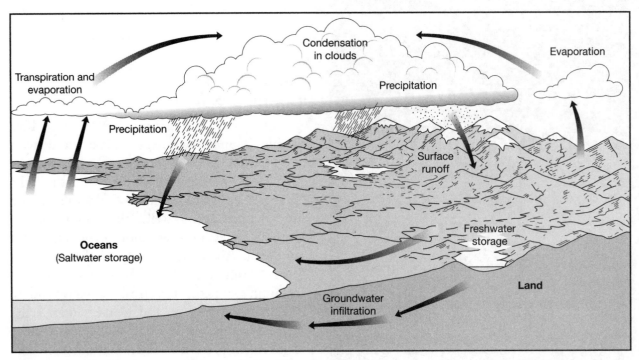

Figure 1.2 Earth's water cycle is a continuous process that does not change the amount of water on Earth, only the form that the water takes.

half of the state's 42 inches of average annual precipitation is returned to the atmosphere via evaporation and transpiration.

Groundwater

Some precipitation runs off the ground. This water is called *runoff*. However, some rain and melting snow seeps into the ground and becomes groundwater. *Groundwater* is water stored beneath Earth's surface. About 22 percent of Earth's fresh water is groundwater, which is accessed through wells and supplies most of the daily household, agricultural, and industrial needs of people around the world. In Pennsylvania, people and industries use more than 1 billion gallons of groundwater each day. In addition to providing many of the state's residents with drinking water, Pennsylvania's groundwater is also used for agriculture and mining.

Because groundwater supplies much of Earth's drinking water, its quality in many countries is closely monitored for contaminants. Some of these contaminants come from natural sources. For example, as groundwater flows through and around soil and rocks, it dissolves certain minerals. Hard water, for example, is the result of high concentrations of calcium in the water. High concentrations of iron and hydrogen sulfide are other natural contaminants that often reduce water quality by giving the water a disagreeable color, taste, or smell.

In addition to natural contaminants, groundwater quality is often affected by human activities. Septic tank systems that are not properly installed and maintained, for example, are sources of groundwater contamination. Pesticides and fertilizers used on farms and lawns also affect groundwater quality, as do landfills, chemical spills, leaking storage tanks, and the salts used on icy roadways. Recent studies on the quality of Pennsylvania's groundwater suggest that the overall quality is generally good. A decrease in the amount of nitrates in some Pennsylvania groundwater sources may have resulted from a combination of changes in agricultural practices and better maintenance of septic tank systems. Increases in other contaminants in some parts of the state have been attributed to a rise in road salting and urban development.

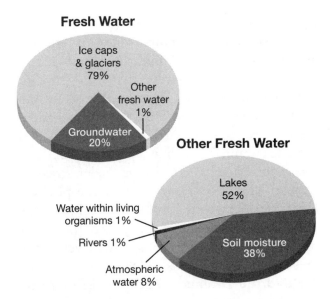

Fresh Water

Ice caps & glaciers 79%

Other fresh water 1%

Groundwater 20%

Other Fresh Water

Lakes 52%

Water within living organisms 1%

Rivers 1%

Atmospheric water 8%

Soil moisture 38%

Figure 1.3 The water supply for humans comes from groundwater and the tiny slice labeled "other fresh water."

Surface Water

Lakes and ponds hold about half the liquid fresh water on Earth's surface. Rivers hold the remainder of the freshwater volume—less than 1 percent. Most of the remaining fresh water is trapped in Earth's soil and air. Rivers begin when runoff flows along tiny channels called rills. Rills merge to form larger bodies of water called creeks and streams. The water in creeks and streams eventually merges to form bodies of water called rivers.

Stream Characteristics

The place where any stream or river begins is called its *source*, or its headwaters. The place where a stream or river ends by flowing into another body of water is called its *mouth*. As a stream flows from its source to its mouth, the water flows in one of two ways. Laminar flow occurs when water moves in straight paths that are parallel to the stream's channel, or bed. Water flowing in this way mixes very little as it moves downstream. Turbulent flow occurs when water moves in tiny circular paths as it flows downstream.

Velocity A stream's *velocity*, or the distance water flows during some period of time such as

meters per second or feet per second, determines whether its flow will be laminar or turbulent. Streams and rivers that move slowly have a laminar flow, but true laminar flow is rarely seen in natural streams. Streams and rivers that move quickly have a turbulent flow. The velocity of a stream or river determines the kind and amount of sediment, or load, that the water can carry.

Sediment Load As streams and rivers flow, they carry sediments in one of three ways. Some of a stream's dissolved load—or sediment carried in solution—enters the water as it flows over rocks and soil. This dissolves some of the minerals that make up these earth materials. Much of a stream's dissolved load, however, comes from groundwater that returns to Earth's surface. In contrast with a dissolved load, a suspended load is sediment such as silt and clay that is in suspension. Most rivers and streams carry the bulk of their loads as suspended loads. The *bed load* of a stream or a river is the sediment carried along the bottom of the channel. The bed load includes larger sediments such as sand, gravel, pebbles, and boulders.

River Deposits In addition to eroding the land over which they move, rivers deposit, or drop, sediment when their velocity decreases. Deposits called bars can form when a river slows down as it travels around a bend in its channel. Bars are made of sand and gravel and are found on the inside of a river bend. As a river's velocity increases, they often migrate to an area of the river that flows more slowly.

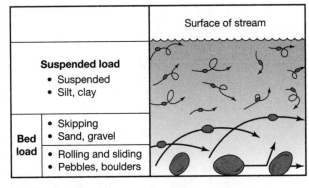

	Surface of stream
Suspended load • Suspended • Silt, clay	
Bed load • Skipping • Sand, gravel	
• Rolling and sliding • Pebbles, boulders	

Figure 1.4 Streams carry sediment at different levels in the water, depending on particle size and weight.

Figure 1.5 Many Pennsylvania farms, such as these along Lake Erie in Erie County, lie on or along a flood plain.

Rivers also deposit sediment when they overflow, or flood, their banks. A flood plain is the part of a river valley that is covered during a flood. Flood plains, like those along many of Pennsylvania's rivers, are very fertile areas of land often used for farming.

Major Drainage Patterns

Pennsylvania has more miles of streams and rivers per square mile than most states. Among the major rivers that run through Pennsylvania are the Ohio, the Allegheny, the Monongahela, the Genesee, the Susquehanna, the Juniata, the Delaware, the Lackawaxen, and the Lackawanna. The drainage patterns of these rivers and their *tributaries*, or feeder streams, depend largely on *topography*, or the physical characteristics of the land. In fact, all drainage patterns are controlled by the types of rocks over which the rivers and streams flow, as well as the presence or lack of folds and faults in the rocks.

Dendritic Drainage Patterns Most rivers and their tributaries form dendritic drainage patterns, which resemble mature trees. The main river or stream is similar to a tree's trunk, and the tributaries form a pattern that resembles a tree's many branches. Dendritic drainage patterns form where bedrock (rock beneath the soil) is uniform and massive, such as in a plains region. As a result, dendritic drainage patterns are mainly a function of the slope of the land over which a river or stream flows.

Radial Drainage Patterns Radial drainage patterns form when streams flow from a

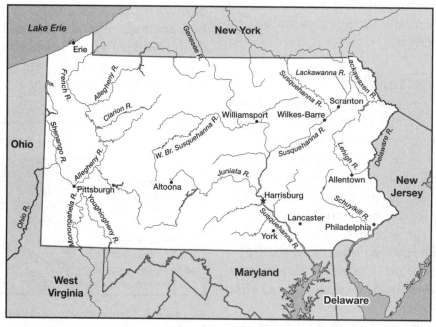

Figure 1.6 Pennsylvania's rivers cover the state, but all drain into the Atlantic Ocean.

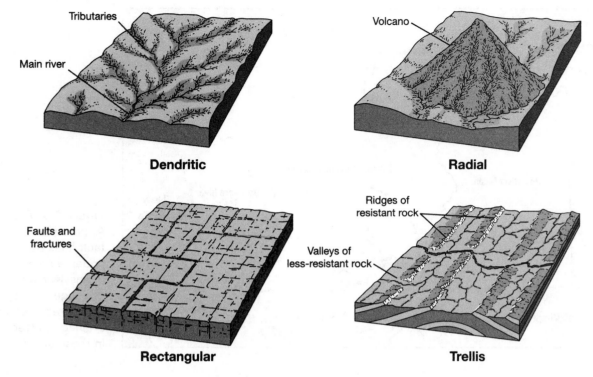

Figure 1.7 The topography of the land determines the drainage pattern of the watershed.

high, central area such as a plateau, volcanic mountain, or other type of uplifted feature. The streams in radial drainage patterns resemble the spokes of a bicycle tire.

Rectangular Drainage Patterns Rectangular drainage patterns form when bodies of rock are broken by a series of faults and other fractures. Rather than the typical rounded curves, the "bends" in rectangular drainage patterns form right angles in streams and rivers.

Trellis Drainage Patterns Trellis drainage patterns are a type of rectangular pattern in which tributary streams are nearly parallel to one another. Trellis drainage patterns form when sections of softer, nonresistant rocks alternate with sections of harder, resistant rocks.

Pennsylvania's Drainage Patterns

Study Figures 1.6 and 1.8, which show the major rivers, drainage basins, and fault lines in Pennsylvania. Many of the drainage patterns in the western half of the state are dendritic patterns. These patterns formed because much

of the rock underlying the soil in this part of the state is massive sedimentary rock.

Locate the thick, black, dotted lines on the south-central portion of the map in Figure 1.8. These lines represent faults, which are fractures in Earth's crust along which movement has taken place. As the Appalachian Mountains began forming hundreds of millions of years ago, so did these faults. Many streams and rivers have developed rectangular drainage patterns as their waters flowed along these fractures in the land.

In southeastern Pennsylvania, the drainage patterns are trellis patterns. The tributaries of the river systems in this area are often nearly parallel to one another but perpendicular to the main stream or river. These drainage patterns formed as the result of folding that occurred when the Appalachians were formed. The folding and subsequent erosion of the rocks left resistant rock layers alternating with nonresistant layers. Streams and rivers now flow in the valleys of nonresistant rocks. The resistant rocks form the ridges that separate the river systems.

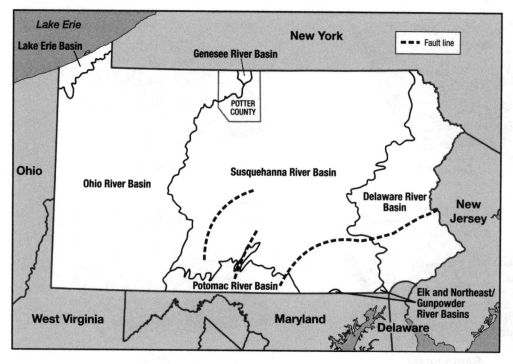

Figure 1.8 The Appalachian fault lines that underlie some of Pennsylvania's drainage basins create rectangular drainage patterns in those areas.

Locate Potter County along the north-central edge of the map above. Here, an unnamed hill rises about 2,520 feet above sea level. This high point marks the boundary between three of Pennsylvania's major drainage basins (watersheds)—the basin that drains either north to the St. Lawrence River or southwest to the Gulf of Mexico, and the basin that drains east into the Atlantic Ocean. What type of drainage pattern would you find at this point?

Lesson Review

1. Why is Earth often referred to as the "Blue Planet"?

2. Explain the connection between evaporation, condensation, and precipitation.

3. The processes of evaporation and transpiration are often combined when referring to Earth's water cycle. Why?

4. What is groundwater, and how is this source of fresh water used in Pennsylvania?

5. Describe three sources of groundwater contamination. How might the sources that are the results of human activities be controlled?

6. Define the terms *source* and *mouth* as they apply to rivers.

7. Contrast the different kinds of loads carried by a stream or a river.

8. Name five major Pennsylvania rivers. Which of these is closest to where you live?

9. Why does a dendritic drainage pattern form in certain areas?

10. What is the principal type of drainage in your area? What can you deduce about the kinds of rocks underlying your area? Are these rocks faulted or folded? Explain.

The Physical Characteristics of a Stream

River Profile Streams and rivers change as they flow from their headwaters to their mouths. These changes can be studied by making a river profile. Below is a profile of a hypothetical river. Study the profile. How does the *gradient*, or slope, of the river channel change from head to mouth?

Base Level Base level is the lowest elevation to which a stream can erode its channel. The local base level of a river or stream can be a lake, a resistant layer of rock, or another river or stream. What is the velocity of a stream or river at its local base level? What do you think is the ultimate base level of all streams and rivers?

Any change in the base level of a stream or river will affect the water body's gradient, its velocity, and its ability to transport its load. How do you think building a dam would affect the base level of a stream or river? How would the dam affect that water body's velocity? gradient? ability to transport sediment?

Discharge The discharge of a stream or river is the amount of water that flows past a given point in a given amount of time. Discharge is usually measured in cubic feet per second, or ft³/s. Discharge is calculated using the following formula:

$$discharge\ (ft^3/s) = channel\ width\ (ft) \times channel\ depth\ (ft) \times velocity\ (ft/s)$$

The data in the table below are discharge values measured along various points of the Susquehanna River in late May 2002. Use a map that shows the cities listed and the data in the table to construct a graph of discharge versus location along the river's course. In which direction does the Susquehanna River flow? How does discharge change downstream? Why?

Place	Discharge (ft³/s)
Danville, PA	38,000
Harrisburg, PA	80,000
Marietta, PA	95,000
Sunbury, PA	60,000
Wilkes-Barre, PA	30,000

The discharge values four days later at each of the various points were 21,000 ft³/s, 32,000 ft³/s, 50,000 ft³/s, 33,000 ft³/s, and 18,000 ft³/s, respectively. How do you think these changes in discharge values affected the velocity of the Susquehanna River at these points on this later date? What do you think would happen to the river channel if the discharge values increased?

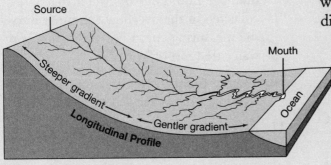

Figure 1.9 A longitudinal profile of a stream shows the change in the gradient.

Lab Study

Runoff, Erosion, and Vegetation

Recall that some rainwater and melting snow seep into the ground and become part of Earth's groundwater system. About 36,000 km^3 of Earth's average annual precipitation, however, flows over the land as runoff. Many factors affect runoff, including topography, climate, and the presence or absence of vegetation. In this study, you will observe how vegetation affects runoff.

Materials

2 large, gift boxes	water	overflow container (bucket or plastic tub)
2 heavy trash bags	measuring cup (2 cup)	
scissors	sprinkling can	stopwatch
stapler	$\frac{1}{2}$" diameter plastic tubing	bricks or books
sod to fill one box	cork to fit tubing	duct tape
soil to nearly fill the other box		

Procedure

1. Completely line each box with a piece of the trash bag. Smooth any wrinkles. Pull the piece of plastic over the edges of the box, and staple it into place.

2. Carefully cut a hole in one end of each box and in the same location in its trash bag. Insert a piece of plastic tubing into each hole, and seal it with duct tape.

3. Half-fill one box with *moist* soil, and gently pat it into place. DO NOT make the soil too wet, and DO NOT compress the soil too tightly.

4. Put the pieces of sod into the other box to form a smooth grass carpet.

5. Use the bricks or books to prop each box up at one end. The higher end of each box should be only 3 or 4 inches from the tabletop. The open edge of the box should be slightly over the edge of the table.

6. Put the overflow container under the table beneath the soil-filled box.

7. Measure 16 ounces of water, and put it into the sprinkling can.

8. Hold the sprinkling can about 6 inches above the higher end of the box containing only soil, and let the water flow gently from the can.

9. Once all 16 ounces of water have been poured onto the soil, begin timing the drainage. When 45 seconds have passed, lift the tubing and cork it to stop the drainage flow. Pour the water that collected in the overflow container into the measuring cup. Record the ounces of water that ran off the soil.

10. Use the runoff to water plants in your classroom or on the school grounds.

11. Repeat Steps 6 through 10 with the box containing the sod.

Conclusions

1. From which box did more water run off in the given period of time?

2. How does vegetation affect runoff?

3. How does vegetation affect erosion by flowing water?

For Discussion

1. Compare your results with those of at least three other pairs of students. Discuss reasons for any large differences in values.

2. How do you think changing the slope of the land (the box) would affect the amount of runoff from the two surfaces?

3. How might the amount of precipitation (the water in the sprinkling can) affect the rate of erosion?

4. Describe what you think would happen if you were to repeat this activity with these same boxes of soil. Remember that the soil in each box has absorbed some of the precipitation. How does the amount of water already in the soil affect runoff?

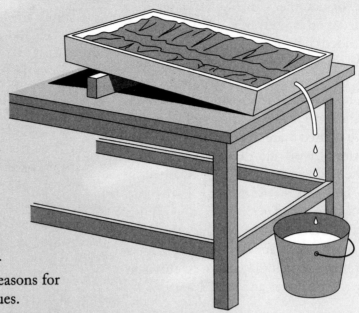

Figure 1.10 This activity illustrates how vegetation affects runoff.

Extension

Runoff and absorption of precipitation also depend on the type of soil. Describe what you think would happen if you were to repeat this experiment using sandy soils or clay-rich soils. Try these experiments.

Data Table	
Box	**Amount of Runoff**
Soil with no vegetation	
Soil with vegetation	

Lesson 1.2
Watersheds

A *watershed,* or drainage basin, is a region drained by, or one that contributes water to, a stream, lake, or other body of water. Watersheds are surrounded by topographic highs called divides. A *divide* is any ridge between two streams along which precipitation runs off. A divide can be several or thousands of feet high. The Continental Divide—which runs through Canada, the United States, and Mexico and into Central America—is an example of a large divide. The Continental Divide creates the separation between the water that drains into the Pacific Ocean and the water that drains into the Atlantic Ocean. Likewise, the watersheds separated by divides can vary in size from a ravine surrounding a single stream to the land drained by a major river and its tributaries.

Pennsylvania's Watersheds

Pennsylvania's watersheds can be described in many ways. For example, because all the fresh water in Pennsylvania eventually drains into the Atlantic Ocean, it can be said that the state itself is one giant watershed of the Atlantic. However, the Pennsylvania State Water Plan organizes the state's freshwater systems into 104 watersheds, which are subdivided into basins and sub-basins. In this lesson, five of the major watersheds in Pennsylvania will be discussed—the Great Lakes Basin, which includes the Erie and Genesee Basins; the Ohio River Basin; the Susquehanna/Chesapeake Basin; the Potomac Basin; and the Delaware Basin.

Great Lakes Basin Only about 1 percent of the Great Lakes Basin lies in Pennsylvania. This part is divided into two sub-basins: the Erie Basin and the Genesee Basin. Some of the major freshwater bodies in the Erie Basin include Pennsylvania's Conneaut, Elk, and Walnut Creeks, all of which drain to the north into Lake Erie. The rivers and streams in Pennsylvania's other Great Lakes watershed, the Genesee Basin, flow through New York State and drain into another Great Lake—Lake Ontario.

Figure 1.11 Coal barges are a common sight on the Ohio River as coal is moved from the mines of Pennsylvania to the power plants and rail stations along the river.

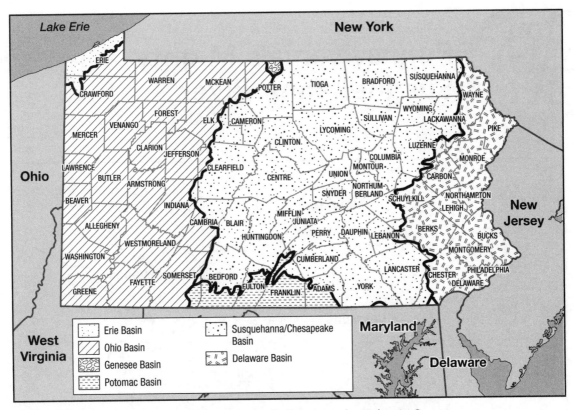

Figure 1.12 All of Pennsylvania's watersheds flow into the Atlantic Ocean.

Ohio River Basin The Ohio River Basin is Pennsylvania's second-largest watershed, covering nearly 16,000 square miles of the state. The basin provides drinking water for an estimated 13 million people, including nearly 3.5 million Pennsylvanians. The headwaters of the largest river in this basin—the Ohio—are in Pittsburgh, where the Allegheny River meets the Monongahela River. Other Pennsylvania water bodies in this basin include Tionesta Creek, Mahoning Creek, Stonycreek River, the Lower and Upper Youghiogheny Rivers, Beaver River, and the Upper Ohio River.

Susquehanna/Chesapeake Basin The Susquehanna River/Chesapeake Bay Basin is the largest watershed in Pennsylvania, covering about 46 percent of the state. The largest river in the basin is the Susquehanna, which has its headwaters in New York State's Otsego Lake and its mouth in the Chesapeake Bay. Major tributaries of the Susquehanna River in the Commonwealth include the Lackawanna, Conestoga, West Branch Susquehanna, and Juniata Rivers and the Loyalsock and Tuscarora Creeks.

Potomac Basin Although the Potomac River does not flow through Pennsylvania, a small portion of the Potomac Basin (about 1,500 square miles out of about 14,700 square miles) is located within the state's borders. Pennsylvania tributaries to the Potomac River include the river's largest, the Shenandoah River, as well as the Marsh, Wills, Tonoloway, Licking, Rock, Conococheague, and Antietam Creeks. These creeks, as well as most of the water bodies in this basin, drain from north to south.

Delaware Basin The Delaware River Basin, which covers about 6,500 square miles of Pennsylvania, is the third-largest watershed in the state. Much of the water from the Delaware River and its tributaries, which include the Lackawaxen River; the Upper, Middle, and Lower Lehigh Rivers; and Maiden and Brandywine Creeks is transferred to the Hudson Basin, which supplies most of New York City's freshwater needs.

Pennsylvania's Mighty Susquehanna River

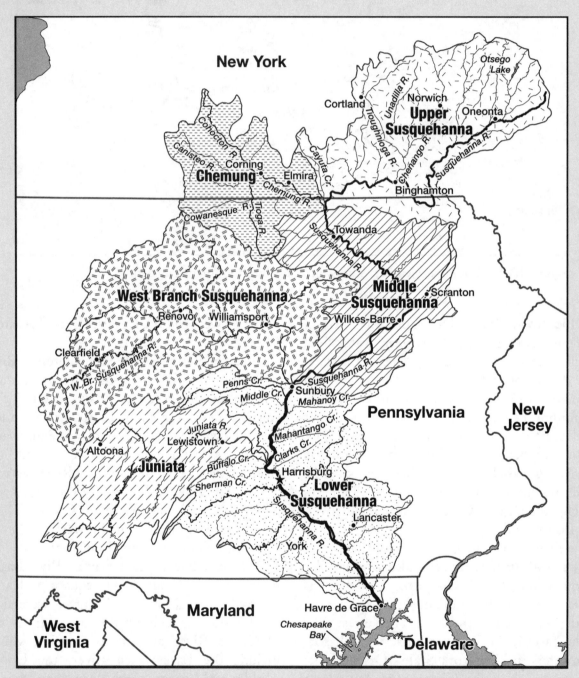

Figure 1.13 Covering almost half the state, the Susquehanna River Basin is Pennsylvania's largest watershed.

You Solve It! *(continued)*

The Susquehanna River is one of Pennsylvania's most important resources. It provides drinking water and recreation for residents of Pennsylvania as well as the state's many visitors. It also is used to power plants that provide electricity for millions of people in the Commonwealth.

The map on the facing page shows the Susquehanna River Basin, its sub-basins, and many of the tributaries that flow into this river. Use the map and what you have learned about rivers to answer the questions below.

Questions

1. In which state is the source of the Susquehanna River located? What is the name of the body of water where the Susquehanna begins?

2. What five major western New York rivers feed into the Susquehanna just as it enters Pennsylvania?

3. What is the name of the creek that feeds into the Susquehanna as the river enters Pennsylvania?

4. Where does the Tioughnioga River meet the Susquehanna River?

5. Name five creeks that enter the Susquehanna River between Sunbury and Harrisburg.

6. What type of drainage pattern is formed by the Juniata River and its tributaries near Lewistown?

7. What type of drainage pattern has developed in the Lower Susquehanna sub-basin?

8. In which state is the mouth of the Susquehanna River? Name the body of water into which the Susquehanna River empties.

9. What are the names of the sub-basins of the Susquehanna River basin?

10. Name the major river in each of the Susquehanna River sub-basins.

11. Describe the direction of flow of the Susquehanna River from its source to its mouth. Use the cities listed on the map in your description.

Lesson Review

1. What is a watershed?

2. How are watersheds separated from one another?

3. How many watersheds are identified by the Pennsylvania State Water Plan?

4. Name Pennsylvania's five major watersheds and the main rivers that drain each.

5. Which of Pennsylvania's watersheds is the largest?

6. What is the ultimate base level of the Susquehanna River?

7. Identify the watershed in which you live. Write a paragraph or two describing the major creeks, streams, and rivers that drain the watershed.

Lesson 1.3
Stream Biology

Streams and rivers are aquatic ecosystems that often are teeming with life. In addition to mosses, grasses, ferns, and other plants found in and along streams and rivers, there are three dominant groups of organisms in most stream communities. These include algae and other protists, invertebrates, and vertebrates.

Algae Algae are plantlike protists that make their own food. For this reason, algae are known as producers, or *autotrophs*. Because they make their own food, algae form the base of most aquatic food chains. Freshwater algae use energy from the sun and dissolved nutrients in a stream or river to make their own food.

Animal-like Protists Some protists have many of the same characteristics as animals. These protists, which include ciliates and paramecia, are aquatic organisms that eat bacteria, sediments that contain bacteria, and algae. Amoeba are protists that engulf their food by flowing around and over it. Protists called *saprotrophs* feed on decayed organic material. Some protists in streams and rivers eat other protists. Such organisms are classified as *raptors*.

Invertebrates Invertebrates are the second major group of organisms that live in and around streams and rivers. The most common freshwater invertebrates include insects, mollusks, and worms. Flies and beetles are among the insects found in nearly every stream or river ecosystem. When in the larval stage, both of these animals live in the water itself. Most of the adults live on the land surrounding the stream. Some insects, however, such as the water striders, can live on the water's surface.

Some flies are *shredders* that eat the tissue of other organisms, organic matter, and wood. Other flies are predators that either ingest their prey whole or pierce its tissues and suck out the fluids. Many beetles catch and engulf prey or feed on decomposed organic matter.

Many freshwater mollusks spend their entire lives in the water, as do some aquatic worms. Most of these aquatic invertebrates feed on algae and plants, and thus are primary

Figure 1.14 The American toad is a native inhabitant of Pennsylvania's streams.

consumers. Some of these animals, however, are either omnivores or carnivores. *Omnivores* eat both plants and animals, and *carnivores* eat other animals.

Vertebrates Aquatic vertebrates are the third major community in a stream or river. Amphibians such as salamanders and frogs are common stream inhabitants. Both of these animals, like all amphibians, depend on water at various stages of their life cycles. Most adult amphibians live on land. Amphibians have a variety of feeding habits. Frogs, for example, are predators that use their sticky tongues to capture flies and other insects. Most salamanders and newts are also carnivores that feed on small insects and their larvae.

Fish are another dominant group of freshwater vertebrates. Some fish are primary consumers of algae. These fish are called grazers, strainers, or suckers, depending on how they feed. Some freshwater fish, such as pike, pickerel, gars, and bullheads, are strictly predators. Other freshwater fish are *detritivores*. Such organisms feed by either shredding sediments that enter the stream or river or filtering their food directly from sediments in the water.

Factors That Affect Freshwater Ecosystems

Many factors affect the presence or absence of organisms in certain parts of a stream or river. *Biotic factors* are the living components of an ecosystem. *Abiotic factors* are the nonliving parts of an ecosystem. Interactions among biotic and abiotic factors determine the numbers and kinds of organisms in any environment, including freshwater ecosystems. Some abiotic factors that affect the biodiversity of a stream or river include temperature, current and velocity, substrate, stream order, amount of sunlight, turbidity, quantities of dissolved substances, pH, and organic matter.

Stream Order Recall that a stream forms over time as runoff flows along tiny channels called rills. These rills join larger streams and eventually flow into a major river. The smallest streams in a river system are first-order streams. First-order streams join to form second-order streams, which in turn meet to form third-order streams. Third-order streams converge to form fourth-order streams, and so on. In the Pennsylvania highlands, nearly 80 percent of the streams are either first- or second-order streams. The rest are either third- or fourth-order streams.

The size or order of a stream relates directly to the organisms that inhabit the ecosystem. For example, first-order streams are home to large insect populations and few, if any, fish. Plants and game fish often dominate third- and fourth-order streams. Larger streams contain diverse populations of algae, fish, and other aquatic organisms.

Temperature Differences in a stream's temperature are caused by several factors. For example, the velocity of the water, as well as its depth, affects the water's temperature. Areas of little or no water circulation tend to experience vertical variations in temperature. Streams and rivers with consistent currents, however, mix the water and often eliminate temperature differences. Water depth also affects the temperature in a stream or river. Because of the exposure to direct sunlight, shallow waters are warmer than deeper waters. Furthermore, the amount of vegetation along a stream or river bank will affect the water temperature.

Seasonal changes certainly affect a stream's water temperature. For example, melting snow can lower a stream's temperature as cold water mixes with the stream. Natural springs entering a stream and a thick tree canopy overlooking it also can lower the water temperature.

Changes in temperature affect the kinds and numbers of species in a river or stream. Some species, such as carp and catfish, live in a wide range of temperatures. Other species, such as some algae, protists, and trout, can survive only in certain water temperatures.

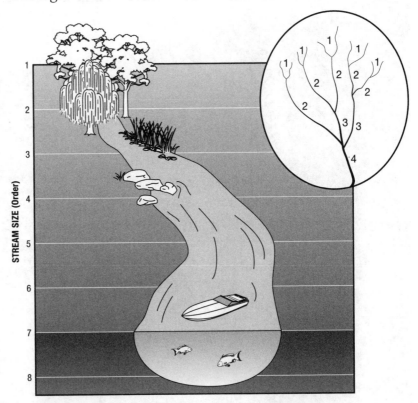

Figure 1.15 The vegetation, insects, and animals living in and around a stream change as the size of the stream changes.

Current and Velocity Unlike ocean currents, water currents in rivers and streams are unidirectional, meaning that they flow in one direction. As the water flows, it carries its load and other substances downstream. Substances in the current, including nutrients, flow quickly over the organisms. If the organisms do not use these substances immediately, they must wait for the current to bring more of them.

Stream currents affect organisms in other ways. The flow of water exerts a force on organisms in the stream. Some species, such as mollusks, can resist this force. A mollusk's muscular foot enables it to attach itself to rocks, plants, or the river channel itself. Other organisms, including streamlined fish, move with or against the current.

Velocity is another abiotic factor that affects organisms in a stream or river. Recall that velocity is the change in distance over time. A stream's velocity changes with its course and its depth. While a decrease in slope reduces velocity, the widening of a river and the smoothing of its bed downstream actually cause an increase in average stream velocity towards its mouth. Stream velocity also is lower at the water's surface and where the water meets the channel bed. Stream velocity is most rapid in the middle of the water column due to the least resistance.

Most species of fish are unaffected by velocity and can live nearly anywhere along a stream or river. Other organisms, such as insects, are generally limited to calmer waters.

Substrate *Substrate* is the material that organisms live in, on, or around. The substrate in a stream or river is made of organic and inorganic particles. Organic substrate includes algae and other small particles of matter that generally are used as food. Inorganic substrates are the pebbles and rocks in the stream and the silt, sand, and mud that make up the stream's channel.

Figure 1.16 Vegetation around waterways helps keep the water temperature lower.

Most invertebrates in a stream or river live on or under rocky substrates. For example, freshwater sponges live their entire lives attached to the tops and sides of rocks and boulders. Other sponges attach to the sides or bottom of the channel.

Some freshwater organisms live *in* the substrate. One type of dragonfly larva lives in the sandy substrate of riverbeds and uses a long siphon to gather oxygen from the water above it. Fishes called bullheads often live deep within the gravelly substrates of many streams and rivers.

In some cases, stream organisms use plants as substrates. Certain flies deposit their larvae on mosses that grow in and near the stream. Insects called midges feed on algae that grows on the leaves. In forested areas some species, such as beetles, use wood as a substrate.

Sunlight The amount of light a stream or river receives also affects an ecosystem's biodiversity. Plants rely on sunlight to make their own food through photosynthesis. A lack of sunlight can adversely affect organisms within an ecosystem. Places in a stream or river that receive little sunlight tend to have fewer organisms than do places where light is abundant and penetrates to great depths.

Turbidity The amount of sunlight that penetrates a body of water depends on the water's clarity, or turbidity. *Turbidity* reflects the amount of suspended matter in the water. Suspended matter in a stream or river includes silt and clay, small organisms called plankton, organic debris, and other nonliving materials.

Several factors affect turbidity. For example, an increase in stream erosion and high water volume increases turbidity. Heavy rains or large amounts of melting snow can cause a sudden increase in water volume and sediment, which increases the stream's turbidity.

Temperature also affects turbidity. Streams and rivers often are very turbid in the spring when melting snow carries large volumes of silt and organic matter into streams and rivers. Warm spring temperatures also promote the rapid growth of plankton, which remain suspended in the water.

Dissolved Solids Recall that streams and rivers carry some of their sediment load as dissolved loads. Some of the dissolved load enters the water as it flows over the riverbed. Most of the dissolved load, however, enters the stream or river from groundwater.

Some of the common elements carried in the dissolved load include magnesium, calcium, iron, sodium, potassium, sulfur, silicon, nitrogen, and phosphorus. These elements are essential to the organisms that live in streams and rivers. Calcium, for example, is a critical element in fishes' bones and mollusks' shells. Silicon is used by microscopic organisms called diatoms to make their shells and by sponges to form their spicules. Phosphorus, potassium, and magnesium are important elements to plant growth.

Excess amounts of some elements, such as nitrogen and phosphorus, can stimulate plant and algae growth. Excessive algal growth is called an algal bloom. *Algal blooms* deplete dissolved oxygen levels in the water and result in the deaths of many organisms.

Dissolved Gases In addition to dissolved solids, rivers and streams contain dissolved gases such as oxygen and carbon dioxide. Of these two gases, oxygen is probably more important in determining the biodiversity of a stream or river.

Oxygen The oxygen in rivers and streams enters the water from the air. The amount of oxygen that enters a river or stream depends mainly on water temperature. As temperature increases, the oxygen that will dissolve in water at atmospheric pressure decreases.

In addition, the amount of dissolved oxygen in a river or stream depends on photosynthesis and respiration. Photosynthesis adds oxygen to the water. Organisms such as fish, insects, spiders, and worms use oxygen to respire. Fish absorb oxygen as water passes over their gills. Beetles and some other insects get oxygen directly from the water or use air tubes to get oxygen from the air. Worms and other invertebrates absorb oxygen through their skins.

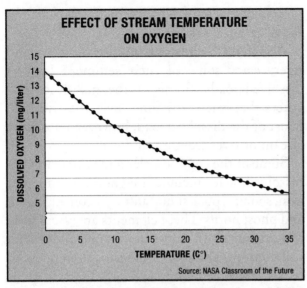

EFFECT OF STREAM TEMPERATURE ON OXYGEN

Source: NASA Classroom of the Future

Figure 1.17 As a stream's temperature increases, the amount of oxygen in the water decreases.

The current of a river or stream also affects the amount of oxygen within it. If current speed decreases, less oxygen is available to organisms living in the water. However, organisms have adapted to compensate for a lower amount of oxygen. Many organisms can increase the current that flows over their respiratory structures. Mayflies, for example, move their gills back and forth to increase the available oxygen. Other insects have small holes in their shells that enable them to create a current through their bodies when oxygen levels in the stream are low.

The decomposition of organic matter also affects the oxygen content of a body of water. Oxygen is used up during decomposition. This process occurs faster in warmer waters than in colder waters.

Carbon Dioxide Most carbon dioxide that enters a stream or river comes from either Earth's atmosphere or its groundwater systems. Decomposition and respiration are other sources of carbon dioxide. As plants photosynthesize and organisms absorb carbonate minerals from the water, carbon dioxide is removed from a stream or river.

Organic Matter Most organic matter in a freshwater ecosystem is used as food. Algae, plankton, bits of leaves and wood, and decaying organisms are a few types of organic matter found in streams and rivers. An excess or lack of these nutrients can have different effects on ecosystems. Too many nutrients, for example, can result in a decrease in oxygen levels. Too few nutrients will result in organisms either traveling to another part of the river or stream in search of food or dying for lack of food.

pH The pH of a solution is a measure of its concentration of specific hydrogen ions. The pH scale, which ranges from 0 to 14, measures a solution's pH. A solution with a pH of 7 is a neutral solution. A solution with a pH value higher than 7 is a basic solution. A solution with a pH value lower than 7 is an acidic solution.

Pure water has a pH of 7—it is neither basic nor acidic. Rainwater and the water in most streams and rivers is slightly acidic. Although most organisms in a river or stream can tolerate slight changes in pH, the acidification of freshwater bodies can greatly reduce an ecosystem's populations. Often, streams that are acidic because of acid rain or snow are acidic for only a short time. Some effects of this short-term acidification include fish kills and decreases in insect populations. Streams that become acidic as the result of mine drainage generally lose many of their bottom-dwelling organisms. This is because mine drainage contains not only acids but also heavy metals and other pollutants. These dangerous substances often settle to the bottom of a river channel and become trapped in sediments. The toxic substances then enter an organism's body through diffusion or as the animal feeds.

Many rivers and streams in Pennsylvania are susceptible to acidification. There are three reasons for this. First, much of Pennsylvania receives some of the most acidic rainfall in the United States. Second, the rocks in much of the state contain minerals that contribute to acidification. Third, Pennsylvania has many coal mines. Fortunately, many of the state's streams and rivers buffer or prevent large changes in pH.

The Upper Perkiomen Creek

The Upper Perkiomen Creek is one of Pennsylvania's richest streams, in terms of biodiversity. American beeches, red and white oaks, black walnuts, river birches, sycamores, and willows are among the dominant trees that thrive along this creek. Among the animals that live in the forests along the banks are gray foxes, moles, rabbits, blue jays, scarlet tanagers, pileated woodpeckers, gray squirrels, bats, coyotes, and white-tailed deer. Tussock sedge, ferns, and skunk cabbage are among the vegetation that thrives in broad, wet meadows along the creek.

Some of the invertebrate aquatic species in the Upper Perkiomen Creek include caddis flies, stoneflies, and mayflies as well as mussels, snails, and crayfish. Other insects that live in and above the creek's leaf litter include ants, beetles, butterflies, bees, wasps, and mosquitoes. Some of the fish that live in the creek and its tributaries are dace, darters, minnows, suckers, brown trout, and native brook trout. Frogs, toads, salamanders, turtles, and snakes such as the northern copperhead also are found along and in the creek.

Use a map of Pennsylvania that shows the Upper Perkiomen Creek watershed as well as guide books and identification keys for Pennsylvania plants and animals to make an ecologic stream profile of the Upper Perkiomen Creek. Your profile should include the creek's source as well as its mouth. On the basis of what you've learned about the ecology of rivers and streams, place the plants and animals mentioned above in their proper habitats. Write a short essay that explains why you placed each animal where you did.

Lesson Review

1. What role do protists play in a freshwater ecosystem?

2. What types of organisms form the base of many aquatic ecosystems? Explain.

3. Name three groups of invertebrates that are found in and around nearly all streams and rivers.

4. What is a shredder? Provide at least two examples of shredders.

5. Explain several different methods of feeding in freshwater fish.

6. Explain the factors that affect the temperature of a stream or river.

7. How does the current of a stream or river affect the organisms that live in the body of water?

8. Describe different types of substrates found in rivers and streams. Name at least one organism that lives in or on each substrate.

9. How do organisms in a stream or river use dissolved inorganic solids?

10. Discuss the factors that affect the amount of oxygen in a freshwater body.

11. Describe how the pH of a stream or river can change. How could these changes affect the organisms that live in the water?

Field Study

Stream Ecology

The types and numbers of organisms that live in a stream or river depend on many biotic and abiotic factors. In this study, you will observe a local creek or stream and gather information about the types of organisms that live in and along it. You will also make observations and measurements of some of the abiotic factors of the ecosystem.

Materials

stream gauge	thermometer	Pennsylvania biological field guides and identification keys
yardstick	collection nets	
collection jars with lids	rubber gloves	map that includes the entire watershed of the stream you are observing
labels	hand lens or magnifying glass	
permanent marker		stereoscopic microscope
pH paper and scale		

Procedure

1. Obtain a copy of the watershed map from your teacher.

2. With your teacher's help, find your location on your map. Mark this point.

3. Follow your teacher's instructions for measuring some of the physical characteristics of the stream, including velocity, temperature, and depth, at four locations. Record your measurements in the data table. Also mark the points on your map where each measurement was made.

4. Follow your teacher's instructions for collecting a water sample at each location. Note each sample location on your map. Label each jar accordingly. Describe the clarity of each sample in your data table. Measure and record the pH of each sample. Tightly close the jars, and take the samples back to the classroom.

5. Use the collection nets to catch either invertebrates or vertebrates. Carefully and quickly examine the organisms while they are in the nets. Follow your teacher's instructions for releasing the organisms back into the ecosystem. *Caution: Always handle live organisms gently and with care.*

6. Use the field guides and identification keys to identify the organisms that you observe. Record your observations in your data table.

7. When you return to the classroom, use the microscope to observe each water sample. Record your observations in the data table.

Conclusions

1. How did velocity, temperature, and depth change with location? Describe any patterns in your data.

2. Were there any differences in pH and clarity at the different locations? Explain.

3. What kinds of protists did you observe at the different locations and in the four water samples?

4. What kinds of invertebrates were found at the different locations?

5. Describe the vertebrates that live in the different locations.

For Discussion

1. Were there any trends in the physical characteristics that you measured? Explain.

2. How might your data compare with similar data farther upstream or downstream?

3. How might your data compare with similar data collected at different times of the year?

Extension

With your teacher or another responsible adult, repeat this activity during another season or after heavy rains. Compare and contrast your findings.

Data Table

Some Observations of _____ Stream/Creek

	Location 1	Location 2	Location 3	Location 4
Depth				
Velocity				
Temperature				
Algae present?				
Invertebrates				
Vertebrates				

Water Samples

	Location 1	Location 2	Location 3	Location 4
pH				
Clarity				
Organisms present?				

Lesson 1.4
Wetlands

A *wetland* is an area that contains unique types of soil, is home to plants adapted to the wet environment, and contains water all year or at certain times during the year. Bogs, swamps, and marshes are some common names for wetlands. A *bog* is a wetland in which soils consist predominantly of decomposed plant material called peat or muck. Mosses are the dominant plants in a bog. Other bog plants include shrubs, some species of evergreens, water lilies, pitcher plants, cranberries, and blueberries. Bogs are very acidic and contain little oxygen because there is very little movement of water into or out of the wetland. Although the lack of oxygen in bogs limits the numbers and kinds of fishes present, bogs often are home to frogs, turtles, insects, and certain birds.

A *swamp* is a forested wetland in which trees and bushes are the dominant plants. Some swamp soils, which drain very slowly, are rich in nutrients; others are not. Swamps can be classified according to the type of tree that dominates the wetland. Cedars, pines, spruces, and hemlocks are found in conifer swamps. Maples, willows, aspens, birches, elms, and oaks are some trees that grow in hardwood swamps. Other swamp vegetation may include dogwoods and alders. Some animals that live in swamps are white-tailed deer, raccoons, herons, egrets, woodpeckers, snakes, frogs, and turtles.

A freshwater *marsh* is a wetland that generally forms at the mouth of a river or in areas where there is poor drainage. The water that fills a marsh comes from nearby creeks, streams, and rivers. Marsh soils are rich in nutrients and support vegetation such as grasses, sedges, bulrushes, and cattails. Other organisms that live in and around a freshwater marsh include beavers, frogs, turtles, raccoons, muskrats, opossums, birds, and of course, insects.

Pennsylvania Wetlands

For legal and regulatory purposes, Chapter 105 of the Commonwealth of Pennsylvania code defines wetlands as:

"Those areas that are inundated or saturated by surface or groundwater at a frequency and duration sufficient to support, and that under normal circumstances do support, a prevalence of vegetation typically adapted for life in saturated soil conditions...."

Figure 1.18 Grasses provide excellent shelter for native creatures that live in a wetland.

Of Pennsylvania's nearly 29 million acres, approximately 407,000 acres are wetlands. Over 4,000 of those acres have been restored as wetlands since 1990. Various wildlife programs also have been developed to maintain and, when necessary, restore these vital environments. Three general types of wetlands are recognized in Pennsylvania: forested wetlands, scrub-shrub wetlands, and emergent wetlands.

Forested wetlands are areas where the dominant plant types include mature woody trees. In Pennsylvania, about 220,000 acres of the state's wetlands are home to red and silver maples, black gums, river birches, and green ashes that tower more than 20 feet above the ground.

Nearly 139,000 acres of Pennsylvania's wetlands are *scrub-shrub wetlands.* These wetlands are so named because their dominant plants are scrub and shrubs as well as trees that are less than 20 feet tall, such as alders and willows. Spicebushes, high-bush blueberries, winterberries, and swamp honeysuckles are among the low-lying vegetation in scrub-shrub wetlands.

Approximately 52,000 acres of all wetlands in Pennsylvania are *emergent wetlands*—marshy areas where plants are rooted in soil but emerge above water. Some common plants of the Commonwealth's emergent wetlands include rushes, grasses, and sedges.

Wetlands at Work

In addition to providing habitat and food for numerous organisms, wetlands serve many other functions. They are spawning grounds and nurseries for many types of aquatic life-forms. Wetlands play a vital role in cycling nutrients through the ecosystem. They serve as buffers that protect land from erosion and from damage caused by flooding and storms. Wetlands also aid in filtering many pollutants from the environment.

Habitat Wetlands are home to hundreds of different species of bacteria, protists, plants, and animals, including many organisms that are threatened or endangered. Endangered species are organisms that soon could become extinct, or die out. Threatened species are those that may

Figure 1.19 The showy lady's slipper is a threatened species in Pennsylvania because of loss of its natural habitat.

soon become endangered. Although wetlands make up about five percent of the total land area of the 48 contiguous states, they are home to nearly 35 percent of the threatened and endangered species in the United States.

In Pennsylvania, many of the more than 500 plant species of concern live in or near wetlands. Scientists also estimate that more than 80 percent of all of the state's amphibians live in and around wetlands most of the time. Twenty-five percent of all of Pennsylvania's 41 species of reptiles spend nearly all of their lives in wetlands. More than 120 species of birds that call Pennsylvania home perform most of their life functions in, on, or around wetlands.

Food Factories Wetlands are considered food factories because they have very high primary productivity rates. Plants, the major organisms responsible for this productivity, form the base of wetland food webs. Some organisms eat the plants that grow above the waterline. Decomposing plant parts, on the other hand, provide food and nutrients for bacteria, fungi, protists, and various wetland invertebrates. In turn, these organisms provide food for many types of wetland vertebrates.

Spawning Grounds and Nurseries According to the United States Forest Service, nearly 200 species of amphibians, as well as all wild ducks, geese, swans, bitterns, and herons, reproduce in wetlands. Wetlands in the flood plains of larger rivers provide spawning habitats for many freshwater fishes, including bullhead, yellow perch, northern pike, and muskellunge. Walleyes and bluegills leave open lake waters to spawn in shallow water wetlands. Coastal wetlands are spawning and nursery grounds for some shellfish and commercial game fish, including salmon, flounder, striped bass, bluefish, and menhaden.

Cycling Nutrients The presence of plants in a wetland not only defines the wetland but also drives this type of ecosystem. Plants make their own food via photosynthesis. During this process, plants and other autotrophs use carbon dioxide and energy from the sun to produce food and oxygen. Plants retain the food they produce. The oxygen, however, is used for respiration by nearly all the *heterotrophs*, animals and fungi that eat plant and animal matter, in the ecosystem. Plants also play an important role in moving other nutrients, such as phosphorus and nitrogen, through the wetland.

Buffer Zones Wetlands are important buffer zones because they can function as sponges. These "natural sponges" absorb excess runoff and slowly release it back into the environment. The ability of wetlands to store water and slow

its flow has several benefits. Wetlands help reduce the likelihood of flood damage to crops. These ecosystems also help control increases in the rate and volume of runoff in urban areas.

Wetlands also aid in protecting coastlines. The roots of all wetland vegetation hold soil in place. Along a coast, wetland plants absorb the energy of waves and break up the flow of stream or river currents. Thus, wetlands in coastal areas buffer storm surges from hurricanes and tropical storms, often preventing severe damage to nearby roads, houses, and other structures.

Pollution Control The number one water pollutant (by volume) in Pennsylvania is sediment. Wetlands play a role in reducing sediment pollution by slowing water movement. This decrease in movement allows the sediment to settle, thus improving water quality for wetland wildlife.

Wetlands also help prevent air pollution. Many wetland plants store carbon rather than releasing it into the air as carbon dioxide. Carbon dioxide is a greenhouse gas that some scientists believe affects global climates.

Suburban Swamps

Because they provided a means to transport goods and fresh water for consumption, Pennsylvania's creeks, streams, and rivers were critical to the development of many cities in the Commonwealth. Unfortunately, urbanization has disrupted and even destroyed many of the wetlands associated with these bodies of water. However, most local and state urban planning in Pennsylvania today is done with a best-practices approach to wetlands.

One important aspect of the best-practices approach is the preservation of open spaces in urban areas. In the greater Philadelphia area, city planners estimate that by 2020, the area will lose approximately 173,000 acres of open space as a result of development. This loss of open space could have many negative effects on the area. First, it may greatly reduce recreational areas. Second, the loss of open space may render the area less attractive to businesses. Third, urbanization may reduce the quality of the air

Figure 1.20 The American coot is at home in Pennsylvania wetlands.

and water in the region. Fourth, the landscapes (concrete and nonvegetated land) of the developed areas may increase the risk of flooding.

The preservation of open spaces has many benefits. For instance, the vegetation in open spaces improves both air and water quality. As a result of photosynthesis, plants remove harmful gases from and contribute oxygen to the air. Plants improve water quality by filtering out harmful substances from the water. Open spaces also provide habitats for wildlife and lessen the chances and effects of flooding.

Urban wetlands are one kind of open space. Some of these wetlands are the remnants of streams and rivers that flowed through areas prior to development. Other urban wetlands develop as a result of poorly or inadequately planned development. Drainage ditches, for example, can become urban wetlands if runoff

collects in these artificial gullies and remains there for at least part of the year. This standing water eventually provides a habitat for a variety of plants, including cattails and reeds, and aquatic animals.

In addition to providing habitat, urban wetlands serve other important functions. They buffer the runoff from pavements, empty lots, and other nonabsorbent surfaces in a city, thereby minimizing flooding. Urban wetlands trap and filter out much of the iron, lead, copper, and other potentially harmful substances present in most urban runoff. Urban wetlands also aid in treating the large volumes of wastewater produced by most cities and towns. When storm runoff and treated sewage are channeled into urban wetlands, the waters receive additional filtering before they are released back into streams and rivers.

You Solve It!

Protecting Pennsylvania's Wetlands

Agencies charged with protecting America's wetlands initially developed and carried out "no net loss" programs. Such programs were intended to simply stop the loss of wetland acreage. In the late 1980s, however, wetland protection programs began focusing their efforts on "net gain" programs. Such programs are designed to increase the quantity and quality of the nation's wetlands resources.

Pennsylvania's commitment to wetland restoration and preservation began in the early 1980s after it was discovered that between 1956 and 1979, the state lost 28,000 acres of wetlands. Since 1990, 4,660 acres of wetlands have been restored in Pennsylvania. Today, an estimated 407,000 acres of wetlands exist throughout the Commonwealth.

Do research to find out about some of the federal and state laws and programs that

regulate and restore wetlands. Summarize your findings in a table. Use the questions below to help you get started with this activity.

- What is the Clean Water Act, and what role does it play in the preservation and restoration of the nation's wetlands?
- How does the Pennsylvania Department of Environmental Protection, or DEP, contribute to the maintenance of wetland environments in the Commonwealth?
- How does the Commonwealth's Dam Safety and Encroachments Act affect wetlands?
- What are Growing Greener Grants, and how do they benefit Pennsylvania's wetlands?
- How does Pennsylvania's Conservation Reserve Enhancement Program, or CREP, benefit wetlands in the state?

1. What is a wetland?

2. Compare and contrast bogs, swamps, and freshwater marshes.

3. How do you think the rate of decomposition in a bog compares with that in a stream or river? Explain.

4. What kinds of animals inhabit Pennsylvania's forested wetlands?

5. Describe each of the six major functions of wetlands.

6. Name six animal species that inhabit Pennsylvania wetlands. How is each dependent on the wetland environment?

7. What are some negative effects of eliminating open spaces in and around cities and towns?

8. Explain the role of wetland plants in removing pollutants from Earth's air and water.

9. How do urban wetlands benefit the areas in which they are located?

10. Compare and contrast "no net loss" and "net gain" programs as they relate to wetland environments.

Use the data in the table below to answer questions 11–14.

Wetland Areas Impacted and Gained in Major Drainage Basins, 1988–1999						
Basin	Acres Lost	Acres Restored or Created by Programs and Agencies*				
		Chapter 105	PWRP	Mining	BAMR	USFWS/NRCS
Delaware	230.8	298.4	5.4	19.9	4.7	194.9
Ohio	313.2	311.1	21	83.2	24.8	1,432.5
Chesapeake Bay	351.7	408.3	23.9	250.2	150.8	1,431.5

*Chapter 105: DEP permitting programs—Wetlands Protection and Dam Safety; PWRP: Pennsylvania Wetland Replacement Program; Mining: Bureau of Mining and Reclamation; BAMR: Bureau of Abandoned Mine Reclamation; USFWS: U.S. Fish and Wildlife Service Partners for Wildlife Program; NRCS: Natural Resource Conservation Service Wetland Reserve Program

11. What was the total wetland acreage affected per basin?

12. What was the total acreage restored or reported in each basin?

13. Compute the net gain of wetlands per basin.

14. What was the total net gain of wetland acreage?

Lesson 1.5
Factors That Affect Wetlands and Watersheds

Wetlands and watersheds are controlled by complex interactions among chemical, physical, and biological factors. Many of these interactions are controlled or influenced by human activities and events. Others are the results of natural events and processes.

Human Activities

According to some estimates, more than half of the original 220 million acres of United States wetlands have been lost over the past 400 years. Some of these ecosystems were totally destroyed by either completely draining or in-filling a region. Others were degraded, or changed in a negative way, by activities associated with agriculture, urbanization, construction, mining, industrial processes, waste disposal, and mosquito control. Some wetlands suffered degradation as the result of pollution by sediment, nutrients, pesticides, and heavy metals. Others were affected by drastic changes in salinity, pH, and dissolved oxygen levels.

Effects of Agriculture Agricultural practices can disrupt or even destroy a wetland in different ways. For example, some wetlands are degraded when food, fiber, or forest products are harvested. Other wetlands are affected when drainage and irrigation ditches are built and maintained. Inefficient irrigation also can cause pesticides, nutrients, pathogens (disease-carrying microscopic organisms), and salts to build up in soil. The accumulation of these substances causes degradation of the water quality in both the soil and underlying groundwater systems.

Agricultural animals also can affect nearby wetlands. Farmers and ranchers use confined facilities to efficiently maintain their animals. However, as a result, vast quantities of waste are produced that can contaminate nearby wetlands if not properly disposed of. Overgrazing is another effect of farm animals on nearby wetlands. Overgrazing exposes soil to erosion by wind and water. This, in turn, increases the amount of sediment that reaches, and often pollutes, a wetland.

Possibly the most harmful effects of agriculture on wetlands are those of the pesticides and fertilizers used on crops. These chemicals

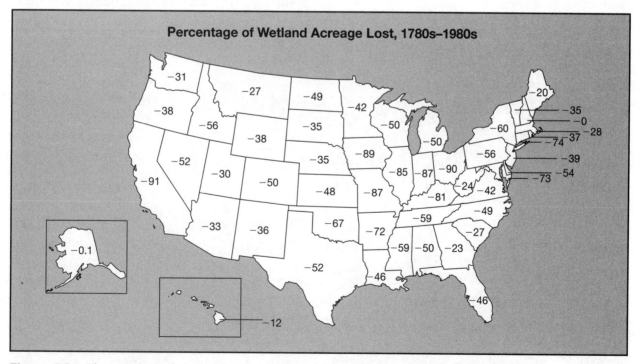

Figure 1.21 The number of wetland acres in the United States has steadily decreased over the past two centuries.

can enter and contaminate wetlands by direct application, in runoff, or by settling out of the air. When these substances reach high enough levels, they can kill wildlife, poison food sources, and destroy the wetland.

Urbanization and Construction The United States Environmental Protection Agency, or EPA, cites urbanization as the major cause of wetland impairment. One product of urbanization is the modern landscape of concrete and other materials that increase the amount of runoff. This runoff carries many pollutants, including sediments, pet wastes, pesticides, salts, and heavy metals into nearby wetlands. Some of the substances carried by runoff also increase the salinity and turbidity of nearby wetlands and decrease the amount of dissolved oxygen in these environments.

The construction of roads and bridges over wetlands can increase the amount of sediment deposited in these ecosystems. Roads also can restrict the movement of some species within a wetland, often resulting in the species' deaths. Paints, cleaners, salt, herbicides, dust-control substances, and other chemicals used on and along roads and bridges also contribute to wetland degradation.

Canals, ditches, and levees divert water away from its natural flow and often are built during urbanization. These structures can change the hydrology of a wetland by increasing the rate at which water flows into and out of an ecosystem. The increased flow reduces the buffering ability of the wetland. Excessive amounts of sediments carried by these structures, for example, can increase turbidity, fill in parts of the wetland, and even smother aquatic vegetation.

Mining Mining operations also can result in the loss and degradation of wetland ecosystems. In central Florida, phosphate mining has eliminated thousands of acres of state wetlands. The mining of peat—a form of organic matter that can be used as fuel—also can destroy wetland ecosystems. In peat mining, vegetation is cleared, parts of a wetland are drained, and roads are built to access the peat.

The mining of rocks and minerals also contributes to wetland degradation. Acid drainage from both active and abandoned coal mines, such as those in Pennsylvania, increases the pH of nearby wetlands and can introduce heavy metals into these ecosystems. Although wetlands are able to filter out some of these pollutants, degradation often occurs over time.

Figure 1.22 The Route 30 bridge in Lancaster County was built over the Susquehanna River.

Industry The construction of office buildings, factories, and processing plants can reduce wetland acreage. The processes carried out in many of these facilities also degrade wetland environments. Water intake, for example, can cause habitat loss or fragmentation. Removing too much water may cause a large area of land to sink. The release of water into a wetland also can cause thermal pollution, which can lead to algal blooms.

Waste Disposal Waste is another common by-product of urbanization. Most urban waste is solid waste that is often taken to landfills. Landfills can pose risks to wetlands. Many landfills in the United States are located within a mile or less of a wetland. Many of the materials that leak out of landfills are extremely toxic to wetland organisms.

Other forms of urban waste include sludge and wastewater treatment plant effluent. These solutions are rich in both nitrogen and phosphorus, and they can cause algal blooms if they are introduced into waterways and wetlands. This excess algae can prevent sunlight from reaching aquatic plants. The lack of light reduces or entirely prevents photosynthesis, which often results in the death of the plants. Algal blooms also remove dissolved oxygen from the water. This reduction in oxygen often kills many of the organisms that live along the bottom of a wetland ecosystem.

Watershed Quality

Many of the human activities that affect wetlands also affect Earth's watersheds. Recall that a watershed, or drainage basin, is the region drained by, or the region contributing water to, a stream, lake, or other body of water. Agencies responsible for monitoring watersheds in the United States use the Index of Watershed Indicators, or IWI, to gather and assess data about aquatic resources. The index also tries to determine whether human activities on the land within a watershed place the basins at risk.

Condition Indicators The IWI includes more than a dozen indicators. Some indicators reflect actual conditions in the watershed. One condition indicator is the presence of contaminated sediments. Contaminated sediments can harm or even kill aquatic organisms. Pollutants in sediments also can pose a risk to humans who eat the contaminated fish or shellfish. In cases in which this indicator is high, fish consumption advisories are issued.

Vulnerability Indicators The IWI includes indicators that measure the vulnerability of a watershed. These indicators show whether human activities produce negative effects on the watershed. One such indicator measures the risk of extinction faced by various organisms in a watershed. If this indicator is high, measures often are taken to protect the species at risk.

Another vulnerability indicator, human population growth, can affect a watershed. A rapid increase in the number of people in an area can place stress on a watershed. The need for fresh water and the amount of runoff produced by humans and human activities are important vulnerability indicators. When both indicators are high, the creeks, streams, rivers, and estuaries in the watershed are at risk of becoming depleted or polluted.

Figure 1.23 Snowy egrets are long-legged wading birds often found in Pennsylvania wetlands.

Dams are another vulnerability indicator. Although dams regulate water flow to some areas, they prevent it from reaching others. In general, dams decrease water circulation. This, in turn, causes an increase in water temperature, a decrease in dissolved oxygen levels, and changes in the salinity and pH of affected water bodies. If not corrected, changes in these quantities often result in the deaths of many watershed organisms.

Health of U.S. Watersheds

A 1999 study of U.S. watersheds uses the Index of Watershed Indicators to suggest that the nation's watersheds are generally "in good health." To determine the health of a watershed, its condition indicators were scored and assigned to one of three categories: *better water quality, water quality with less serious problems,* and *water quality with more serious problems.* Then the watershed's vulnerability indicators were scored to create two categories: *high* and *low.* The two sets of indicators were combined to provide an overall description of water quality.

The results of this study suggest that about 23 percent of the nation's watersheds have more serious water quality problems today than they once did. About 15 percent of all U.S. watersheds have better water quality today than they did in the past. About one in three watersheds in the United States has some kind of water quality problems.

The map on this page shows the overall quality of Pennsylvania's watersheds as measured by the 1999 IWI study. What is the overall quality of watersheds as shown on the map? Find your county on the map. How does your watershed health compare with that of surrounding counties?

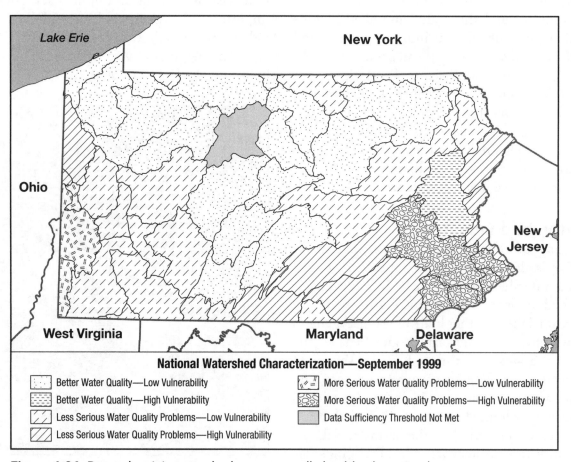

National Watershed Characterization—September 1999

Better Water Quality—Low Vulnerability		More Serious Water Quality Problems—Low Vulnerability	
Better Water Quality—High Vulnerability		More Serious Water Quality Problems—High Vulnerability	
Less Serious Water Quality Problems—Low Vulnerability		Data Sufficiency Threshold Not Met	
Less Serious Water Quality Problems—High Vulnerability			

Figure 1.24 Pennsylvania's watersheds are generally healthy, boasting better water quality and less vulnerability.

Figure 1.25 Sinneahoning Creek is buffered by trees, grasses, and bushes.

Pennsylvania's Stream ReLeaf Program

In addition to the negative effects that humans and human activities can have on wetlands and watersheds, they also can produce positive effects on these freshwater systems.

Many governmental agencies in the United States have established programs to preserve and restore riparian (streamside) buffers. Pennsylvania's Stream ReLeaf initiative was launched in 1997 with several general objectives. First, restoration of streamside buffers should occur on both private and government-owned lands. Restoration should be effective enough that it improves the waters along which it takes place. Second, all existing streamside buffers should be conserved to protect and improve forest diversity. Third, public education should provide interested persons with an understanding of the importance of streamside buffers to both present-day and future Pennsylvanians. Fourth,

public relations activities should raise awareness about streamside buffers. These activities also should generate enthusiasm for the program and encourage participation. Fifth, data on streamside buffer programs should be collected, evaluated, and reported. This objective allows all interested parties to track the program's progress.

Since the launch of Pennsylvania's Stream ReLeaf program, individuals in many private organizations, watershed associations, and community water-monitoring groups have planted forest buffers along many of the Commonwealth's streams and rivers. Streamside buffers, especially those that are at least 100 feet wide, are critical to many ecosystems. These buffers help remove sediment and chemicals in runoff. These forest buffers also provide shade and canopy to regulate temperature. Streamside vegetation aids in cycling nutrients through an ecosystem and provides habitat and food for many of the organisms that live on and around this vegetation.

Streamside buffers also benefit human communities by protecting groundwater recharge areas. These buffers also provide flood control by absorbing much of the rain and runoff in an area. Streamside buffers can be used to manage storm water. Channeling storm water into the buffers allows the water to be filtered. This filtering process helps reduce both nutrient and sediment loads. Forested streams also offer recreational and educational opportunities for people in the community. Streamside buffers also provide windbreak, shade, and scenery to an area.

Pennsylvania's Watershed Education Program

Teachers and their students in grades 6 through 12 can learn more about watersheds and wetlands through Pennsylvania's Watershed Education program, which is sponsored by the Department of Conservation and Natural Resources' Bureau of State Parks. The program combines classroom knowledge with field research, hands-on ecological investigations, and community service to produce "environmentally literate" people.

Objectives of Watershed Education, or WE as it is commonly called, include developing an appreciation for the local watershed and understanding the effects of human activities on the drainage basin. WE also strives to spark interest in aquatic ecosystems by encouraging hands-on observations of the physical, chemical, and biological characteristics of the bodies of water in a watershed. The results of these studies are shared with other schools, organizations, and agencies that are working to protect the watershed.

Natural Events Affect Watersheds and Wetlands

Many of the human activities and events that affect watersheds and wetlands have been presented. Along with humans and human activities, nature also plays a role in changing Earth's watersheds and the organisms that inhabit them. Some of these changes are beneficial to ecosystems; others are not.

Floods Floods are important to watersheds because they move nutrients and organic materials downstream. Floods, which can be seasonal or the result of severe weather, enrich a river's flood plain by depositing large quantities of silt onto the river's banks. Floodwaters can even change the shape and size of a river channel. In cases of severe flooding, entirely new channels may form.

Floods also can have a negative impact on a watershed. They can destroy wetland forests that thrive along a river's banks and carry organisms away from their native habitats. Flooding also can trigger landslides, causing massive amounts of sediment to flow downhill.

Erosion and Deposition Water constantly changes the land over which it flows by eroding and depositing sediment. The amount of sediment moved, or eroded, by a stream or river determines the shape of a channel. Channel shape, in turn, affects some of the river's physical factors such as velocity, discharge, and gradient, as well as stream biology. Sediment transport is directly related to the amount and severity of precipitation that the watershed receives. Likewise, deposition of sediment in and along a stream or river is related to severe weather, including drought and storms.

Drought A *drought* is a period in which the amount of precipitation that falls in an area is lower than normal. Obviously, droughts reduce the volume of water in a watershed. This reduction in water can affect the clarity, salinity, temperature, pH, and amount of sediment in the water bodies involved. Severe changes in these properties

Figure 1.26 Students test the water from their local river for pH and contaminants.

can have adverse effects on the organisms that inhabit the watershed. Periods of drought can also cause some bodies of water to disappear completely. The lack of suitable breeding and feeding grounds can cause decreases in many populations of organisms, including certain amphibians and birds.

Volcanic Eruptions A volcanic eruption is another natural event that can greatly alter a watershed. For instance, the 1980 eruption of Mount Saint Helens triggered massive mudslides that dammed and enlarged a nearby lake. Forests were burned or buried by the ash and other volcanic debris that rained over the area. The ash and dust filled streams and rivers, killing many organisms that inhabited these bodies of water.

Fires Wildfires can affect a watershed in different ways. Fires can damage or destroy vegetation in affected areas, causing an increase in the amount of runoff in an area. Fires that cover large areas in a steep, sloping watershed can cause an increase in erosion by moving water. Very intense wildfires can cause an increase in the temperatures of nearby water bodies, which in turn affects organisms that live in and around the waters.

Wildfires can also be beneficial to a watershed's vegetative cover. Some pines, for example, can reproduce only when their cones are exposed to intense heat. After a fire, the cones open and disperse seeds into the soil.

Wind Winds associated with severe weather can carry and drop large quantities of sediment into a body of water, reducing its clarity and increasing its turbidity. Wind is also partly responsible for the length of time a river or lake keeps its winter ice cap. The ice cap, in turn, affects certain physical and biological aspects of the water body.

Global Climate Change Natural, large-scale changes in climate occur about every 10,000 or so years. When Earth's overall climate is colder, much of the fresh water is locked up in glaciers, and the sea level drops. During warmer climates, the sea level rises. Various studies suggest that Earth's climate is warming and the sea level is rising. Increases in sea level can disrupt coastal wetlands by flooding, which causes wetlands to shift toward land. The rising sea level also can cause salt water to move into coastal wetlands. This influx of salt water changes the salinity of an ecosystem. These changes often result in salt-tolerant species replacing freshwater organisms. The influx of salty water also can inundate the wetlands with water, covering the wetland plants and changing the wetland into an open water environment. This change in environment is happening at a relatively rapid pace in the state of Louisiana.

Figure 1.27 Most of Pennsylvania's coastal wetlands are found along Lake Erie.

Case Study

The 1999 Summer Drought

Pennsylvania's average annual volume of precipitation is about 33,000 billion gallons. If annual precipitation is higher than normal, this value may reach 40,000 billion gallons. In a drought year, however, annual precipitation falls to about 22,600 billion gallons. In the past century, numerous droughts have affected Pennsylvania's watersheds. One of the most recent examples occurred in the summer of 1999. That period of severe water shortage affected Pennsylvania's economy, many of its people, and its freshwater systems.

Pennsylvania uses five parameters to assess drought conditions. The first is to compare the volume of stream flow in a watershed with the same time period on record. The second is the difference between actual precipitation and what is normal for that time. The third parameter is the storage level in a number of reservoirs in the state and in nearby states. The fourth parameter is the groundwater elevation in different places when compared with past elevations. The fifth parameter is the Palmer Drought Index, or PDI. This index measures soil moisture around the state.

From April to August 1999 the Northeast, which includes Pennsylvania, experienced the driest time of the twentieth century. The graph above shows, in inches, normal and irregular precipitation from July 1998 through August 1999. In Pennsylvania, this lack of rain was coupled with extreme temperatures. Temperatures exceeded 90°F on 15 of 31 days in July in the south and southeastern parts of the state, making the summer of 1999 the second-driest on record in Pennsylvania's history.

The monthly PDI for January 1900 through August 1999 for Pennsylvania is shown on the next page. Note that PDI values for 1999 reached −4.0, which indicates

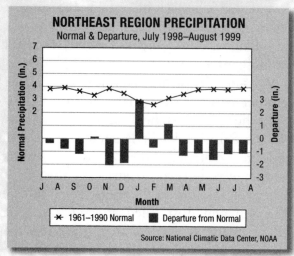

Figure 1.28 The Northeast Region was below normal precipitation levels for much of 1998 and 1999.

extreme, long-term drought. However, also note that the PDI indicates that the 1999 drought was not the worst long-term drought on record. The drought of the 1960s lasted much longer than the 1999 drought. However, the worst drought in Pennsylvania history (as measured by the magnitude of the PDI) occurred in 1930 and 1931.

Pennsylvania defines three stages of drought preparedness. A *drought watch* is a period during which governmental agencies, public water suppliers, water users, and the public are alerted to the possibility of drought. A request for voluntary water conservation is made with the goal of reducing water consumption by 5 percent. A *drought warning* is a period during which measures are taken to avoid or reduce shortages, to relieve stressed sources of water, and to find new sources of fresh water. The goal of the conservation measures during a drought warning is to reduce overall water usage by 10 to 15 percent in affected areas. A *drought emergency* is a period during which agencies, suppliers, and users, including the general public, are asked or even required to take measures to reduce water consumption by at least 15 percent.

On July 20, 1999, then-Governor Tom Ridge declared a drought emergency for 55 Pennsylvania counties, saying that Pennsylvania's water supply was at dangerously low levels. Ridge also said, "The water levels we're seeing today—in the middle of the summer—are on par with levels we would see in September or October. Groundwater levels typically won't begin to recharge until … the fall." By August 1999, Ridge had requested that the United States Department of Agriculture, or USDA, "declare all 67 counties [in the state] a federal drought disaster." Estimates of crop and livestock loss from the 1999 drought in the mid-Atlantic region, which includes Pennsylvania, reached $1.5 billion.

Some southern and all eastern counties in Pennsylvania were hardest hit by the drought. Not until precipitation from Hurricane Floyd and subsequent storms fell in late summer and early fall did the state's groundwater systems recharge to near normal levels. In August, groundwater levels were below normal in 92 percent of observation wells in the Delaware River Basin. Hurricane Floyd recharged the wells and left only 15 percent of them at below-normal levels. In the Susquehanna River Basin, 66 percent of observation wells were below normal before the hurricane, and other severe storms recharged half of them.

During the 1999 summer drought, stream flows throughout the mid-Atlantic region were well below normal. Some streams and rivers were at their lowest levels ever. The reduced stream flow caused many shallow wells in Pennsylvania to dry up. Susan Rickens of Pennsylvania's Department of Environmental Protection said that the large amount of runoff early in 1999 and the lack of spring and summer rains were particularly hard on groundwater levels. "We could be in this [drought] for a prolonged period," she said.

The reduction in stream flow also caused salt water to move 11 miles up the Delaware River from its normal position. This saltwater influx affected many wetland organisms. Some bay grasses were unable to adapt to the changes in salinity and died off. This resulted in a reduction in food supplies for certain waterfowl as well as habitat for young crustaceans. Changes in salinity also limited the spawning habitat of some perch and bass and subjected some oyster populations to diseases.

Pennsylvania suffered another severe drought in the fall of 2001, which many experts argue was still in effect in May 2002. On May 8, 2002, Governor Mark Schweiker announced that he was returning 24 counties in the state to normal status, but extending the drought emergency in 20 other Pennsylvania counties for another 90 days. Schweiker said, "… groundwater levels are still so low [in some areas] that extending the drought emergency for 20 of our counties is the right thing to do. Residents in the drought-emergency counties must remember to conserve water whenever possible."

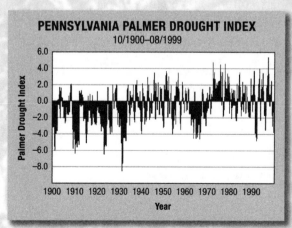

Figure 1.29 The Palmer Drought Index shows the level of soil moisture in Pennsylvania.

Water Conservation

Water is an important natural resource that always should be conserved. Work with other students to list at least ten ways in which you can conserve water. List at least ten more ways in which your community can conserve water. Compare your lists with the lists of other groups.

In the next column are some of Pennsylvania's nonessential water use restrictions during a drought emergency. Debate with another student whether these restrictions should be enforced regularly. Describe exceptions that might be plausible in various cases.

Some Pennsylvania Water Use Restrictions During Drought Emergencies

- Use of any water for watering grass
- Use of any water for watering athletic fields
- Use of fresh water for irrigation and watering of outdoor gardens, landscaped areas, trees, shrubs, and other outdoor plants
- Use of any water for ornamental purposes, including fountains, artificial waterfalls, and reflecting pools
- Use of any water for washing or cleaning of mobile equipment, including automobiles, trucks, buses, trailers, cars, wagons, railroad cars, campers, and boats
- Serving water in eating or drinking places

Lesson Review

1. Describe three negative effects of agriculture on wetlands.

2. Explain how municipal waste disposal can affect wetlands in the United States.

3. Contrast the two types of IWI indicators, and give two examples of each.

4. What are the objectives of Pennsylvania's Stream ReLeaf Program?

5. How do streamside buffers benefit human communities?

6. Describe how floods and droughts affect wetlands and watersheds.

7. How does global climate change affect coastal wetlands?

8. How might a drought affect watershed forests?

9. Contrast the three stages of drought preparedness in Pennsylvania.

10. Describe some of the effects the summer 1999 drought had on Pennsylvania and its residents.

Chapter 2

Renewable and Nonrenewable Resources

Every day we use resources such as batteries, fabric, lights, water, soap, toothpaste, food, electricity, paper, concrete, automobiles, and gasoline. The list is almost endless.

From where do these resources come? They come from Earth, either in raw form or as materials used to make new products. We often take many of them for granted, forgetting how our lives would be different without them.

Lesson 2.1

Earth's Resources

Until recently, most experts defined natural resources as only those things that provide people with manufacturing materials or energy. That definition now has expanded to include all of Earth's organisms, air, water, and soil, as well as materials such as oil, gas, and ores that are removed from the ground.

Renewable Resources

Traditionally, plants, animals, and other economically important organisms were the only resources labeled as renewable because they were able to reproduce, or replenish, themselves in a reasonable amount of time. Most scientists today, however, define reasonable time as within the period of a human life span. Therefore, a *renewable resource* is any material or energy source that cycles or can be replaced within

Figure 2.1 From the moment we get up in the morning, we begin to use resources.

Figure 2.2 Wheat is grown in Pennsylvania, providing a renewable food and fiber resource as long as the soil is protected and maintained.

the period of a human life span. Renewable resources include crops, soil, wind, sunlight, water, organic matter, and geothermal energy. People use these resources every day.

Food and Fiber Food and fiber are renewable agriculture resources such as the crops grown for human and livestock consumption, wild and planted forest crops, and wild and domesticated animals. These resources can be harvested or raised indefinitely, unless their use exceeds their rate of reproduction. If the resources are used faster than they can be replanted or can reproduce themselves, the resource will become exhausted, or used up.

Soil Soil is a mixture of living and nonliving materials—tiny rocks, minerals, organic matter, water, and air—that provides habitat for plants and organisms. Soil forms over a period of thousands of years when rocks are exposed to wind, water, and other agents of change. The rate at which soil forms varies with the climate of the area. Hot, humid climates form larger amounts of soil more quickly, but dry climates

form very small amounts of soil over longer periods of time. Because it does take thousands of years for soil to form, it may seem incorrect to classify soil as a renewable resource. However, soil is renewable as long as the living organic matter in the soil remains fertile. If soil is abused to a point at which it can no longer sustain life, then it becomes a nonrenewable resource.

Wind Wind is air in motion. Wind blows because Earth's surfaces are not evenly heated. Wind is a resource because it can be used to generate electricity, and it is renewable because it is inexhaustible.

The Sun The light provided by the sun is another resource that is essentially inexhaustible. Sunlight is *solar energy* and is vital to our planet because it provides heat and light. Experts have estimated that at the sun's current rate of production, it is capable of providing energy in the form of light and heat for the next 5 billion years. However, without the sun Earth would not be capable of supporting life as we know it. The sun provides the light energy needed by autotrophs to produce their own food. Autotrophs, in turn, become the food sources for heterotrophs. The sun is also the source of all energy resources. Energy from the sun is released as heat or light when fuels are burned.

Water The amount of water on Earth today is the same as it was when Earth formed almost 5 billion years ago. About 326 million trillion gallons of water are found in, on, and above our planet, covering approximately 70 percent of Earth. This water simply changes form as it moves throughout Earth via the water cycle.

As you learned in Chapter 1, of the total amount of water on Earth, only about 3 percent is fresh water. However, a clean, constant supply of fresh water is essential to every community. In many parts of the world, however, unpolluted fresh water is becoming scarce. Many streams, rivers, and lakes, as well as the ground-water they feed, are contaminated. Groundwater and other freshwater systems are being depleted faster than natural processes can recharge them. Thus, although water is generally considered a renewable resource, its use and quality must be carefully monitored to protect it.

Biomass Fuels *Biomass fuels* are organic matter that contain stored solar energy. Most biomass fuels are plant parts such as wood products, dried vegetation, crop residues, and aquatic plants, all of which produce energy upon combustion. Other biomass fuels are derived from animal wastes.

Biomass has become one of the most commonly used renewable energy sources in the last two decades. In fact, biomass accounts for almost 15 percent of the world's total energy supply and provides as much as 35 percent of the energy used for cooking and heating in developing countries.

Geothermal Energy The heat generated deep within Earth is another renewable resource. This form of energy, called geothermal energy, is fueled by the decay of radioactive elements. *Geothermal energy* is heat that is transferred by water, which can be brought to the surface and used to drive electric generators as well as to heat homes and other buildings.

Figure 2.3 Not only is water a vital resource for human and animal consumption but it also provides a habitat for millions of species.

Nonrenewable Resources

A *nonrenewable resource* is a material or energy source that cannot be replaced during the time of a human life span. Most of Earth's nonrenewable resources took millions of years to form. Therefore, before they do become depleted, we must conserve them while searching for alternative resources.

Ores Mineral deposits from which valuable metals and nonmetals can be recovered at a profit are called *ores*. Metallic ores include iron, aluminum, copper, zinc, lead, silver, gold, and manganese, among others. Most of the iron mined in the United States comes from rocks that formed billions of years ago when Earth's atmosphere was oxygen-poor. At that time, simple blue-green algae lived in the oceans and produced oxygen as a waste product. The dissolved iron in the water combined with that oxygen to form what are known as banded iron formations. Today, the bands of these ore deposits are alternating layers of several iron-rich minerals.

Many of the other metallic ores formed when very hot solutions percolated through cracks in Earth's rocks. The very high temperatures of these solutions caused chemical reactions that formed minerals rich in metal. Gold, silver, and other precious metal deposits also formed when hydrothermal fluids changed existing rocks into precious metals.

Nonmetallic ores include fluorite, salt, clay, sand, gravel, diamonds, gypsum, sulfur, talc, and quartz, among others. Many of these nonmetallic ores are used in fertilizers, cements, building materials, and fiber optics. Salt is used in food preparation and preservation and to de-ice roads, sidewalks, and bridges. Diamonds and other gemstones are commonly used as jewelry, but some are also used to make industrial abrasives.

Rocks as Resources Rocks are mixtures of one or more minerals. Common inorganic, economically important rocks of Pennsylvania include marble, sandstone, granite, limestone, shale, and slate. Most of these rocks are used as ornamental stones in buildings and the grounds that surround them.

Pennsylvania's Rock and Mineral Resources The people who inhabited Pennsylvania

Figure 2.4 This quarry in Monroe County mines sandstone, an economically important rock in Pennsylvania.

thousands of years ago used many of the iron-bearing minerals found in the state's rocks as pigments. They made pottery using the clay and talc found throughout the state. Metallic minerals such as iron, lead, copper, nickel, and zinc were among the ores mined in and around present-day Philadelphia and other major Pennsylvania cities at the turn of the 20th century. Today, however, there are no metal mines in operation in Pennsylvania. The major nonmetallic resources mined in the Commonwealth today include coal, limestone, granite, slate, sand, gravel, and clay.

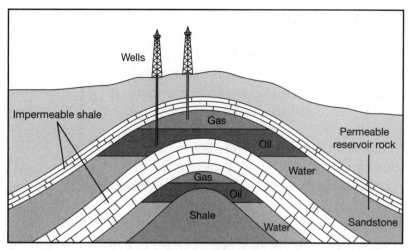

Figure 2.5 As mountains formed, the underlying rocks folded, creating structural traps. Gas, oil, and water are often trapped between layers of impermeable shale.

Fossil Fuels

When wood, charcoal, peat, coal, oil, and natural gas are burned, stored, or fossilized, energy is released. These fuels are called *fossil fuels*. Fossil fuels are nonrenewable resources because they take millions of years to form. In most developing countries, wood, charcoal, and peat are the major fossil fuels burned to provide energy. In developed countries, coal, oil, and natural gas are the primary sources of energy.

Coal Coal is a fossil fuel that forms when wetland plants die, become buried, and undergo physical and chemical changes over millions of years. The first stage in coal formation is peat, a porous brown mass of organic matter in which twigs, roots, and other plant parts can still be recognized. Peat, which is about 50 percent carbon, is used as a fuel in many developing nations as well as in some European countries.

Over time, peat becomes compressed and some of the oxygen, hydrogen, and water in the organic matter are forced out. These changes, as well as increases in temperature, cause peat to become lignite, a soft, brown organic material that is about 70 percent carbon. Eventually, increases in pressures and temperatures change lignite into bituminous coal, or soft coal,

containing about 85 percent carbon. Ultimately, bituminous coal becomes anthracite, or hard coal. Anthracite contains very little water, oxygen, or hydrogen and is more than 90 percent carbon. This high carbon content makes anthracite a very clean-burning coal.

The leading producers of coal are the former Soviet Union, which produces about 50 percent of the world's coal resources; China, which produces about 20 percent; and the United States, which contributes about 15 percent. Much of the coal produced in the United States is lignite and bituminous coal. The coal fields of western Pennsylvania are bituminous coal, whereas the coal mined in the eastern part of the state is anthracite.

Petroleum and Natural Gas Petroleum, or oil as it is commonly called, and natural gas are other nonrenewable fossil fuels. Oil and gas are the remains of plants, bacteria, algae, and other microscopic marine organisms. Oil and gas begin to form when more organic matter is produced than is destroyed. This condition is common in coastal marine waters. During millions of years of burial, chemical and physical reactions take place that change the organic matter in liquid and gaseous compounds.

Although Pennsylvania does not produce significant amounts of oil and gas today, these fossil fuels played an important role in the state's economic development. An oil well drilled in Titusville, Pennsylvania, in 1859 marked the beginning of the 19th-century oil boom in the United States. Since then, oil and natural gas have been used as fuels and in the manufacture of lubricants, fertilizers, plastics, and many other substances we use every day.

The rocks in which oil and gas form are called source rocks. But because oil and gas are fluids, they often migrate and collect in nearby rocks called reservoir rocks. Oil, because it is denser than gas, is found near the bottom of the reservoir. Gas, on the other hand, migrates to the top of a reservoir. The reservoir shown on the previous page is called a structural trap. It formed when oil and gas migrated from the source rock and became trapped in the reservoir rocks when all of the rocks in the area were folded.

Global Energy Use and Production

Experts say that the world's total energy consumption increased by nearly 50 percent from 1973 to 1993. Many energy experts anticipate these upward trends to continue in most countries. Global coal use, for example, is expected to increase more than 50 percent over the next two decades. Developing nations, especially Asia, will require the greatest increase in coal consumption. In those countries, coal is the main heating source in homes, and as the population continues to increase, so will the demand for coal. The amount of oil needed is also expected to rise rapidly, predominantly in areas such as China, India, and Thailand. In these Asian countries, the number of motor vehicles per capita is still very low, but as consumers' incomes continue to increase, the number of vehicles is expected to increase as well.

Study the graph on this page, which shows projected global energy use through the year 2010. Notice that developed nations belonging to the OECD, or Organization for Economic Co-operation and Development, consume more than half of all commercial energy. Members of the OECD include Australia, New Zealand, Canada, the United States, the European Union, Iceland, Japan, Mexico, and the United Kingdom. Experts predict, however, that over the next few decades, developing and primarily agricultural nations such as Africa and most of Latin America, and transition economies such as those in central and eastern Europe, the former Soviet Union, and much of Asia will increase their share of energy use to nearly 40 percent. This potential increase in the energy consumption of developing nations can be attributed to impending rapid economic expansion, population growth, and the replacement of traditional biomass fuels with fossil fuels such as coal, oil, and natural gas.

Using more fossil fuels will increase air pollution and produce more greenhouse gases, both of which will likely accelerate the global warming trend. What other effects will a growth in global energy use produce?

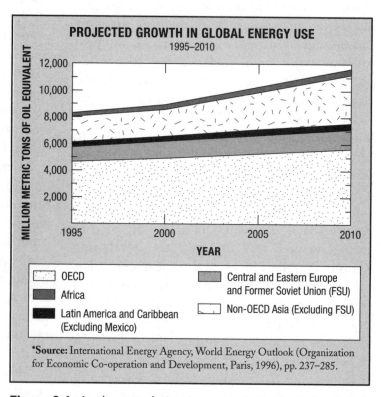

Figure 2.6 As the population increases expotentially, global energy use is also expected to increase.

Field Study

Reducing Dependence on Fossil Fuels

The United States produces only about 11 percent of the world's oil but consumes almost 26 percent of that total. This petroleum provides about 40 percent of the energy used in the country. About 60 percent of oil is used for transportation. How can we reduce our dependence on oil and other fossil fuels?

Materials	
pencil	ruler
paper	calculator

Procedure

1. Use the pencil, paper, and ruler to make a three-column table with eight rows. List each of the statements below in the first column, one per row.

   - Give incentives for building energy-efficient houses and other buildings.
   - Build power plants that use alternative energy such as nuclear energy, hydropower, and wind energy.
   - Give incentives for gasoline conservation efforts.
   - Build more fuel-efficient motor vehicles.
   - Increase prices at the gas pumps to encourage conservation.
   - Develop more domestic petroleum resources.
   - Develop and build public transportation systems.
   - Increase taxes on conventional fuels.

2. Survey at least ten adults to determine the three most effective ways of those listed to reduce the U.S. consumption of fossil fuels.

3. Record the responses with tally marks in the second column of the table.

4. As a class, compile the results, and determine what percentage of survey participants responded to each suggestion. Put these values in the third column of the data table.

Conclusions

1. How did your results compare with those of other students?

2. What were the three most effective ways of reducing fossil fuel consumption?

For Discussion

1. Which three statements do you and your classmates think would be most effective in reducing fossil fuel dependence? Which would you support?

2. Are any of these methods being used in your community?

3. Which three of these possibilities do you think would be most easily implemented in your community? Why?

Extension

With a partner, research federal programs that are working to curb U.S. dependence on the amount of oil it imports. Post your results in a public area of your community.

Alternative Energy Resources

In developed nations today, most energy is provided by coal, oil, and natural gas. Because these fossil fuels are nonrenewable resources, other sources of energy, or alternative energy resources, must be developed and used. Some currently used alternative energy sources include the sun, wind, geothermal energy, hydropower, nuclear power, and even trash. Another promising energy alternative being developed is hydrogen fuel.

Solar Energy Solar energy can be used to heat buildings and water and provide electricity to power lights and appliances. A passive solar heating system is one in which the sun's energy is collected through large south-facing windows, absorbed by tiles or bricks, and released when the air above the absorbing materials is cooler than the materials. Solar cells, or photovoltaic cells (PVs), can convert solar energy directly into electricity to pump water, light highways, and power electrical systems located far from power lines. Another method used to harness solar energy is solar thermal systems, which concentrate sunlight to produce heat, which in turn causes water to boil and produce steam. The steam rotates a turbine and causes it to move. The turbine is attached to a generator that produces electricity.

Wind Wind is already used in many developed countries to produce electricity. The blades on a wind turbine drive a generator, much like a steam turbine. The longer the blades on the wind turbine and the faster the wind speed, the more electricity the turbine generates. Groups of turbines are called wind farms. The turbines of a wind farm are connected to electric utility power lines to provide electricity.

More than two dozen wind turbines are already installed in five locations around Pennsylvania. The current turbines provide enough electricity to power about 2,800 households. These wind facilities were built in response to consumer demand. Farms, private residences, businesses, hotels, colleges, and universities across Pennsylvania have chosen to use renewable wind energy to supply their electical needs.

Hydropower Energy from rivers and streams can be captured to produce electricity. Dams create large bodies of water that can be released to flow through turbines that are connected to generators. Twenty-three dams in Pennsylvania generate electricity. Hydropower plants generate about 10 percent of the total electricity produced in the United States.

Geothermal Energy Geothermal energy is heat from deep within Earth that can be used to produce electricity. The water in geothermal reservoirs, which may be hundreds or thousands of feet beneath the surface, can be brought to the surface as either hot water or steam. Nearly two dozen countries, including the United States and France, generate some of their electricity using geothermal heat. The capital of Iceland, Reykjavík, receives all of its heat from the volcanic geothermal reservoirs in the area.

Figure 2.7 The Kinzua Dam, near Warren, Pennsylvania, rises 179 feet above the Allegheny River and is 1,877 feet long. The dam regulates the water level of the Allegheny Reservoir, and the discharge water can be used to generate electricity.

Nuclear Power Nuclear power is an alternative energy resource that uses the fission, or natural splitting, of a specific form of uranium to generate electricity. The fission process releases energy as heat that turns liquid water into steam. That steam drives turbines that generate electricity. Currently, 25 countries generate some of their electricity in nuclear power plants. In France, about 75 percent of the electricity needs are supplied by nuclear energy. In the United States, more than 100 nuclear reactors provide about 20 percent of the nation's electricity. Pennsylvania is home to nine operating reactors in five locations—Beaver Valley, Three Mile Island, Peach Bottom, Susquehanna, and Limerick—that generate more than one third of the energy produced in Pennsylvania. One of those reactors, Three Mile Island, is located about 10 miles south of Harrisburg, Pennsylvania. In 1979, Three Mile Island suffered a partial reactor meltdown that is considered the most serious nuclear accident in United States history. That accident brought to a standstill the development of nuclear power in the United States. Some plants that were already completed at the time have never been allowed to open, and no nuclear power plants have been commissioned since the Three Mile Island meltdown.

Trash Trash is another alternative energy resource. Trash can be burned in power plants to generate electric power. Municipal waste-to-energy plants in the United States currently generate about 2,500 megawatts of electricity. This amount is equal to the same amount of power produced by several large coal-burning power plants. Pennsylvania alone has seven waste-to-energy plants that handle almost 19 million tons of waste per year.

Trash can also provide fuel as it decomposes. Decaying food scraps and other wastes produce methane, the main ingredient in natural gas. Energy alternative experts propose that wells be drilled into landfills to release and capture the gas. Pipes could then transport the methane so that it could be processed and burned to produce steam to generate electricity.

Hydrogen Hydrogen is the H in H_2O. Because three fourths of Earth's surface is covered with water, the supply of hydrogen seems almost as inexhaustible as solar energy. Hydrogen is an extremely clean way to produce energy. Hydrogen fuel cells emit only a small amount of heat and water instead of pollutants and toxins. Because of these low emissions, energy experts believe that hydrogen is the fuel of the future. Hydrogen is now being used on a small scale to produce energy to power automobiles.

A hydrogen fuel cell works much like a battery. Hydrogen is pumped to the cell's negatively charged side. There, the gas breaks into its subatomic particles—protons (positively charged particles) and electrons (negatively charged particles). Oxygen is then pumped into the fuel cell's positively charged side. A metal membrane prevents the electrons from moving to the positive side and forces them through a circuit that produces electric current. The membrane allows protons to pass through to join the oxygen in the positively charged part of the cell, where the protons combine with the oxygen to form water. The water is then released from the cell, and the process begins again.

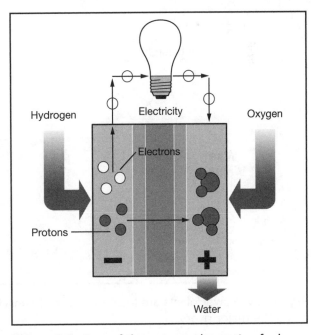

Figure 2.8 One of the newest alternative fuel options is a hydrogen fuel cell. Fuel cells are being used in some places in public transportation and in some newer vehicles.

Fossil Fuel Production and Consumption in Pennsylvania

Like people in many states, Pennsylvanians use more petroleum and natural gas than is actually produced in the state. In 1999, for example, Pennsylvania produced about 1.5 million barrels of oil and used approximately 2.5 billion barrels. In that same year, 1.7 million cubic feet of natural gas were produced in Pennsylvania, compared with the 672 billion cubic feet used. Coal is another major fossil fuel used in Pennsylvania. In 1999, Pennsylvanians produced about 7.6 million short tons of coal and used more than half of it—about 4.5 million short tons.

Although Pennsylvanians' reliance on fossil fuels is relatively high, the more than 12 million people who live in the state also use several types of renewable resources to provide their annual energy needs. This is shown on the map below. Of the total energy generated in Pennsylvania in 1999, coal generated just over half of that and nuclear power plants generated another third. Natural gas and petroleum each fueled about 2 percent of the electricity generated. Hydroelectric plants fueled a little more than half a percent of the electricity generated in 1999 in the Commonwealth, and all other sources fueled about 5 percent.

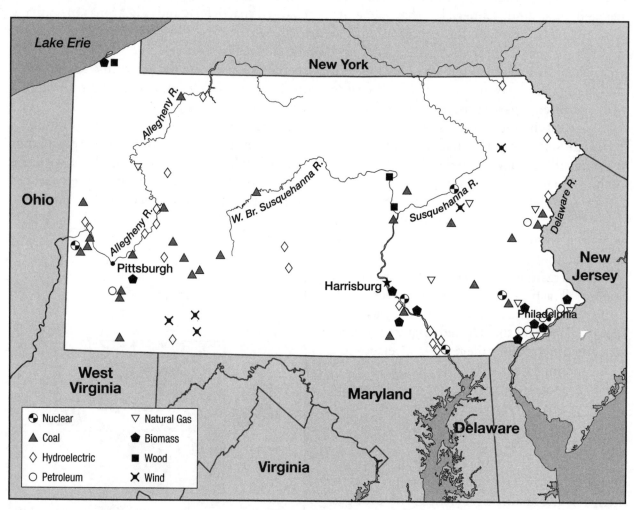

Figure 2.9 Power plants are located all over Pennsylvania, but mostly along the major rivers.

Electricity Generation in Pennsylvania

Use the information from the lesson and the map on the facing page to answer the following questions about generating electricity in Pennsylvania.

1. Where are most of the state's power plants that use petroleum as the major fuel?

2. What types of fuel are used to generate electricity in the Pittsburgh area?

3. Name Pennsylvania's nuclear power plants.

4. Locate the wind generating plants in the eastern part of the state. What makes this area of Pennsylvania suitable for wind power?

5. Where are most of the coal-powered, electricity-generating plants in Pennsylvania?

6. Are there any biomass plants in the state? If so, where are they found?

7. Where do you think the wood to run Pennsylvania's wood-powered facilities comes from?

8. Along which two major rivers are most of Pennsylvania's hydroelectric plants located?

9. According to the map information alone, what type of fuel is used to generate the electricity in your area?

10. Which fossil fuel was used to generate the most electricity in Pennsylvania in 1999? Do you think the use of this fuel in the Commonwealth will increase or decrease in the next decade or two? Explain your answer.

Lesson Review

1. What is a renewable resource?

2. Explain why food and fiber are renewable resources.

3. What is soil, and what affects its rate of formation?

4. What are biomass fuels, and where are these fuels primarily used today?

5. Define a nonrenewable resource, and list at least five examples of such resources.

6. What are the major nonmetallic ores mined in Pennsylvania today?

7. Compare and contrast energy consumption in developed and developing nations.

8. How is the global use of coal expected to change over the next 20 years?

9. Explain three types of solar heating systems.

10. Explain how a hydrogen fuel cell works.

11. Identify three alternative energy sources.

12. What disadvantages are associated with using energy from the sun and wind?

Lesson 2.2
Availability of Resources

Nearly every resource from food to fuel needs to be removed from Earth and processed in some way before it can be made available to the consumer. Some extraction and processing methods are relatively simple and involve little or no equipment and energy. Other resource removal and processing methods are complex and involve sophisticated machinery run by computers. The availability of our natural resources is related to the costs of extracting and processing them.

Removing Earth's Resources

Advances in technology have affected our use of natural resources. Inventions involving both simple and complex machines have made the removal of most resources very efficient and cost-effective.

Harvesting Food and Fiber Early farmers and foresters often relied on nothing more than a hoe, a sickle, an animal-drawn cart, an ax, and a handsaw to plant and harvest their crops and timber. Since the early 1900s, however, many kinds of machines have revolutionized farming and forestry in most countries. Instead of using a hoe in their fields today, farmers may use a cultivator or a disk to remove weeds. Both are pulled by tractors and remove weeds by digging up the soil. Cultivators have hoelike parts that look like claws and turn the soil between rows, and disks have sharp, round blades that turn the soil in the spring.

Sickles have been replaced by machines such as windrowers and combines. Windrowers cut swaths of grasses or forage crops into neat rows to dry in the sun. The windrows are turned periodically with other machines so that they dry evenly, and they are then baled for food or bedding. A combine cuts the crop and removes the seed from its protective layers. The combine's header cuts the grain, which is then delivered to the threshing machine. The threshing cylinder rubs the grain out of the protective heads and sends it to the cleaning shoe. The cleaning shoe uses air to separate dirt and chaff from the grain, which then falls into an auger where it is transported to the storage tank.

Figure 2.10 Today's agricultural equipment increases production efficiency. This tractor powers the baler, which then drops the bales of straw into the hayrack. With sides on the hayrack, only one person is needed to bale this field of straw.

In the past, harvesting timber in developed nations was done with a simple ax and a handsaw. Today, however, most trees are felled with chain saws or circular saws. These saws are used to make wedge-shaped cuts into the trees, causing them to fall. Chain saws are also used to remove the unwanted limbs. Bark removal is sometimes done with an ax or a device called a spud, which consists of a chisel and spade. The timber is then hoisted by cable systems onto trucks or other heavy equipment and transported out of the forest for further processing.

Quarries A *quarry* is an excavation pit in Earth's crust from which rock resources are removed. Some of the rock removed from a quarry is used as dimensional stone for buildings, columns, flooring, and countertops. This rock is removed as large slabs—which often weigh several tons—by drilling closely spaced holes into the rock formation to separate the dimensional stone from the rest of the rock body. Crushed stone is another common quarry product that is mined by setting off a large number of blasts to fragment the rock. Tens of thousands of tons of crushed rock can be produced from a single blast. The broken rock is then crushed into smaller pieces and often sorted by size before it leaves the quarry.

Oil and Gas Wells Some of the hydrocarbon wells drilled in Pennsylvania, Ohio, and other neighboring states in the late 1800s and early 1900s were drilled specifically for oil. At the time, the natural gas associated with the oil was considered useless and was often flared, or burned. Today, however, much of the gas, along with the oil pumped from wells, is collected, processed, and eventually sold.

Oil and gas wells today are drilled using a complex set of machines, engines, pumps, pipes, and drills that is collectively called a rig. A rig has four major systems: the power supply system, the mechanical system, the rotating equipment, and the circulation system. The power system is made up of many engines and motors that provide the energy needed to operate the rig. The mechanical system includes numerous winches and pulleys used to lift heavy

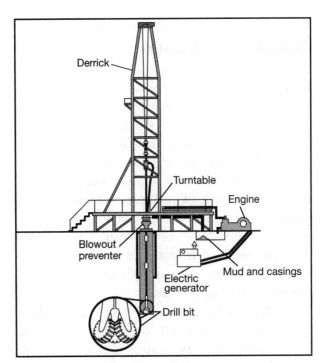

Figure 2.11 Oil rigs drill through rock reservoirs to reach oil reserves. These rigs are replaced by oil pumps after oil is flowing.

loads. The rotating equipment is composed of pipes, cables, turntables, and drill bits, which all spin and turn as they drill deeper into the crust to produce the well. The circulation system consists of pumps and pipes that cycle mud and water through the hole to prevent damage to the drill bit and to keep the hole from imploding.

After the well is complete, the flow of oil is started by pumping either acid or a gritty liquid into the well. In a limestone reservoir, the acid creates channels in the limestone. The oil then flows from these channels into the well. The gritty liquid contains ingredients such as sand, walnut shells, and aluminum pellets and is used in a sandstone reservoir. This mixture is forced into the well and exerts pressure on the rocks, causing fractures to form. Oil then moves along these fractures into the well.

When oil is flowing into the well, the rig is removed from the site and a pump is placed on the wellhead. An electric motor in the pump drives a gear box that causes the long metal arm of the pump to move up and down. This plunging motion creates a suction that draws the oil up through the well.

Natural Events Can Affect Resource Availability

Technology plays a major role in extracting Earth's resources and making them available to consumers. But the availability of natural resources also depends on natural disasters, including severe weather, biological infestations, fires, and natural oil seeps, among others.

Severe Weather Periods of excessive precipitation or lack of precipitation can lead to flooding and drought, respectively. Both of these weather-related extremes can cause crop damage. Too much water can cause crops to rot. Too little water causes plants to yield less, or even to wither and die.

Unseasonably cold weather can also reduce the availability of some food and fiber crops. Citrus fruits such as lemons and oranges, for example, are one food resource easily affected by cold weather. When temperatures drop into the low 20s (°F) or teens for several days in a row, the fruits become damaged and can even freeze. In 1990, a long cold snap in California's San Joaquin Valley caused more than $780 million in agricultural damage—most of which affected citrus crops.

Biological Infestations Biological infestations occur when unwanted organisms enter or infect a natural resource. Many of these unwanted organisms are *pathogens,* which are organisms that cause disease. Pathogens are found in all freshwater bodies. Drinking water as well as water for other domestic and commercial needs is treated to remove these potentially dangerous organisms. Sometimes, however, pathogens enter the water supply and contaminate it. *Cryptosporidium,* or crypto as it is often called, is a pathogen whose eggs can enter surface water when heavy rains increase the amount of animal wastes in runoff. In 1987, although the municipal water system had met all state and federal drinking water standards, 13,000 people in Carrollton, Georgia, became ill with cryptosporidiosis, the disease caused by crypto. In 1993, approximately 400,000 people became ill and several died in Milwaukee, Wisconsin, when the municipal drinking water, which was within governmental standards, was contaminated with *Cryptosporidium.*

Natural Oil Seeps Oil spills are accidents that result from human activities. Oil seeps, however, are natural events that can affect the quality and quantity of some of Earth's resources. As much as 1.5 million barrels of oil may enter Earth's oceans from natural seeps every year. Fortunately, when these seeps occur, various biological and chemical processes break down the oil over time. However, when the oil does mix with water, it can contaminate freshwater drinking sources upstream and affect some of the aquatic organisms used as human food sources.

Fire Between June and September 1988, wildfires burned and destroyed millions of acres of forests in Yellowstone National Park and surrounding areas. Although the fires played an important role in regenerating forest ecosystems, the timber industry in this part of the United States lost millions of dollars as a result of the fires. Fires associated with volcanic eruptions can also affect forest resources. The 1980 eruption of Mount Saint Helens, for example, destroyed almost 99,000 acres of timber-rich land by blanketing the area in ashes and gas that approached 1,000°F.

Figure 2.12 When Mount Saint Helens erupted in 1980, thousands of acres of forest land were destroyed.

Middle Atlantic Census Division Energy Consumption

In this activity, you will evaluate some effects of consumer desires on natural resources in the Middle Atlantic Census Division, which consists of New Jersey, New York, and Pennsylvania. You will also compare energy uses in this part of the country with those of the total United States.

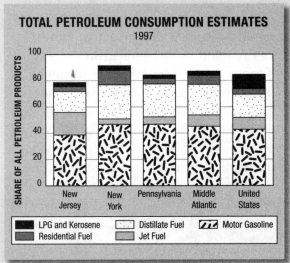

TOTAL PETROLEUM CONSUMPTION ESTIMATES
1997

SHARE OF ALL PETROLEUM PRODUCTS

New Jersey • New York • Pennsylvania • Middle Atlantic • United States

Legend:
- ■ LPG and Kerosene
- ▨ Residential Fuel
- ▦ Distillate Fuel
- Jet Fuel
- ▨ Motor Gasoline

Source: Energy Information Agency

Figure 2.13 The dense population, number of flights, and amount of industry in the Middle Atlantic region all contribute to the region's high petroleum use.

- According to the U.S. Energy Information Administration, the major fossil fuel resources used in Pennsylvania are coal and natural gas. In New York, natural gas provides the most fossil fuel energy. Explain why.
- Winter energy costs in the Middle Atlantic are higher than those for the United States as a whole. Why?
- The per-household demand for electricity for air conditioning in the Middle Atlantic Census region is lower than the U.S. average. Why?

Use the graph at left to answer the following questions.

1. How does Middle Atlantic petroleum consumption compare with U.S. consumption as a whole?

2. Why do you think New York uses more residential fuel than either New Jersey or Pennsylvania?

3. After the gasoline used in motor vehicles, which fuel is consumed in the largest quantity in New Jersey? Why?

4. How does Pennsylvania's consumption of petroleum products compare with that of the United States as a whole?

Lesson Review

1. What are two modern farming machines used to prepare soil and control weeds?

2. Explain how an agricultural combine works.

3. What types of products are generally removed from a quarry? How is each mined?

4. Explain the function of each of the major systems of an oil rig.

5. Name four natural events that can affect the availability of timber.

6. Discuss ways in which global warming will affect Pennsylvania's forests.

Case Study

Natural Events Affect Pennsylvania's Forest Industry

Nearly 60 percent, or more than 17 million acres, of Pennsylvania is covered with hardwood forests. The industry supported by many of these forests provides more than 100,000 people with jobs and contributes about $5 billion to the state's economy each year. Like many of Earth's biological resources, Pennsylvania's forests are affected by many natural events, including severe weather, fire, biological infestations, and global warming.

In 1999, for example, Hurricane Floyd's damaging winds toppled thousands of trees at Ricketts Glen State Park in Luzerne County. Hundreds of acres of black cherry, red maple, and mixed oak were damaged or destroyed by the storm, which was a serious financial loss for Pennsylvania's timber industry. The downed and damaged timber also increased the risk of wildfire. Helicopter-assisted logging operations began a year later to clean up the damage. The valuable logs were removed, but the treetops were left to add biomass and nutrients to the forest floor and to help protect new seedling growth from foraging deer.

Also in 1999, the combination of below-average rainfall, a long period of warm weather, and the previous mild winter resulted in the most widespread and damaging drought on record in Pennsylvania and surrounding states. Many trees died from drought-related diseases including crown dieback—when the branch tips in the crown of the tree die—and stem and branch cankers.

Drought conditions can intensify the damage that other pests can do. In 1999 alone, insect defoliation in Pennsylvania totaled 333,595 acres. The greatest damage was caused by gypsy moths. Both an increase in the gypsy moth populations and a decrease in gypsy moth mortality rates contributed to the loss of many Pennsylvania oaks and some conifers.

On the other hand, drought can have a positive effect on forests as well. From 1994 through 1998, for example, a fungal disease called sycamore anthracnose caused extensive crown dieback, crown thinning, and tree mortality throughout Pennsylvania's sycamore forests. But because many fungi prefer moist habitat, the 1999 drought that affected the Commonwealth caused this particular disease to subside well into the year 2000.

Most forest fires in Pennsylvania are caused by careless human activities. Others are the result of the spontaneous combustion of forest debris. The 1999 fire season in Pennsylvania was more severe than normal because of the drought conditions in the state. One of the more costly fires occurred in the Tobyhanna State Park, where a bog fire burned for more than two weeks. That

Figure 2.14 High winds can damage or destroy even mature trees.

area is off limits to forest firefighters on the ground because of the unexploded shells that were left over from artillery training from World Wars I and II. Thus, Army and National Guard helicopters dumped more than 200,000 gallons of water on the fire, which covered about 20 acres. Fire-fighting foams were also dropped from the helicopters to contain the fire.

Another natural event that has already affected and will continue to affect Pennsylvania's forests is global warming. Scientists are researching global warming and using computer models to show the effects of changes in global temperatures and annual precipitation. The study indicates that global climate changes over the past few decades have already caused warblers to move their nesting sites north more than 40 miles. Losing warblers could increase forest pest problems, resulting in a loss of timber production. Global warming could also reduce the blue jay populations in Pennsylvania and surrounding states. Blue jays are primary distributors of oak seeds, so a decrease in the number of blue jays will result in fewer oak forests in the area.

Fisheries will likely suffer from the effects of global warming, too. An increase of a few degrees in air temperature will increase the number of warm water streams and affect most of the state's trout species. The many brook trout that inhabit Pennsylvania's streams, for example, require clean, clear, cool waters. Increased water temperatures over the past few decades have already forced many of these fish to move to higher, cooler streams. The change in distribution of these trout is expected to continue. Brown and rainbow trout, on the other hand, are less sensitive to temperature fluctuations and have moved into the brook trout ranges, causing more competition among the trout.

Figure 2.15 The stream habitat of Pennsylvania's brook trout is threatened by warmer waters.

Forest plants would be affected by global warming as well. An increase in temperature of just over 5 degrees Fahrenheit would change the appropriate temperature range for 7 to 11 percent of the vascular plants found in North America. These species could become extinct unless they were able to migrate rapidly or adjust to the temperature increase. A climate change would also favor exotic, invasive weed species that spread and adapt to environmental changes quicker than native species do.

Unfortunately, these natural events are not the only factors affecting Pennsylvania's forest resources. Human activities and actions, too, are stressing the Commonwealth's forest ecosystems. Acid precipitation and acid mine drainage are degrading numerous patches of forests as well as many of the freshwater bodies within the forest ecosystems. Exotic species are rapidly displacing many of the state's native plants and animals. Loss of habitat and the increasing demand for lumber as the result of urbanization are also taking their toll on Pennsylvania's forest resources.

Lesson 2.3
Distribution and Management of Natural Resources

In nearly every house in Pennsylvania, a flick of a switch provides electricity to light a room or to power a computer. Turning a knob provides the gas or electricity used for cooking. Furnaces convert the energy stored in fuel into heat that keeps the house warm in the winter. Electricity powers the refrigerators that keep many food and fiber resources fresh. What makes all of these things possible?

Pennsylvania Coal

Pennsylvania produces more than half of its electricity in coal-burning power plants around the state. Most of the coal that is used as fuel in these plants, in fact, is the bituminous coal that is mined from the nearly 22 billion tons of coal reserves in the western part of the state. Pennsylvania's anthracite, or hard coal, which is found as scattered deposits in the eastern half of the state, plays a relatively minor role in fueling the state's power plants.

Mining Pennsylvania's Coals Much of the bituminous coal mined in Pennsylvania is removed from underground coal mines that generally employ one of two methods to extract the coal. Most underground coal is mined by the *room and pillar method*, whereby rooms are cut into the coal bed, leaving a series of pillars, or columns of coal, to help support the mine roof and control the flow of air. Generally, rooms are about 20 to 30 feet wide and the pillars are up to 100 feet wide. When the workers have removed most of the coal from the mine, they remove as much coal as possible from the remaining pillars until the roof falls in. When this retreat mining is complete, the mined area is abandoned.

The *longwall method* of underground mining accounts for over one third of the underground coal production in Pennsylvania and surrounding states. In longwall mining, a cutting head moves back and forth across a coal seam, causing pieces of coal to fall onto a flexible conveyor for removal from the mine. Longwall mining is done using special roof supports that are moved as the seam is cut. The roof in the mined-out areas falls as the supports are advanced.

Some of Pennsylvania's coal seams are mined using surface mining techniques. Draglines, bulldozers, and front-end loaders are used to remove the overburden from the coal seam. Explosives are then used to loosen the coal. As with underground mines, there are several types of surface coal mines. Area surface mines are used in flat terrain and consist of a series of cuts hundreds of feet wide. The overburden from one cut is used to fill in the mined-out area of the preceding cut. Contour surface mining follows a coal seam along the side of the hill. Open pit mines are developed in areas where coal seams are relatively thick.

Coal and the Environment

Compared with most of the coal mined in the United States, Pennsylvania's bituminous coals contain a large amount of pyrite, a mineral often

Figure 2.16 Most of the electricity in Pennsylvania is generated in coal-burning power plants such as this one in Elderton, Pennsylvania.

called fool's gold. Pyrite is made of iron and sulfur. When pyrite is exposed to air and water, sulfuric acid and iron hydroxide form. These two substances are often referred to as *acid mine drainage*. Acid mine drainage can form in surface coal mines when the overburden is broken and removed, exposing the pyrite in the coal to air and rainwater. Acid mine drainage can also form in deeper mines when air enters the mines and the oxygen in the air reacts with the pyrite. When acid mine drainage enters freshwater resources, it lowers the water's pH and covers the river channels with iron hydroxide, which gives the channels a yellowish-orange color.

Acid mine drainage is the major source of water pollution in Pennsylvania. To date, state and federal government agencies have invested nearly $500 million to correct many of the environmental problems associated with this type of pollution. Also, as a result of past pollution by acid mine drainage, the Pennsylvania Department of Environmental Protection cannot, by law, issue any permit for new coal mining if that mining will create acid mine drainage.

Coal mining, and, in fact, the mining of any resource, can greatly alter the landscape. Prior to the late 1970s, most mined land was abandoned when mining was complete. Fortunately, the 1977 Surface Mining Control and Reclamation Act requires all mining companies to restore mined land to its original condition by reconstructing the land's topography and by replanting vegetation. This restoration of the land is called *reclamation.*

Coal also affects the environment when it is burned. Emissions such as sulfur dioxide and nitrogen oxide combine with water vapor in the air to form sulfuric and nitric acids. When these acids combine with precipitation and fall to Earth, lakes, rivers, and streams become contaminated and many aquatic organisms are harmed. Acid precipitation also leaches aluminum from the soil, which can be extremely toxic to many species of aquatic organisms and damages crops and trees by leaching nutrients from the plants' leaves.

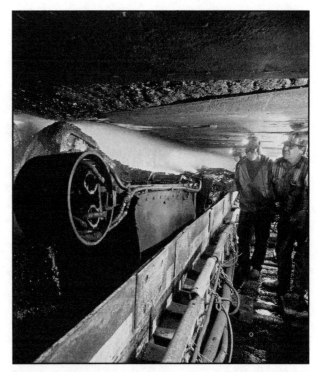

Figure 2.17 Continuous mining uses a conveyor belt to transfer coal from the mine to the surface.

Pennsylvania Power Plants

More than half of the electricity generated in Pennsylvania is produced in coal-burning power plants. However, nearly 40 percent of all of the electricity produced in the Commonwealth is generated at nuclear power plants. Currently, hydroelectric plants provide only a very small amount of the electricity produced in the state.

Coal-burning power plants Most of the coal-burning plants in Pennsylvania are steam-turbine plants. In such power plants, the coal, which is usually bituminous coal because of its high heating value, is burned in a combustion chamber to produce heat. The heat converts water in a boiler into steam, which flows through tubes and into a device called a superheater. Extremely hot gases surround the steam-filled tubes in the superheater and cause both the temperature and pressure of the steam in the tubes to increase.

The superheated, high-pressure steam is then used to drive a turbine. A steam turbine has a series of wheels that are mounted on a shaft. As the steam is forced quickly through the turbine, it pushes against the blades on the wheels and causes the wheels and the turbine shaft to spin. The shaft then turns the rotor of the electric generator to produce electric power.

After the steam has passed through the turbine, it enters a device called a *condenser*. In the condenser, the steam passes over pipes filled with cool water. Because heat flows from a region with a higher temperature to a region with a lower temperature, the water in the pipes absorbs the heat from the steam, causing it to cool and condense to form liquid water. This water is then pumped back to the boiler to be turned into steam again.

At many power plants, the water from the condenser pipes is pumped to a cooling tower. A series of decks in the tower allow water to cool as it flows over each successive deck. The cooled water is recycled through the condenser or is discharged into a nearby lake, river, or other body of water.

As in most conventional power plants, the chemicals and particulate matter released during combustion of coal cause air pollution when they are released into the atmosphere. The air quality surrounding these plants is monitored to ensure that the plant's emissions are within the legal limits set for various chemicals and particulates. A number of Pennsylvania's coal-burning power plants use pollution control equipment that limits the release of these pollutants. Such equipment, however, does not fully eliminate the air pollution created by the coal-burning plants.

Nuclear power plants Nuclear plants use a nuclear reactor to split the nuclei of uranium atoms. This splitting, which is called fission, generates enormous amounts of energy. This energy is used to convert water into steam, which drives a turbine that powers an electric generator and produces electricity. As the steam leaves the turbine, it cools, condenses to form liquid water, and is recycled through the plant.

Nuclear power plants use much less fuel than coal-burning plants to produce an equal amount of electrical power. Nuclear plants also cause much less air pollution than fossil-fuel burning plants. However, because the fuels used in nuclear plants are radioactive materials, they pose safety hazards at the plant. Numerous safety systems are present in nuclear plants to help prevent and quickly deal with accidents. Nuclear plants also create radioactive wastes that must be properly disposed of to prevent radiation contamination.

Hydroelectric plants Only about half a percent of the electricity generated in Pennsylvania is provided by hydroelectric power plants, which convert the energy of falling water into electricity. A hydroelectric plant allows water from a reservoir to flow through a tunnel or pipe to the plant's water turbine. As the water flows through the turbine, it causes the turbine's shaft to turn. The spinning shaft drives the generator to produce electricity.

Hydroelectric power plants cost less to operate than fossil-fuel plants. Other advantages of such plants are that they do not pollute the air and they produce no wastes. The number of hydroelectric power plants is limited, however, by the availability of the water needed to run them as well as the finite availability of suitable locations for dams and reservoirs.

From Power Plant to Consumer

After electricity is produced, it must be distributed to the consumer. In the United States, most electricity travels through overhead wires from the power plant to the consumer. Some types of industries can use the electrical current directly from the transmission lines. Most other uses require that the voltage be decreased before the power is distributed. Power substations use devices called step-down transformers to reduce the voltage needed by most consumers.

Conservation

All of Earth's resources—renewable and nonrenewable—are important in that they supply humans and organisms with the materials and energy they need in their everyday lives. Proper management of all of Earth's resources is critical to prevent exploitation, pollution, destruction, or neglect of the resources so that they are available in the future. The wise use and management of Earth's natural resources is *conservation*.

Many organizations and agencies are working around the globe to help conserve and protect Earth's many resources. One organization, Global Response, is an environmental action and educational network that works with local governments and people to protect the environment in all regions of the world. One of the projects recently undertaken by Global Response is to prevent the lenga forests of Tierra del Fuego, an island shared by Chile and Argentina, from being clear-cut by multinational logging companies. Another of Global Response's current projects is to prevent destruction of an Australian wetland lake that would result from gold mining along its shores.

Another multinational group working to conserve Earth's resources is Conservation International, or CI. One of this group's major projects is focused on conserving the Guinean Forests of West Africa. Some of the goals of this project are to increase the understanding of biodiversity and to raise public awareness about threats to biodiversity conservation. Conservation International works to create protected areas in regions of high biodiversity, focusing their efforts on key endangered species to prevent their extinction. Like most conservation groups, CI works closely with local communities and businesses to develop conservation policies and practices that protect Earth's natural resources.

The International Energy Agency, or IEA, is another organization consisting of 26 countries that are working to ensure the conservation of Earth's oil supply. Members of the IEA share energy information, coordinate their energy policies, and cooperate in the development of rational energy programs. The group also works to promote rational energy policies with nonmember countries, industry, and international organizations. The participating countries strive to improve the world's energy supply and demand structure by developing alternative energy sources and increasing the efficiency of energy use.

In addition to international organizations and agencies, many governments play an active role in resource conservation. The United States Environmental Protection Agency, or EPA, for example, was established in 1970 to repair damage already done to the environment as well as to establish new criteria to protect human health and the air, water, and land upon which all life depends. Engineers, scientists, and environmental protection specialists at the EPA work closely with other federal agencies, state and local governments, and Native American groups to develop and enforce regulations under existing environmental laws. The EPA also works with industries on a variety of voluntary pollution prevention programs and energy conservation efforts.

Figure 2.18 Ecosystems around the world need to be protected from destruction.

Information Systems and Natural Resources

An information system collects, stores, processes, and communicates information. Information systems in a hospital might assist with admissions, track patient care, manage pharmacy inventory, and generate bills. A business may use its information systems to manage its operations, supply services, and compete in the marketplace. State and municipal governments rely on information systems to provide basic services to citizens.

There are five main components of an information system. Obviously, there are the people involved in the agency, organization, or business. Computers, which are often called hardware, process and store the information. Software is any program that is used on the computer. Databases are collections of related records. The telecommunications system includes computers and the wires and cables that link them to other computers in the same office or anywhere in the world.

How do information systems affect the management and distribution of natural resources? Use what you have learned about Earth's natural resources to answer the following questions.

- An on-line learning module on common crop pests consists of printable materials. How could this module be revised to make it more useful to more farmers?
- How might computerized decision-making programs be beneficial to people working in a nuclear power plant?
- How might a database of locational information be useful to a mining company interested in reconnaissance mining?
- How might statistical software be used to manage electricity demands?
- How might computer modeling help engineers design a hydroelectric power plant in an earthquake-prone area?

Lesson Review

1. Explain two ways that electricity is generated in Pennsylvania. What energy source generates the majority of Pennsylvania's electricity?

2. Compare and contrast two types of underground coal mining methods.

3. Describe four negative effects that coal mining and the use of coal as fuel have on the environment.

4. Explain the advantages and disadvantages of coal-burning, nuclear, and hydroelectric power plants.

5. List the steps involved in getting electricity from a power plant to the consumer.

6. Name four global organizations or agencies, and describe how each works to promote conservation of Earth's resources.

7. How might an information system ensure that oil moves through a pipeline without causing an increase in pressure that could damage the pipeline?

Lesson 2.4
Solid Waste Management

Recall that most of Earth's natural resources must be processed before they can be used. The operations involved in converting the raw materials into finished parts or products make up the manufacturing process. In addition to the goods produced during this process, manufacturing also produces wastes. Some of these wastes are released into Earth's atmosphere or waterways, where they may cause pollution. Other wastes are recovered and sold, recycled within the factory, or taken to landfills for disposal.

Manufacturing Pennsylvania's Steel

The first step in most manufacturing processes is extracting the raw materials from a resource. The iron ore used to make steel in Pennsylvania's steel mills is first crushed to increase the concentration of the iron. Next, the iron ore is separated from the crushed rock. Then the ore is smelted—air or oxygen is blown in at the bottom of an enormous vat containing the iron ore, coke, and limestone. Coke and limestone are the other two key ingredients needed to produce pig iron. The air or oxygen causes the coke to burn, which removes oxygen from the ore. The limestone then fuses with the other impurities and is removed from the ore. The final product of this process is pig iron.

Pig iron is converted into liquid steel by refining the iron in furnaces containing recycled iron and scraps of steel. This primary method of steel making uses the electric-arc method. High-current electric arcs are used to melt steel scrap and convert it into liquid steel with a certain chemical composition and temperature. The Bethlehem Lukens Plate facility in Conshohocken, Pennsylvania, uses the electric-arc method of steel making as well as the secondary ladle method. The ladle, a large cylindrical container, sits beneath the primary steel furnace and receives the liquid steel. The ladle is used for holding and transporting liquid steel. All metallurgical work takes place in the ladle.

Figure 2.19 Steel manufacturing, one of Pennsylvania's main industries, produces many wastes. Many manufacturers have pollution control programs in place to reduce or reuse many of these wastes.

Steel making, like any manufacturing process, produces wastes. However, many steel manufacturers have resource recovery and pollution control programs in place. Many of the gaseous wastes produced in electric arc furnaces are captured using emission-control equipment. Some of the heat associated with these emissions can be captured for reuse in other heating processes. The water used to quench hot steel is often recycled within the factory. Likewise, much of the solid waste generated in the steel-making process is recovered. Some of the dust or sludge is sold to other manufacturing companies or buried in landfills. If the iron content of the dust is sufficient, the dust can be reused in the steel mill's blast furnaces. If not high enough in iron, the dust can be sold to other industries for use as a raw material in brick, cement, sandblasting, or fertilizers.

Municipal Solid Waste

In the United States alone, manufacturing processes, people, and institutions produced more than 230 million tons of solid waste in 1999. This amount of trash equals almost 5 pounds of waste per person per day. Most of this waste is paper, yard waste, food, and plastics. This waste, which is often called *municipal solid waste,* or MSW, is disposed of in different ways.

Landfills A *landfill* is a regulated area where wastes are placed in the land. Some landfills are made by digging pits in the land; others are constructed on the sites of old quarries or mines. A pit, quarry, or mine is usually lined with plastic sheets that are reinforced with several feet of clay on the bottom and sides of the landfill. The plastic liner and the impermeable clay prevent most substances from leaking out of the landfill and into the ground and water around the landfill.

The wastes in a sanitary landfill are compacted and covered with several inches of soil on a daily basis to help reduce odors and to control litter, insects, and rodents. Frequent groundwater monitoring is also necessary near landfills to determine whether potentially dangerous waste materials have escaped from the landfill. Newer landfills in Pennsylvania are equipped to collect and treat any liquids leaching from the landfill. Another potential problem associated with landfills is the gas (landfill gas, or LFG) that forms when trash decays. LFG consists of about 50 percent methane, about 50 percent carbon dioxide, and a small amount of organic compounds. Methane can contribute to local smog and global climate change. Some landfills, however, capture these gases, convert them into fuel, and use them to supply energy.

The number of landfills in the United States has decreased sharply in the past decades for various reasons. Some landfills were closed because they posed environmental problems as a result of leakage and hazardous waste disposal. Others simply became full and had to be closed. The decrease in available landfill

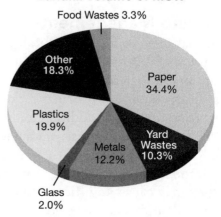

Landfill Volume of MSW

Figure 2.20 Landfills are constructed in many layers to prevent contamination of the soil and water around them and to handle odors, gases, and waste volume.

space has led to waste disposal problems in many states. Pennsylvania, however, is not one of these states. According to recent statistics, people in Pennsylvania recycle about a quarter of their MSW and dispose of just over 3 million tons of waste in landfills each year. The surplus landfill space, however, is being filled by nearly as much out-of-state waste that is being transported into Pennsylvania. Because waste is a commodity according to federal law, it is protected under the interstate commerce laws. Therefore, states cannot ban its importation. Some Pennsylvania lawmakers, environmental groups, and state agencies, however, are working to resolve this issue.

Combustion To reduce the amount of landfill space needed for municipal solid waste, some local governments and private operators can dispose of trash by controlled burning, or combustion. Burning municipal waste has several benefits. Combustion of trash reduces the volume of the waste up to 90 percent and the mass of the waste up to 75 percent. Burning waste at extremely high temperatures destroys harmful compounds and disease-causing bacteria. Burning trash also generates energy, and when combustors are fitted with appropriate devices, they can convert water into steam to generate electricity.

Combustion, unfortunately, also can pollute the air. A variety of pollution-control technologies have been developed to reduce most of the dangerous substances emitted in combustion smoke and to meet the legal limits for these emissions. One such technology is a scrubber, which uses a liquid spray to neutralize acidic gases in combustion smoke. These are already used in coal-burning power plants. Filters are another pollution-control device that remove ash particles from the smoke.

Combustion facilities are often called waste-to-energy, or W-T-E, facilities. Some W-T-E plants are mass burn plants in which everything but hazardous materials is burned together. As the waste burns, energy is produced and is converted into electricity. Other W-T-E facilities are refuse-derived fuel plants. In these plants, the trash is first processed to remove materials that do not burn well and materials that can be recycled. The burnable waste then is either shredded or packed into pellets and burned.

Bioremediation Plants Many states, including Pennsylvania, dispose of some of their MSW in bioremediation plants. This type of W-T-E plant uses heated tanks filled with bacteria to break down municipal solid waste. By-products of this process include carbon and methane. The methane is then burned to produce heat and electricity, most of which is used at the plant itself.

Composting *Composting* is another biological method of waste disposal in which worms, bacteria, fungi, and other organisms decompose piles of fruit and vegetable food scraps, wood, and lawn clippings. Composting usually begins when microorganisms—bacteria and fungi—and worms digest and excrete the organic matter in the pile. As these biological processes occur, the temperature of the waste rises and more organisms are attracted to the waste pile. The product of composting is a dark brown substance called humus, which is very rich in nutrients. Humus is an important part of good soil.

Figure 2.21 The waste generated by people in the United States is disposed of in many ways. The compost generated from this pile of waste at a landfill could be used to fertilize gardens, yards, nurseries, or indoor plants.

Lab Study

Vermicomposting

Yard clippings and food scraps make up about a quarter of the solid waste generated in U.S. households. Composting this waste can greatly reduce the amount of waste that ends up in landfills or incinerators and can provide rich organic material to be added to gardens, houseplants, and yards. Vermicomposting uses worms to turn organic matter into nutrient-rich compost.

Worms feed on the decomposing plant material, and as they digest the organic matter, they return important nutrients to the soil through castings, or worm waste. Worms also help improve soil structure as they move through it, improving aeration and allowing plant roots to penetrate the soil more easily.

Materials		
shallow 10-gallon bin (plastic, wood, or glass) with lid	black plastic garbage bag	scale
earthworms	potting soil or topsoil	fruit and vegetable scraps, eggshells, leaves, grass clippings, nonrecyclable paper, tea bags, coffee grounds
soil	blender	
newspaper	water	
	spray bottle	

Procedure

1. Rinse your container and its lid with water to remove any residues that may be harmful to your worm colony. Do not use soap, which can leave a residue. Leave your lid ajar, or drill holes in the lid to allow air into the bin.

2. To prepare bedding for the bin, tear black-and-white newspaper pages into $\frac{1}{2}$- to 1-inch strips. Place the strips in a large garbage bag, and moisten them with water (to the moistness of a damp sponge but not dripping wet).

3. Layer the strips loosely in the bin. Add strips until the bin is about three-fourths full.

4. Sprinkle 2 to 4 cups of potting soil or outdoor topsoil over the bedding, which will provide microorganisms and grit to aid the worms' digestion.

5. Weigh your worms to determine how much food to feed them. Worms consume approximately three times their weight per week. So, if you start with a pound of worms, add three pounds of food per week.

6. Add your worms to the bedding and soil layers.

7. Place a full sheet of dry newspaper on top of the bedding to maintain moisture and discourage fruit flies.

8. Feed your worms fruit and vegetable scraps such as cores and peels and other nonmeat and nondairy remains from the kitchen such as bread, cake, beans, tea bags, or coffee grounds. Try to avoid citrus peels or rinds, which attract fruit flies. Cut, break, or grind (in a blender) food particles to small sizes, approximately $\frac{1}{4}$ inch. Food should be moist but not soaking wet. To avoid odors, lift up the layer of bedding, and bury the scraps underneath.

9. Cover the bin with the lid to keep the bin dark and cool. Remove the cover every couple of days to add air to the bin.

10. Make weekly observations of the contents of the bin. Describe your observations.

Important: Keep the bin away from heat. Do not store it on the windowsill.

Extension

Use what you have learned about vermicomposting to start your own compost bin at home. You may want to research other composting techniques on the Internet.

Reduce, Reuse, and Recycle

More than half of the hundreds of millions of tons of MSW produced each year in the United States is sent to landfills. Reducing, reusing, and recycling waste are ways to decrease the volume of waste sent to landfills or burned.

Source Reduction The United States has often been referred to as the "throw-away society." Disposable cups and plates, tissues, plastic bags and bottles, and other single-use items make up much of the waste in the United States. *Source reduction* alters the design, manufacture, or use of materials to reduce the amount and toxicity of the waste generated. Source reduction also includes purchasing durable goods and products with little or no extra packaging. Because source reduction prevents waste, it is the preferred method of waste management.

Source reduction also involves reducing toxic wastes. Using environmentally friendly cleaning products, using the smallest amounts necessary, and sharing products with hazardous ingredients are ways to reduce toxic wastes.

Reusing products rather than throwing them away is another key to waste management. In the United States, more than 6,000 reuse centers exist around the country. Some of these centers collect building materials or supplies and furniture no longer used in schools and offices

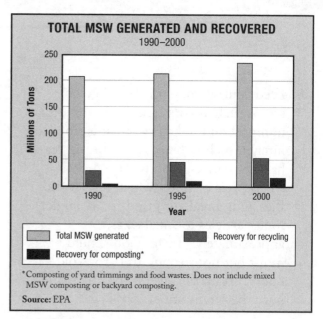

Figure 2.23 Recycling and composting continue to reduce the total MSW that ends up in landfills.

and redistribute the items for reuse. Nonprofit organizations such as Goodwill and the Salvation Army contribute to source reduction by collecting and distributing usable items such as toys, furniture, household items, and clothes.

Reducing waste has numerous environmental benefits. For example, waste reduction conserves natural resources because manufacturing new products uses energy, water, and other resources *and* produces more wastes. In 1999 alone, more than 50 million tons of MSW were source-reduced in the United States.

Recycling *Recycling* is a series of activities that reuse a product's raw materials to manufacture new products. The first step in the recycling process is to collect recyclable materials such as paper, glass, aluminum, steel, and plastics. In many communities, this is done through curbside pick-up, drop-off and buy-back centers, and deposit-refund programs. Recyclables are then sent to a facility for sorting and cleaning and are eventually sold.

The next step in recycling is manufacturing. Recyclables such as glass, plastics, steel, and aluminum are melted down and reformed to produce new products. Paper, on the other hand, is shredded and mixed with water to form a slurry, pressed, and dried to produce recycled paper.

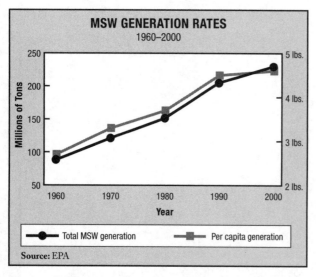

Figure 2.22 More than 230 million tons of waste were produced in 2000. That is almost 5 pounds per person.

The recycling loop is complete when recycled products are purchased. Buying recycled products creates an economic incentive for recyclables to be collected, manufactured, and marketed as new products. Buying recycled products also saves resources for future generations.

About 42 percent of all paper, 40 percent of all plastic soft drink bottles, 55 percent of all aluminum drink cans, and 56 percent of all steel packaging is now being recycled in the United States. Paper, especially newsprint, is recycled to produce more paper and is used on farms as livestock bedding and to enrich soil. Not all glass can be recycled because different kinds of glass require slightly different manufacturing processes. Glass beverage bottles can be recycled, however, and some states require consumers to pay a deposit on the bottles that is refunded when the bottles are returned.

Plastics also vary in the way that they can be recycled. Code numbers from 1 through 7, which are generally on the bottom of the containers, indicate the type of plastic and how it must be recycled. In general, plastics with lower numbers are easier to recycle than those with higher numbers.

Metals that are commonly recycled include steel and aluminum. Scrap steel has been an integral part of the steel making process for many years now. In fact, almost 25 percent of all the steel manufactured around the world today is made from scrap steel.

Yes, It Can!

Prior to the 1970s, all aluminum cans were manufactured from raw materials. Environmental awareness, as well as cash for empty aluminum cans, created recycling incentives. Recycling aluminum cans helps divert more than 2 billion pounds of aluminum from landstreams. In addition to keeping this aluminum out of landfills, recycling saves about 95 percent of the energy used to process raw aluminum. In 1995 alone, aluminum recycling saved the equivalent of enough electricity to light a city the size of Pittsburgh for nearly six years.

Aluminum cans can be recycled into new cans in as few as 60 days. The first step is to collect the cans and send them to a recycling center. At the recycling facility, the cans are cleaned, crushed, and baled. After they have been processed, the used cans are sent to the manufacturing plant, where they are shredded, melted, and mixed with raw aluminum. This mixture is then cast into ingots that are allowed to cool. The ingots are rolled into long, thin sheets that are coiled and sent to can manufacturing plants.

Aluminum beverage cans, which are made of only two pieces—the body of the can and its top—are made from the aluminum sheets. Then they are sent to soft drink companies for filling and sealing. Soft drink companies send their products to distribution companies that send the products to the consumer. When the cans are recycled by the consumer, the process starts again.

Lesson Review

1. Briefly explain the steps involved in steel making.

2. Explain some of the resource recovery and pollution control methods used in the steel manufacturing process.

3. What makes up the bulk of municipal solid waste in the United States?

4. Contrast three methods of managing solid wastes.

5. Explain various aspects of source reduction as it pertains to solid wastes.

6. List the steps involved in recycling metallic resources.

7. Explain the steps and processes involved in recycling aluminum cans.

The 3 Rs—Reduce, Reuse, Recycle

Part 1—Scavenger Hunt

Look around your house, your school, and your community for at least ten items made from completely new materials and at least ten items made, at least in part, from recycled materials. Organize your findings in the data table provided by your teacher. Compare your results with those of at least four other students.

Part 2—Packaging

The primary purpose of most packaging is to protect products and parts during shipping. However, packaging is also designed to sell products and parts. Packaging can account for 10 to 15 percent of the cost of a product and from 40 to 50 percent of consumer waste.

- Think about the many products in grocery stores, toy stores, department stores, and other types of stores. Determine at least ten items in which the packaging is for protection. List at least ten items in which the packaging promotes sales. Name at least ten items in which the packaging does both. Organize your findings in the data table provided by your teacher.

- For each item listed, determine whether any of the packaging is excess packaging, regardless of its purpose. Estimate the percentage of the excess packaging. For example, many over-the-counter medicine bottles are only about three-fourths full of medication. Cotton balls are often stuffed in the bottle to fill the excess space, which is usually between $\frac{1}{2}$ and 1 inch. Record your observations and estimates in the table.

- Determine the composition (paper, plastic, metal, glass, other material) of the packaging for each item in your lists. Record your observations. Determine whether the packaging is recyclable.

- Which of the items in your table would you encourage people to buy because of the packaging alone? In other words, which products and items contain little or no excess packaging or packaging that can be recycled?

- Choose five items from your table, and describe how you would redesign the packaging so that it is not excessive but still protects the items. What kinds of materials would you use for your packaging?

Figure 2.24 Try to choose products with the least amount of packaging or with packaging made from recycled materials.

Chapter 3

Environmental Health

Many pollutants contaminate Earth. Car exhaust, cigarette smoke, house pets, factory smokestacks, and construction sites, for example, are a few of the many pollutants of Earth's atmosphere. Sediment, animal wastes, microscopic organisms, and toxic wastes from industrial processes wreak havoc on the layer of water near Earth's surface called the hydrosphere. The solid ground we walk on, called the lithosphere, can be contaminated by radioactive wastes, leaking storage tanks, landfills, pesticides, and some household cleaning products, among other pollutants. The biosphere, which consists of every living organism on Earth, is polluted when those organisms are exposed to pollutants that enter the air, water, and soil. However, pollution may not always be chemicals or particles. In certain circumstances, pollution can be a temperature change caused by a manufacturing process.

Fortunately, over the past several decades, people have become more aware of how their actions affect the environment. In addition to this public awareness, laws and other legislation have been enacted to reduce or even prevent pollution of Earth's ecosystems. These concerted efforts are aimed at helping the planet recuperate from the damage that has been done to it and keeping the planet healthy for future generations.

Figure 3.1 Pollution such as this oil spill along the Delaware River in Pennsylvania can have long-lasting negative effects on the environment.

Lesson 3.1
Pollution and Human Health

People depend on Earth's hydrosphere, atmosphere, lithosphere, and biosphere for many of their needs, from the water we drink to the air we breathe to the soil we use to grow crops. When these resources become polluted, they affect our health.

Water Pollution

Most people take potable, or drinking, water for granted. Turning on a spigot in developed nations often produces a clear stream of fresh water. Although the water may be clear, however, it is not necessarily clean. Water for household use in most countries is treated to remove dangerous pollutants. Some pollutants, unfortunately, still enter bodies of fresh water that are used for human consumption. Most of these pollutants enter the water when rain, melting snow, or irrigation water runs over land or through the ground and picks up pollutants. When these polluted waters enter a standing body of water such as a stream, river, lake, or ocean, they deposit the pollutants, which then can enter Earth's groundwater systems. Two of the most common water pollutants that enter Earth's water systems in this way are sediment and nutrients. These substances wash into water bodies from farmland, animal feeding facilities, construction sites, and other areas in which the ground is disturbed.

Other types of pollutants directly enter the water. *Effluent* is the wastewater from factories and refineries that is released directly into urban water supplies.

Effluent often contains harmful by-products of manufacturing processes. Some effluent is heated wastewater that can pollute the waterway it enters by raising the temperature of the waterway and killing many forms of aquatic life. According to the EPA, the amount of effluent pollution discharged by industries around the country is more than three times greater than the amount discharged by U.S. sewage systems.

Another type of effluent is sewage. *Sewage* is polluted water that contains human waste, garbage, and other household wastewater. In most countries, sewage is treated with screens, filters, and chlorine and other chemicals to remove dirt, organic matter, and other contaminants from the water. In the United States, about 80 percent of all sewage goes through treatment plants; another 10 percent passes through septic tanks before it is allowed to seep into the ground. The remaining 10 percent is untreated and passes directly into Earth's water systems.

One of the products of sewage treatment is sediment, which is commonly called sludge. In the past, most sludge was dumped directly into water bodies or taken to landfills. Today,

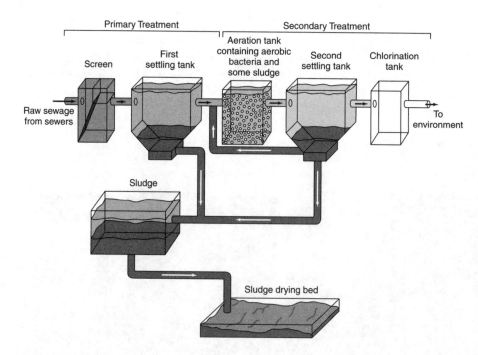

Figure 3.2 In wastewater-treatment plants, sewage passes through two steps in which sludge settles out of the wastewater.

however, much of the sludge from water treatment processes is dried or may be composted, tested, and used as fertilizers for forests and crops. The chemicals that can be found in the sludge usually determine where the sludge can be spread. In some cities, sludge is mixed with water and is either sprayed over vegetation or pumped directly into the soil.

Water Pollutants and Human Health

Most water pollutants can be dangerous to human health. Lead that leaks into water supply systems from pipes and pipe solder, for example, may cause brain damage, especially in children. Iron and manganese are other metals that can pollute water supplies and are harmful when ingested in large amounts. Hydrogen sulfide gas is an industrial waste that gives water a rotten-egg odor. Hydrogen sulfide, too, is harmful to humans in large concentrations. Radioactive substances and their decay products, which are used in hospitals and some research facilities, can cause some types of cancer if they make their way into water supply systems.

Although the majority of developing countries have treatment centers for water and waste, untreated or improperly treated sewage can be harmful to humans because it contains microbes. *Microbes* are very tiny pathogens, or organisms that cause disease. Microbes can be protists, bacteria, or viruses. Some common water-related illnesses caused by microbes are cholera, dysentery, malaria, cryptosporidiosis, and giardiasis.

Cholera Cholera is an intestinal infection caused by water or food that is contaminated by the bacterium *Vibrio cholerae*. When these bacteria enter the human body, they produce toxins that cause cells in the intestines to secrete fluids faster than they are produced. Cholera symptoms include watery diarrhea, and in many cases vomiting. Cholera can quickly lead to dehydration and even death if not promptly treated.

Drinking and eating contaminated water and food spreads cholera. Peeling fruits and vegetables before eating them, as well as thoroughly cooking food and preventing it from coming into contact with raw foods, can prevent most incidences of cholera. This waterborne disease can also be prevented by avoiding contaminated water and ice. Cholera is usually treated with rehydration fluids and antibiotics.

According to the World Health Organization, or WHO, the seventh pandemic of cholera is in progress, mostly in developing countries. A *pandemic* is an outbreak of a disease that affects an exceptionally high portion of a population and occurs over a very large geographic area. The seventh cholera pandemic began in 1961 when *V. cholerae* caused a large number of cases of cholera in Indonesia. The disease spread rapidly to other countries of eastern Asia, India, the former Soviet Union, Iran, and Iraq. In 1970, cholera invaded West Africa, making its way around the globe and eventually infecting hundreds of thousands of people in Latin America.

Dysentery Dysentery is an illness caused by several types of bacteria. People infected with dysentery have bloody diarrhea and abdominal cramps and often have rectal pain. Because the immune system of an infected person attempts to fight the illness, the person also has a fever. Less frequent, but more serious, complications of dysentery include seizures and kidney failure.

Health care officials believe that dysentery is most likely spread through person-to-person contact and by eating and drinking contaminated foods and water. Antibiotics used to treat the illness are often effective for only one or two years after being introduced. In some cases, resistance to antibiotics develops during the course of an individual's treatment. Dysentery has caused epidemics in some parts of the world, including Central America and much of Africa, over the past several decades.

Malaria Malaria is a parasitic disease transmitted by mosquitoes that breed in still bodies of water. The parasite is transmitted to humans when they are bitten by certain female mosquitoes. Inside the human host, the parasite infects the liver and red blood cells. Malaria symptoms typically include flulike symptoms—headache, fever, and vomiting. If left untreated, malaria can be life threatening. Most malaria cases occur in tropical and subtropical regions of the world, causing at least one million deaths each year.

Cholera, dysentery, and malaria are, unfortunately, common diseases in developing nations. These diseases are very rare in developed countries around the world, including the United States. Waterborne diseases that have affected large numbers of people in the United States in recent years, however, are cryptosporidiosis and giardiasis. Both of these diarrheal illnesses are caused by animal-like protists called protozoa.

Cryptosporidiosis Cryptosporidiosis is an illness that occurs when cryptosporidium cysts enter the human body and excyst, or "hatch." The opening of the cysts allows millions of protozoa to complete their life cycles within the host's intestines. Symptoms of cryptosporidiosis, which typically appear within one week after the ingestion of the cysts, include persistent diarrhea, nausea, abdominal cramps, weight loss, and sometimes dehydration. Cryptosporidiosis usually lasts between 10 and 14 days, but it can become chronic and last up to one or two months. The illness can be fatal for people with weakened immune systems.

Cryptosporidiosis is a gastrointestinal disease that cannot be transmitted through a cut in the skin or by touching the blood of an infected individual. Cysts are usually transmitted from the environment to humans through inadequately or improperly treated drinking water. The cysts may also be introduced into the body by eating contaminated food or by fecal-oral transmission. Children are particularly susceptible to this illness because they can acquire the protozoa through fecal-oral transmission.

Cryptosporidium is often present in surface waters. To prevent the cysts of these protozoa from entering drinking water supplies, water must be properly treated with multiple barriers— such as chemicals, filters, and disinfectants. The distribution pipes and storage facilities must also be monitored to prevent recontamination. If cryptosporidium cysts are suspected of being present in water, a rapid boil for one full minute will destroy the cysts.

Giardiasis Giardiasis is similar to cryptosporidiosis in its infection methods, typical symptoms, method of transmission, and prevention. Often, the feces of an infected person or animal are passed into both water and food sources. Giardiasis is often found in Pennsylvania streams. The illness differs, however, in that giardia cysts can be killed with chlorine if exposed to the chemical for a sufficiently long period of time. Also, unlike cryptosporidiosis, medication can be prescribed to eliminate the giardia parasites from the human host.

Waterborne Disease Outbreaks in Pennsylvania

From 1971 to 1985, Pennsylvania reported more waterborne disease outbreaks associated with drinking water supplies than did any other state. Since 1979, eight documented giardiasis outbreaks and one cryptosporidiosis outbreak have occurred in the Commonwealth. The Pennsylvania Department of Environmental Protection's Safe Drinking Water Program has since taken a multiple-barrier approach to protecting the state's public water supplies. Agencies involved in the program closely

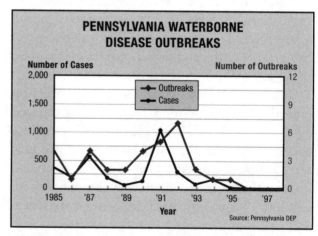

Figure 3.3 Rigid testing standards, careful monitoring, and improved treatment systems have dramatically reduced waterborne diseases in Pennsylvania.

evaluate and monitor the state's water treatment plants to make sure that harmful microbes, including protozoa, are removed from drinking water. Dramatic improvements in the state's drinking water systems during the 1990s have led to sharp reductions in waterborne diseases, as shown by the graph on the previous page.

Air Pollution

In many parts of the world today, air pollution is a serious problem that results from both natural events and human activities. Forest fires caused by either lightning or arson, for example, send smoke and ash billowing into the air. Dust storms such as those that plagued Beijing in 2002 forced people to wear surgical masks in and around their schools, homes, and offices to prevent inhalation of the dust. Burning fossil fuels releases not only energy but also harmful gases into the air. Industrial processes, driving cars, and operating other motor vehicles also release harmful substances into the air. These last two sources of air pollution—industrial processes and motor vehicles—are two of the major sources of air pollution today. Some of the pollutants released from these two sources include ozone, carbon monoxide, sulfur dioxide, nitrogen dioxide, particulate matter, and numerous other toxic substances.

Ozone Ozone, O_3, is a form of oxygen that has a very important function high in Earth's atmosphere. It protects Earth's inhabitants from harmful solar radiation that can cause skin cancers and cataracts and can harm the natural processes in Earth's ecosystems. Ozone close to Earth's surface, however, is a pollutant that can cause upper and lower respiratory tract illnesses if the levels are high enough. Ozone-induced illnesses include eye irritation, coughing, shortness of breath, nausea, wheezing, and headaches. Ozone has been associated with increased development of chronic respiratory

Figure 3.4 Power plants emit many toxins into the air, and weather conditions can concentrate this pollution, making the air dangerous for people to breathe.

illness as well as increased incidence of emergency room visits and hospitalizations for asthma and respiratory diseases.

Carbon Monoxide Carbon monoxide, CO, is a colorless, odorless gas that forms from the incomplete burning of fuels. Automobile exhaust gases include carbon monoxide as do gases from industrial furnaces. Burning charcoal and cigarette smoke also are high in carbon monoxide. Very small amounts of this gas in the bloodstream can produce toxic chemical reactions that result in illness or even death. Symptoms of low-level carbon monoxide exposure include headache, fatigue, and flulike symptoms. Symptoms of moderate to high levels of exposure include impaired vision and hearing, problems with fine motor skills, and lack of concentration, among others. A high level of carbon monoxide exposure can be fatal.

Sulfur Dioxide Sulfur dioxide, SO_2, is a pollutant that forms when coal containing pyrite is burned. The sulfur from the pyrite combines with the oxygen present during combustion

Figure 3.5 Air pollution is a common problem in most of our urban communities.

to form sulfur dioxide. This gas then combines with moisture in the air to form sulfuric acid, which damages plants and harms other organisms, including humans. Health problems that are associated with exposure to high concentrations of SO_2 include difficulty breathing, respiratory illnesses, decreased lung functions, and aggravation of existing heart disease.

Nitrogen Dioxide Nitrogen compounds, including nitrogen dioxide, NO_2, form when fuels burn. Nitrogen dioxide is present in the pollutant known as smog, a combination of smoke and fog. Smog is common in industrial areas or in areas in which there are many motor vehicles. Nitrogen dioxide gives smog its brown color and can cause eye irritation, stuffy nose, coughing, sore throat, lung inflammation, and various illnesses of the human respiratory system. Many cities around the United States monitor the levels of various pollutants, including nitrogen, in the air. When the levels are high or the conditions for smog to form are likely, smog alerts and warnings are issued.

Particulate Matter Particulate matter is the solid particles present in air. Some particulate matter is soil and construction dust carried by the wind. Other particulate matter, especially in and around large cities, contains tiny bits of tire rubber, asbestos from brake linings, and diesel and motor vehicle exhaust, among others. Particulate matter causes irritation and illnesses of the human respiratory system as well as certain kinds of cancers.

Toxic Substances Most of the pollutants discussed thus far can be toxic at high enough levels. Scientists, doctors, and other air quality experts, however, classify nearly 200 various metals and compounds as toxic pollutants. Lead, for example, is a metal that is highly toxic when ingested or inhaled. Lead can cause cancers of the lungs and kidneys and has adverse effects on the human cardiovascular and nervous systems. Lead is emitted into the air when leaded fuels are burned and from certain industrial processes, including the manufacturing of batteries and the smelting of lead.

Another toxic air pollutant is mercury, which is emitted into the air primarily by large coal-burning power plants. Other forms of mercury enter and pollute the air when certain ores are mined or as the result of various manufacturing processes. Modern plants and factories have developed measures that greatly reduce the amount of mercury and other toxins released into the air. Emissions from these plants are closely monitored and regulated. Any form of mercury can permanently damage the brain and other parts of the nervous system, the kidneys, and developing fetuses. Some of the effects of mercury on the nervous system include irritability, shyness, tremors, changes in vision or hearing, and memory problems. Exposure to high levels of mercury vapors may damage human lungs; cause nausea, vomiting, and diarrhea; increase blood pressure and heart rate; and cause rashes and irritation of the eyes and mucus membranes.

Allergies and Asthma

Allergies and asthma are respiratory system diseases often caused or triggered by both outdoor and indoor air pollutants. An *allergy* is a reaction by the body to a foreign substance that, in similar amounts and circumstances, is harmless to most other people. Substances that produce allergic reactions are called allergens. Typical allergens include molds, bacteria, pollens, photocopier fumes, cigarette smoke, drugs, lint, animal dander, dust, foods, dyes, and various outdoor air pollutants. Many allergies can be controlled with medication, avoidance of the irritating substance, or both.

Asthma is a disorder of the lungs in which airways tend to constrict, resulting in episodes of breathlessness, wheezing, coughing, and tightness of the chest. Asthma, like many allergies, can be triggered by dust mites, animal dander, pollen, air pollutants such as smog, cigarette smoke, medications, and exercise. Asthma can also be caused by bacterial infections. Asthma that develops in young children is often the result of an inherited susceptibility to allergens. Asthma that begins in adulthood may also develop in response to allergens, but viruses, certain medications, and exercise may cause the disease as well. Some cases of adult asthma are linked to exposure to certain materials in the workplace. Asthma, like allergies, can be controlled with medication. In most cases, however, asthma is a more serious disease than most allergies.

Pennsylvania Air Quality

Over the past decade or so, the number of motor vehicles on Pennsylvania's roadways has increased. This increase in vehicles, however, has not resulted in higher levels of air pollutants in

Figure 3.6 Many states now have stringent emission regulations and require vehicles to be tested regularly. In Pennsylvania, the Drive Clean inspection program helps reduce emissions by ensuring that vehicles in the state are properly maintained.

most parts of the state. In other areas, pollution levels have decreased as a result of environmentally conscious acts such as the use of motor vehicles that emit fewer exhausts, the burning of cleaner fuels, and increases in the number of motor vehicle maintenance and state inspections.

The Bureau of Air Quality, part of Pennsylvania's DEP, works with industry, businesses, schools, and communities to limit air pollution through a coordination of various government efforts. The bureau issues permits, regulates emissions, approves air quality plans for construction sites, and works to modify all air pollution sources. The bureau also enforces Pennsylvania's clean air requirements by monitoring air quality throughout the state.

Various air quality programs exist throughout Pennsylvania. The Clean Mower Rebate Program, for example, offers rebates in certain counties to people who turn in working gasoline-powered lawnmowers, weed trimmers, and edgers and replace them with electric-powered machines. The Alternative Fuels Incentive Grant Program provides financial assistance and information on alternative fuels and vehicles. The Small Business Assistance Program provides small businesses with information about pollution prevention practices and ensures that small businesses are considered when new regulations are developed. The Drive Clean Pennsylvania program ensures that motor vehicles registered in the state are properly inspected and maintained. The Ozone Action Partnership works to reduce ground-level ozone, which is harmful to all of Earth's organisms.

Common Soil Pollutants

As with Earth's water and air, many of the substances that pollute the soil are the result of human activities. Agriculture, for example, contributes a large percentage of soil pollutants in the form of sediment, pesticides, animal wastes, and fertilizers. Irrigating crops in poorly drained areas results in standing water, which eventually evaporates and leaves the soil polluted with salts. Some of the solid wastes buried in landfills can leak into the soil and contaminate

it with harmful substances. Industrial processes can release toxic substances including lead and mercury into the air and water; eventually these heavy metals make their way into the soil, where they pose risks to humans and other organisms that depend on the soil. Mining practices can pollute soil by releasing acid mine drainage into the land. Oil and gas wells, as well as underground petroleum tanks, can contaminate the soil if they are not properly sealed, allowing oil and gas to leak into the environment.

Another soil pollutant is the radioactive waste that is generated by nuclear power plants, hospitals, and some industries and research facilities around the world. There are two types of radioactive wastes: high-level waste (HLW) and low-level waste (LLW). HLW is waste that is highly radioactive, which means that it can pose health risks for thousands of years. Most HLW is used nuclear fuel from power plants. Other HLW includes certain nuclear reactor components and some industrial radiation gauges. Disposal and storage of HLW is the responsibility of the United States government.

LLW is radioactive waste that consists of trash or other materials that have been contaminated by radioactive materials. LLW contains small amounts of materials that emit radiation. Unlike HLW, most of the radioactive elements in LLW decay to safe levels in about 100 years. Therefore, LLW does not pose as much risk as HLW, but it still is, in fact, radioactive waste. LLW disposal in the United States is the responsibility of individual states. Much of the LLW disposed of by plants, industry, and institutions in Pennsylvania includes contaminated clothing, filters, and paper and glass items used in medicine, manufacturing, and scientific research; certain kinds of resins; some radiation gauges; and some reactor components including ash and solidified waste.

An LLW disposal facility is currently being proposed for Pennsylvania. The Pennsylvania facility will be designed to isolate the LLW and monitored closely to ensure that the wastes pose no potential health risks for the environment and the organisms that inhabit it.

Indoor Pollution

When most people hear the word *pollution,* they associate it with the outdoors. Indoor pollutants, however, are common in many households and pose many health risks. Materials used to remodel homes—including recarpeting or putting in new cabinets—often emit fumes that adversely affect some people. Paints, cleaning products, oils, and pesticides are just a few household items that contain hazardous components. If mishandled or misused, these products can become household hazardous waste (HHW) and pose risks to humans and the environment.

There are several ways to reduce the risks posed by common household products. First, the instructions for use should be read and followed exactly as they appear on the labels. Second, only the minimum amount needed to do the job should be used. Third, leftover portions of the products should be given to others to use or disposed of according to the manufacturer's label. To deal with household hazardous waste, many communities have set up collection programs to prevent these wastes from being disposed of in landfills or burned in combustion plants. These programs ensure the safe disposal of HHW in facilities designed to treat or dispose of the wastes properly. At the same time, manufacturers are designing newer household products that give off significantly fewer toxins and thus reduce the amount of indoor pollution.

Manufacturing Common Household Cleaning Products

In addition to the risks they pose during and after use, the manufacture of many common household-cleaning products can pollute the environment and pose risks to human health. Ammonia, which is used in various cleaning products, is made by combining nitrogen and hydrogen gases under high pressures and temperatures. Not all of the hydrogen and nitrogen combine, however, and they are recirculated through the process. Nitrogen can

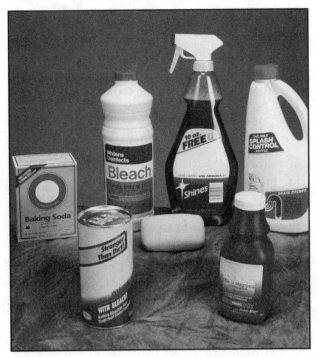

Figure 3.7 Household cleaning products must be handled properly and carefully to reduce their risks to the environment or to human health.

pollute the air if it escapes and combines with oxygen to produce nitrogen dioxide.

The manufacture of chlorine bleach is another process that can pollute the environment. This process uses an electric current to break down salt water into sodium hydroxide, hydrogen, and chlorine. The sodium hydroxide is mixed with water. Chlorine is then added to form sodium hypochlorite, the active ingredient in liquid chlorine bleaches. Chlorine gas is a poisonous, yellowish-green gas with a strong, unpleasant odor that irritates the upper respiratory systems and the lungs when inhaled.

The manufacture of laundry detergents also involves the use of many substances that can pollute the environment, including petroleum by-products, methyl alcohol, sulfuric acid, and alkalis. Detergents are made by combining a synthetic surfactant with bleaches, fabric brighteners, suds stabilizers, and substances that help prevent the dirt from re-adhering to the fabric after it is removed. This mixture is then processed into granules, flakes, tablets, or a liquid.

Lab Study

Air Pollutants in Rainwater

Some air pollutants dissolve in water in the atmosphere to produce solutions that are either very acidic or very basic. In this study, you will make observation chambers to determine how two substances can diffuse, enter the air, and form pollutants.

Materials

4 clean, dry petri dishes with lids	cotton swabs	lab apron
solution of 6M NH_3	stopwatch or clock with a second hand	copy of grid provided by your teacher
solution of 6M HCl	sheet of white paper	
universal indicator solution in dropper bottles	safety goggles	

CAUTION: *Wear your safety goggles and lab apron at ALL times during the activity. Ammonia (NH_3) and hydrochloric acid (HCl) are caustic solutions that can cause burns and damage skin and clothing. Handle them only as your teacher instructs. Should you spill or accidentally come in contact with either of these solutions, notify your teacher immediately and wash thoroughly with water.*

Procedure

1. Remove the lid from one petri dish, and place the dish face up on a copy of the grid provided by your teacher.

2. Place drops of indicator solution on the lid as shown by the dots on the grid. Try to make the drops the same size. Remove any misplaced drops with the cotton swabs, and dispose of the swabs as indicated by your teacher.

3. Place 1 drop of the NH_3 solution on the bottom half of the petri dish over the cross on the grid.

4. Carefully but quickly cover the dish with its lid. Carefully place the dish onto the sheet of white paper.

5. Ammonia evaporates very quickly. Observe changes in color of the indicator drops as the ammonia disperses throughout the dish. Notice the "eye" that forms in the center of each indicator drop. Also observe the order in which the drops change color.

6. Use a clean dish and repeat Steps 1–5, but use the stopwatch or clock to measure how fast the ammonia disperses. Record all of your observations and the time in your data table.

7. Repeat the entire procedure as outlined above, but replace the ammonia (NH_3) with hydrochloric acid (HCl).

Conclusions

1. Why did the "eye" form as the indicator drops changed color?

2. What does the "eye" imply about the solubility of the "pollutant" (ammonia or hydrochloric acid) in water?

3. What happened to the size of each "eye" as time passed?

4. Which indicator drops on the grid changed color the fastest? Explain.

5. Which "pollutant" moved faster?

6. Use the color chart that comes with the indicator solution to determine whether the "pollutants" in this study formed acids or bases in solution. Which of the "pollutants" contributes to acid rain?

For Discussion

1. Explain how you think the size of a raindrop would affect its ability to dissolve gaseous pollutants in the air. Would acid rain be more acidic than fog in the same area? Explain.

2. How can you alter this experiment to speed up the movement of the "pollutants"? To slow them down?

3. Remote regions in Canada show the effects of corrosion by acid rain, yet there isn't any air-polluting industry within hundreds of miles of these regions. Use the results from this study to explain this phenomenon.

Extension

Try to germinate seeds wrapped in a moist paper towel in each of two petri dishes—one of which contains the "pollutant" NH_3, the other containing the "pollutant" HCl. When the seedlings begin to grow, observe and compare their rates of growth, coloration, and overall health. Make a display of your results, including a graph comparing the growth rates in each "polluted" dish.

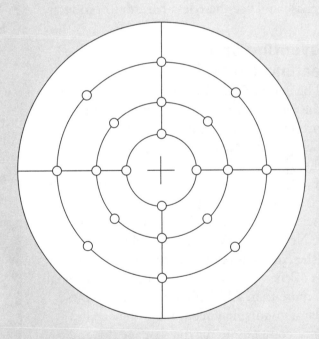

Figure 3.8 This grid shows where to place your drops in the petri dishes.

Cleaning Up Around the House

Many of the commercial cleaning products commonly used around the house can be replaced with solutions and substances that are less harmful to the environment. Make a list of at least ten cleaning products in your home. Read the labels. Are any of the following words used: *danger, warning, caution, toxic, corrosive, flammable,* or *poisonous*? Make a data table in which to record the name of each product, what it is used for, and any information about the product's components. Research to find environmentally-friendly replacements for each product. Then encourage family members to purchase and use these less hazardous products.

Preventing and Cleaning Up Pollution

The costs of cleaning up pollutants as well as the hazards inflicted on humans and the environment can be enormous. The costs associated with cleaning up the almost 11 million gallons of oil spilled by the supertanker *Exxon Valdez,* for example, exceeded $3 billion in cleanup and settlements. Many cases associated with that spill are still pending. The New York State Love Canal settlement for the contamination and cleanup of 23,000 tons of chemical wastes dumped into the canal was more than $250 million. Although these dollar amounts may seem high, they really cannot compensate for the damage done. Thousands of marine and shore organisms perished as a result of the *Valdez* oil spill. Many fishers were left without jobs for extended periods of time. People who lived in the vicinity of Love Canal suffered adverse health effects including cancers, birth defects, and numerous other serious illnesses.

The best solution to any pollution is to prevent it from happening. Pennsylvania's environmental policies do this by incorporating an understanding of and a respect for ecological values into the state's existing social structure. These policies work to challenge and change attitudes that do not reflect an overall sensitivity for the environment. The Commonwealth's environmental plan includes principles to address these challenges:

- Every person is a part of the total ecosystem and should be recognized as a trustee of Earth's resources.
- The dependency of people on air, water, and land resources should be acknowledged for the long-term survival of society.
- The complex interrelationships of the natural environment are to be recognized and respected.
- Resources are to be managed according to the natural capabilities of the total environment.
- Human activities can create adverse impacts on human health and the natural environment and are to be minimized.

Figure 3.9 Dispose of household cleaning products, hazardous waste, and other household recyclables in your community disposal program.

You Solve It! *(continued)*

Using these principles, Pennsylvania has enacted many regulations at both the local and state levels that protect farmlands, watersheds, floodplains, coal resources, water supplies, air quality, and open spaces in urban areas. One of the first environmental laws passed was the Purity of Waters Act, passed in 1905 to ensure supplies of clean drinking water around the state. This act was repealed in 1974 by the Safe Drinking Water Act that protected public drinking water supplies. The Surface Mining Conservation and Reclamation Act of 1945 prevents pollution from surface coal mining. In 1961, the Delaware River Basin Compact created the Basin Commission along the Delaware River to protect this watershed. In 1964, the Project 70 Land Acquisition and Borrowing Act created a $70 million program to acquire land for conservation purposes. The Pennsylvania Solid Waste Management Act was passed in 1968 to prevent pollution from the disposal of solid waste. It was repealed in 1980 by the Solid Waste Management Act, enacted to regulate the treatment and disposal of municipal, residual, and hazardous wastes. Also in 1980, the Building Energy Conservation Act authorized communities to adopt standards for energy conservation as part of local building codes.

Recent acts and laws in Pennsylvania include the 1990 legislation that banned hauling food in vehicles that had contained waste or hazardous chemicals. In 1992, municipalities were given more flexibility in bidding procedures to market recyclables. Many amendments related to environmental laws and regulations were also made during 1992. The Phosphate Detergent Act was amended to extend its expiration date. The Municipalities Planning Code was amended to allow the practice of forestry. The Vehicle Code to establish an enhanced vehicle emission-system inspection program was also amended. In 1996, the Waste Tire Recycling Act created the Waste Tire Remediation Program. Act 125, passed in 1998, provides for the cleanup of waste from state forest lands. Act 174, also passed in the late 1990s, established Neighborhood Improvement Districts. Act 57, passed in 1999, provides emergency agriculture drought relief.

Although this list may seem long, it mentions only some of the environmental regulations governed by the state of Pennsylvania in its commitment to protect and preserve the environment. Try to find out about other Commonwealth laws and acts and their environmental impacts.

Lesson Review

1. What is effluent, and what risks does it pose to humans and the environment?

2. List five water pollutants and the effects each has on human health.

3. Describe four gases that pollute the air and the effects of each on human health.

4. How do some farming practices pollute the soil?

5. Compare and contrast high-level and low-level radioactive wastes.

6. What are some of the principles of Pennsylvania's environmental policy?

7. Name five Pennsylvania acts or laws and the impact of each on the environment.

Lesson 3.2
Earth—One Enormous Ecosystem

Ecology is the scientific study of interactions between organisms and their environments. Ecologists collect and analyze quantitative data, such as how one population of organisms might increase or decrease when the number of its predators changes. Ecologists also gather descriptive data on factors such as the mutually beneficial relationships that exist between some ants and acacia trees in subtropical regions. All of the interactions between biotic and abiotic factors in an ecosystem can be summarized by some basic principles of ecology. One of the principles of ecology states that everything is related to everything else. The simplest disturbance in any natural process sets off a chain reaction. For example, a decrease in mosquito populations is seemingly beneficial to humans, but the absence of these insects disrupts the food chains of many organisms, including tadpoles and fish. These animals feed on mosquitoes and their larvae.

A second principle of ecology states that everything must go somewhere. In other words, nothing can really be thrown away. When an object or substance is released into the environment, it will settle somewhere. If mercury, for example, enters an aquatic environment, it is absorbed by certain mollusks. Fish that eat these mollusks will absorb the mercury into their tissues. Humans who then eat the infected fish are also exposed to this highly toxic metal.

A third principle of ecology is that nature knows best. Earth and the myriad of life-forms that inhabit the planet have evolved for billions of years. Humans simply share the planet with the rest of the biosphere. Short-term changes in the environment, such as many of those made by humans, are often likely to do more harm than good.

Aldo Leopold, a famous ecologist, always stressed that humans must live in harmony with Earth and that whatever is taken from nature is simply borrowed. The resources removed from anywhere on our planet are not free and need to be returned at some point in time either by natural processes or by human activities.

Figure 3.10 Earth's ecosystem is delicately balanced between its resources and organisms.

Nonpoint Source Pollutants

Many pollutants are *nonpoint source (NPS) pollutants* that are carried far from their sources by rain and melting snow. NPS pollutants are eventually deposited in soil or into freshwater and groundwater systems. Common NPS pollutants include fertilizers and pesticides from farms and residential areas; oil, grease, and toxic chemicals from residential areas and factories; sediment from barren landscapes, construction sites, farms, and forests; and bacteria and nutrients from livestock, pet wastes, and faulty septic systems, among others.

NPS pollution is the leading cause of water quality problems throughout the United States and in many other countries. NPS pollutants have harmful effects on drinking water supplies, recreational areas, fisheries, and wildlife in general. Some of the responsibility of reducing NPS pollutants belongs to federal governments. Some NPS pollution problems are state responsibilities. In Pennsylvania, for example, legislation regulates mining and logging practices to minimize their effects on freshwater resources. The DEP Bureau of Land and Water Conservation directs the efforts of the state's Chesapeake Bay Program. This program works to restore the health of the Chesapeake Bay by finding better ways to control key NPS pollutants.

Individuals can prevent or eliminate NPS pollutants, too, by keeping litter, pet wastes, leaves, and debris out of street gutters and storm drains because these channels drain directly into watershed bodies. NPS pollutants can also be reduced by sparingly using lawn chemicals and disposing of all used household chemicals properly. Controlling soil erosion by planting ground cover to stabilize erosion-prone areas also reduces NPS pollutants.

Figure 3.11 Some factories reduce point source pollution by using cooling ponds to cool and filter effluent before it reaches a waterway.

Point Source Pollutants

Point source (PS) pollutants are contaminants that are discharged or emitted from an identifiable source. PS pollutants include output from factory pipes, leaking landfills, wastes from food processing plants and slaughterhouses, domestic sewage, and factory smokestacks, among others. In 1996, Pennsylvania ranked among the top ten states for PS emissions.

Fortunately, many local and state regulations are in place to prevent and reduce PS pollution throughout the Commonwealth. Many industries and municipal facilities in Pennsylvania comply with these laws. Some factories and municipalities have even taken the initiative to reduce their PS pollutants more than is required by law.

Case Study

Chesapeake Bay Program

The Chesapeake Bay Program is a multi-jurisdictional partnership that is working to restore and protect Chesapeake Bay and its resources. Since the program began in 1987, federal and state partners have met many goals and are working toward others to reduce PS and NPS pollutants in and around the bay. One of the goals of the program is to ensure sound land use in the bay area by limiting development and monitoring the effects of continued growth in the area.

Habitat restoration is another goal of the program. Partners are working to reduce and eliminate blockages in waterways that prevent fish from migrating. Environmentally conscious fishery management is ensuring that adequate spawning and breeding grounds are available for the numerous species of fish in the bay and the rivers that feed it. Restoring and protecting wetlands, including forest buffers, are other ways program participants are working to restore habitat in the Chesapeake Bay watershed.

Another major goal of the Chesapeake Bay Program is to restore and protect water quality in the watershed by reducing both PS and NPS pollutants. This goal is achieved in different ways. Farmers are encouraged to plant buffer strips at the edges of crop fields and to practice conservation tillage and strip cropping to reduce the amount of sediment that can be eroded from their fields. Animal waste management methods such as storing manure and preventing it from entering runoff are other ways in which farmers can reduce both NPS and PS pollution in the bay watershed. Municipal facilities can reduce PS pollution of the bay area by maintaining septic systems and upgrading existing wastewater treatment facilities. Individuals can contribute to the bay management program by reducing household wastes, limiting their use of lawn and garden chemicals, planting trees, and conserving all of the resources they use.

Perhaps one of the biggest challenges facing the partners in the Chesapeake Bay Program is reducing nutrient PS pollutants. In 1985, nutrient PS pollutants contributed a quarter of the total nitrogen delivered to the bay from all sources. This amount was reduced to 22 percent in 1996. PS pollutants accounted for 37 percent of the phosphorus emptied into the bay in 1985 and 25 percent in 1996. The table below shows the number of facilities by state that released PS nutrients into the Chesapeake Bay watershed in 1999.

Point Source Nutrient Discharge by State in the Chesapeake Bay Watershed, 1999

Jurisdiction	Number of Facilities			
	Municipal	Industrial	Federal	Total
Virginia	70	18	3	91
Pennsylvania	124	18	1	143
Maryland	62	8	5	75
D.C.	2	0	0	2
New York	18	0	0	18
Delaware	3	1	0	4
West Virginia	9	3	0	12
Total	288	48	9	345

Source: Chesapeake Bay Program

One proposed method of removing both PS and NPS nutrients and other organic matter from the Chesapeake Bay watershed is biological nutrient removal, or BNR. BNR is a process that includes two major steps. Nitrification is the first step, which converts ammonia (NH_3) to compounds called nitrites. Nitrification is accomplished by extending the aeration time of wastewater in a conventional treatment plant. This prolonged period of exposure to air allows nitrogen-consuming bacteria to grow. The second step in BNR is denitrification, which allows the bacteria to convert nitrites into nitrogen gas. This step of the process is accomplished by using a tank that operates under oxygen-free conditions.

Figure 3.12 Recreational boats pollute air and waterways with fuel spills and gaseous emissions.

Advantages of BNR include a reduction in energy costs when compared with traditional nitrogen removal processes. Urban treatment plants, for example, spend nearly $150 per pound of nitrogen reduced. Conservation tillage and animal waste management each cost about $7 per pound of nitrogen reduced. BNR methods of nitrogen reduction only cost about $4 per pound of nitrogen reduced. BNR also uses about 50 percent fewer chemicals than do traditional methods and reduces the amount of sludge produced by 5 to 15 percent.

In addition to PS nutrients, many PS toxics are released into the Chesapeake Bay area. Mines, factories, shipping ports, and recreational boating contribute substantial amounts of copper, mercury, and highly toxic organic contaminants to the watershed's tributaries. Many of these sources also release toxic chemicals into the air. The extent and severity of toxic impacts varies widely throughout the bay watershed. A 1993 study identified three hot spots, or regions of concern—areas with probable chemical contaminant-related problems. These areas are the Anacostia River in Washington, D.C.; the Baltimore Harbor/Patapsco River in Maryland; and the Elizabeth River in Virginia. Regional action plans were developed in 1996 to reduce, correct, and prevent future chemical contamination in these areas. Fortunately, some industries in these regions have reduced their emissions of toxic materials.

The 15 million individuals who live in the Chesapeake Bay region also play an important role in reducing and preventing pollution there. Putting fewer miles on cars, installing and maintaining low-flush toilets, using environmentally friendly cleaning products, and conserving electricity and water are just a few simple lifestyle changes that can help restore and protect the Chesapeake Bay region.

Detecting Pollutants

Some pollutants, such as acid mine drainage, can often be detected by simply observing the color of the affected water body and its channel or by using pH paper to test the acidity of the water. The noses, eyes, and throats of many individuals can often "detect" ground-level ozone and smog. Most pollutants, however, are detected and measured using state-of-the-art technologies.

Detecting Hazardous Wastes Seismic vibrations, for example, can be used to image and characterize the waste materials in underground storage tanks. The resulting images can be studied to learn about the construction of the tank, as well as the kinds and amounts of waste materials stored in the tank. Other surveillance and measurement systems are used on storage sites that have become obsolete and are being demolished or dismantled. Before any decontamination or dismantlement (D&D) work can be done, facilities are analyzed and the D&D work at that site is carefully planned so that the release of harmful substances is prevented or at least minimized.

Toxic metals emission monitoring equipment commonly consists of an argon plasma spectrometer, a sampling interface, and a sampling system. These three components simultaneously measure concentrations of all hazardous metals once per minute. Such equipment can be used to measure and monitor the metallic hazardous wastes emitted at combustion and incinerator facilities.

Detecting Air Pollutants Various types of state-of-the-art equipment are used to monitor and measure air pollutants. A continuous emission monitoring system, or CEMS, is made up of several tools that measure the gas or particulate matter concentration in the air. These measurements are often entered into a computer program that determines whether the emissions exceed local, state, and federal air pollution standards.

A Fourier Transform Infrared spectrometer, or FTIR, can measure more than 100 of the 189 hazardous air pollutants listed in the Clean Air Act Amendments of 1990. Because the FTIR can measure multiple compounds simultaneously, it has a definite cost advantage over traditional devices that measure one or only a few pollutants at a time.

On the Drawing Board Some pollution monitoring devices are still in their development phases. Some researchers specializing in environmental monitoring and detection of chemicals, for example, are developing an electronic tongue. This device could be dipped into water bodies or industrial waste streams to "taste" and analyze the contents. A "brain" would then interpret the data. These electronic tongues could be placed into a river or waste stream for continuous pollutant monitoring. Other researchers are working to develop the world's smallest "electronic nose," a device that could sense and process environmental odors or chemicals much like the human nose does.

Natural Events and Environmental Health

Recall that natural events such as forest fires and natural oil seeps can pollute Earth's air, soil, and water bodies. Other natural events that affect environmental health are El Niño, its counterpart La Niña, and volcanic eruptions, among others.

El Niño El Niño is a disruption in the relationship between Earth's hydrosphere and atmosphere system in the tropical Pacific Ocean. El Niño, which occurs roughly every four years, can result in floods, droughts, hurricanes, and other types of severe weather. El Niño can also disrupt ecosystems around the world. Normally, trade winds blow from east to west, causing an increase in warm surface water in the west Pacific. To replace this water that has been blown to the west, cold nutrient-rich waters rise up from deep in the ocean along the coast of South America. These nutrient-rich waters support a diversity of marine life. When El Niño occurs, the trade winds die down and the water that had accumulated in the western Pacific migrates westward. This then causes the nutrient-rich upwellings of coastal waters to subside, drastically reducing the food supply, which often kills many marine organisms.

Volcanic Eruptions Many volcanic eruptions send tons of gases, ash, and dust high into the atmosphere. The 1991 eruption of Mount Pinatubo in the Philippines, for example, produced eruption columns that extended 25 miles above Earth's surface. These plumes of gas and dust injected about 30 million tons of SO_2 into the lower stratosphere. The SO_2 combined with the air and formed sulfate aerosols, or suspended atmospheric particles, that spread rapidly around the globe. The aerosol cloud dramatically decreased the amount of sunlight reaching Earth's surface. As a result, climates in the Northern Hemisphere were cooler for a few years. Aerosols also deplete ozone levels. In 1992, the Southern Hemisphere's ozone hole increased to an unprecedented size, and ozone depletion rates around the globe were faster than they had ever been before.

Some of the volcanic ash and dust generated during the eruption was blown through the atmosphere by the intense winds of a typhoon that coincided with the eruption. Fine ash fell as far away as the Indian Ocean, and satellites tracked the ash cloud as it moved several times around the globe.

In the late 1990s, the environmental effects of Mount Pinatubo's eruption could still be observed. Ash and other larger pieces of volcanic debris had blanketed the countryside. Avalanches of searing hot ash, gas, and pumice fragments had flowed down the mountain and had filled valleys with as much as 660 feet of volcanic debris. The thick deposits that filled many of the nearby valleys were still very hot; many had temperatures as high as 900°F. Even today, many experts fear that these hot spots could retain this heat for many more decades. When surface water or groundwater comes into contact with these hot deposits, the deposits explode and send more fine ash downwind. During the eruption, many rice paddies and sugarcane fields were also buried and won't be usable for many years.

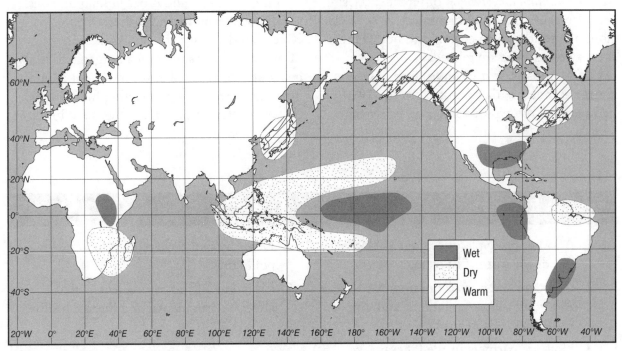

Figure 3.13 El Niño causes the climates of certain areas of the world to become wetter, drier, or warmer than normal.

You Solve It!

Natural Occurrences, Ecosystems, and Human Health

Floods, hurricanes, drought, volcanic eruptions, wildfires, biologic infestations, and global warming are just a few natural events that disrupt ecosystems. Many of these occurrences can also affect human health. Use current references and the Internet to find out about the effects of each of the events below. Then try to find out about other natural events and their effects on Earth's ecosystems and organisms.

Red Tides The magnitude of El Niño in 1997–1998 was exceptionally high. For example, a series of red tides, or algal blooms, occurred in Hong Kong territorial waters in 1998 and resulted in the loss of $32 million in fish kill damage. The alga responsible for the damage was *Gyrodinium auteolum*. A different species of alga also caused harmful blooms in 1997–1998 along the south China coast. Find out whether these two red tides are related.

Los Alamos (Cerro Grande) Fire The Cerro Grande fire that occurred in the 1990s had many of the typical effects on ecosystems that wildfires usually do. Land was damaged, and timber was lost. The loss of vegetation resulted in the deaths of livestock and wildlife and increased erosion in many areas. Find out about the hazards this particular fire posed for human health.

Global Warming and Human Diseases Recent studies suggest that global warming is increasing the geographical range and virulence of diseases in humans, animals, and plants. The increase in the number of cases of dengue virus in Latin America, West Nile virus in the United States, and Rift Valley fever in the Middle East appears to be closely related to the increases in global temperature. Find out more about the effects of global warming on these and other human diseases.

Global Warming and Other Organisms Recent studies have concluded that the health of many of Earth's nonhuman organisms is also being affected by global warming. Find out how global warming is affecting mosquitoes, oysters, butterflies, eelgrass, frogs, and birds.

Lesson Review

1. Another principle of ecology is "We all live downstream." Explain.

2. Compare and contrast nonpoint source and point source pollutants, and give at least three examples of each.

3. How are partners in the Chesapeake Bay Program working to restore the watershed?

4. Describe four devices used to detect pollutants.

5. List some of the natural events that affect environmental and human health.

Lesson 3.3
Biodiversity and Environmental Health

Biological diversity, or *biodiversity*, is the variety of living organisms on Earth. The number and type of these organisms vary by habitat. The biodiversity in and along a typical Pennsylvania stream might include mussels, trout, clams, algae, dragonflies, beetles, moths, butterflies, turtles, white-tailed deer, rattlesnakes, bats, rats, skunks, oaks, willows, skunk cabbage, and ferns. When the stream's habitat is in equilibrium, the number of species is balanced by the resources within the stream and vice versa. If the habitat becomes stressed or damaged, its organisms and resources are no longer in equilibrium. In these cases, the removal of even a single species from the stream's habitat could greatly disrupt the biodiversity of the whole system. The health of every ecosystem is directly related to its biodiversity.

Biomonitoring

In the past, the health of an ecosystem was often determined by collecting water and air samples and analyzing them for pollutants. Today, most ecosystem monitoring incorporates biological factors as well. This biological approach to monitoring an ecosystem's health is called *biomonitoring*. The basic premise of biomonitoring is that certain types of organisms occur and thrive within a limited range of conditions. When these conditions change, the numbers and distribution of organisms in the affected site also change.

Nearly all water-quality monitoring done in the United States and Europe today employs biomonitoring techniques. The organisms most commonly used in stream and river biomonitoring studies are bottom-dwelling invertebrates. These organisms are used for several reasons. First, they are present in nearly every aquatic ecosystem and are relatively easy to identify and collect. Second, these animals have limited mobility and thus cannot easily avoid poor water-quality conditions. Third, they are sensitive

Figure 3.14 Snails are excellent indicators of ecosystem health.

to a wide range of environmental impacts, including pollution.

Aquatic invertebrates often used in biomonitoring include crustaceans such as crayfish, side swimmers, and pill bugs. Mollusks such as clams, mussels, and snails are also excellent bio-indicators, as are mites, earthworms, and leeches. Most aquatic bio-indicators, however, are the insects in the ecosystem, such as mayflies, stoneflies, damselflies, beetles, dragonflies, caddisflies, true flies (crane flies and black flies), and dobsonflies.

After the invertebrate bio-indicators have been caught with nets or screens, they are identified and counted. This information—type and number of organisms—is then compared with information gathered at a different time in the same stream. In some studies, the information is compared with information collected at the same time in different streams.

Chester County Streams— A Success Story

Since 1969, government agencies have been sampling the biological and chemical parameters of the streams in Chester County, Pennsylvania. The initial goals of this program were to evaluate overall stream quality and to determine the effects of urbanization on stream ecosystems. The current goals are to use the data to monitor present stream conditions and to determine any trends. Without monitoring, there is no way to determine whether changes in land use or environmental policies are affecting water quality. The data collected by the Stream Conditions of Chester Country Program indicate that the quality of Chester County streams has greatly improved since 1970. The biodiversity in 37 of the 40 monitored streams is more varied and consists of more pollutant-sensitive species than did the same streams in the early 1970s.

Humans and Species Extinction

According to many biomonitoring studies, the health of numerous ecosystems across Pennsylvania and throughout the United States has improved since monitoring began. Despite this encouraging information, however, experts estimate that up to 50,000 species are becoming extinct each year. The renowned Harvard biologist E. O. Wilson has estimated that this current rate of extinction is 10,000 times that which is "normal" or "natural." The major cause of species endangerment, which can lead to extinction, is habitat loss. Common causes of habitat loss in the Commonwealth include sprawl, pollution, logging and mining, and forest fire suppression.

Sprawl Urban sprawl is unplanned development that results in more and more suburbs. Urban sprawl contributes significantly to air and water pollution. Sprawl is also a major cause of habitat loss. Trees are cut and removed, wetlands are drained and filled, and grassy areas are paved as development occurs. Sprawl has become a significant problem in southeastern Pennsylvania. In the Philadelphia metropolitan area alone, one acre of open space per hour is currently being developed, often at the expense of urban ecosystems.

Pollution Pollution of the air, water, and land results in habitat degradation and eventually

Figure 3.15 Sprawling urban development causes habitat loss and air and water pollution. Urban sprawl is a significant problem in many cities across the United States.

habitat loss. Pollutants also affect organisms directly. The past widespread use of the pesticide DDT in Pennsylvania and elsewhere, for example, has affected various species of birds. The global number of bald eagles and peregrine falcons has dramatically decreased as the result of DDT exposure. This pesticide affected the birds' reproductive systems, making their eggs extremely thin-shelled. The fragile eggs often did not survive incubation. Fortunately, since the mid-20th century, DDT has been banned in most parts of the world, and some of the species affected by its use are slowly recovering.

Logging and Mining Logging Pennsylvania's forests and mining its coal fields have destroyed many wildlife habitats. The extraction of timber and fuel has also polluted many ecosystems around the state with sediment, soil, and acid mine drainage. However, laws and regulations have been enacted to minimize and even prevent further loss of habitat that could lead to the extinction of many species in the Commonwealth.

Fire Suppression The ecological succession of many pine forests, including those in southern Pennsylvania, depends on naturally occurring forest fires. When these fires are suppressed, the forest ecosystems are altered immensely. Fire suppression can leave native plants very vulnerable to competitors. The competitors often grow faster than the native plants but do not become adapted to withstand periodic fires. This disruption of ecological succession can eventually destroy the habitat.

The Passenger Pigeon— Gone But Not Forgotten

Passenger pigeons were once abundant in the trees of north-central and northwestern Pennsylvania. An estimated five billion birds inhabited much of North America in the middle to late 1800s. As North America's forests were cleared for agriculture, community development, and industry, however, the passenger pigeon lost important feeding, roosting, and nesting areas. This loss of habitat, coupled with an unregulated harvest of the

Figure 3.16 The passenger pigeon looked very similar to a mourning dove but was larger in size.

birds, eventually caused the demise of the passenger pigeon.

Attempts were made to save the bird, but they were too late. In 1873, for example, Pennsylvania's General Assembly adopted a legislative package that included a law making it illegal to discharge a firearm within a quarter-mile of a wild pigeon rookery. The law also made it illegal to shoot at roosting pigeons. The fine was very steep for the time—$25 per offense. Unfortunately, the law was largely ignored. Two years later, the General Assembly enacted legislation that prohibited killing or disturbing passenger pigeons on roosts or in nesting grounds. This legislation also charged nonresidents $50 for a license to trap or net the pigeons. In 1881, another act made it unlawful to discharge firearms within a mile of a pigeon roost or to remove young pigeons from their nests. Despite these laws, however, passenger pigeons were nesting only sporadically in Pennsylvania by the early 1880s. Within a decade, they were scarce throughout the entire eastern United States. The last passenger pigeon died in the Cincinnati Zoo in Ohio in 1914.

Field Study

Backyard Biodiversity

Ecosystems vary in size and can be as large as an ocean or as small as a puddle on the ground; as large as one of Pennsylvania's forests or as small as your backyard. In this study, you will observe a portion of your backyard, the school grounds, or another grassy area to determine the biological diversity of the ecosystem. After analyzing your observations, you will hypothesize how the extinction of one of the species in the ecosystem might affect the health of the system.

Materials		
yardstick	pencil	Pennsylvania biological field guides and identification keys
four 36-inch sticks	colored pencils	
string	graph paper	
magnifying glass	copy of data table	

Procedure

1. Use the yardstick, sticks, and string to mark off an area (3 yd × 3 yd) that will not be disturbed for the duration of this study. Try not to disturb the enclosed area as you work, and make sure that the area contains different kinds of plants, including grass, weeds, shrubs, and at least one tree. If possible, include some flowers in the roped-off area.

2. Let your ecosystem readjust to having been disturbed by your work for a day or so.

3. Go back to the area, and make a bird's-eye view, or map view, of the area on the graph paper. Before you start, determine a reasonable scale to use for your sketch. As before, try not to disturb the roped-off area as you work.

4. Walk around the perimeter of the area, and use the magnifying glass to observe, identify, and count or estimate the number of plants and animals that you can see in the ecosystem. Record your observations and measurements in the data table.

5. Make sketches of the organisms in their proper places on the map view of the ecosystem.

6. From a distance, and at different times of the day, observe the roped-off area for organisms such as squirrels, birds, and rabbits that might be frequenting the ecosystem.

7. Repeat Steps 3–6 three more times over the next three weeks. Make a new map each time you return to the ecosystem. Remember to date each map so that you can easily compare the maps when the study is complete.

Conclusions

1. What kinds of plants were present in the ecosystem? What role do plants play in any ecosystem?

2. What kinds of invertebrates did you observe in the roped-off area? What role does each of these organisms play in the ecosystem?

3. Did you observe any vertebrates in or near the roped-off area? If so, what were they? What role does each vertebrate play in the ecosystem?

4. How did the information on your maps change over time?

5. How would you describe the species diversity of the ecosystem?

6. Pick one of the organisms—plant or animal—from the ecosystem. Write a paragraph or two explaining how the extinction of this organism would affect the health of your ecosystem and other similar ecosystems.

For Discussion

1. How do you think the biodiversity of a similar ecosystem in another part of the community might compare with that in your ecosystem?

2. Compare your paragraph on ecosystem health and species extinction with those of students who chose different organisms. Discuss the information.

Extension

Repeat this study at a different location, but with a similar ecosystem. Compare and contrast your findings.

Data Table		
Some Observations of _____ Ecosystem		
Organism	Number of Individuals	Role Organism Plays in the Ecosystem

Blue Pike

Stizostedion vitreum glacum, or the blue pike, was declared extinct in September 1983. This fish was once an important part of the Lake Erie ecosystem as well as the area's commercial fishing industry. Blue pike were one of the few species of Lake Erie fish to spawn in deep water, preferring the clearer, eastern two thirds of the lake. The 20 million pounds of blue pike caught each year contributed an estimated $150 million, in today's dollars, to the commercial fishing industry.

Scientists hypothesize that several factors led to the blue pike's extinction. The fish were unable to tolerate the increasing amounts of pollutants entering Lake Erie over the years. The pollutants, together with the introduction of nonnative species, caused changes in the pike's habitat. Overfishing, wetland drainage, and dam construction probably contributed to the fish's extinction as well.

Use this information together with current literature to write two or more paragraphs that detail the extinction of the blue pike and how this extinction affected the Lake Erie ecosystem.

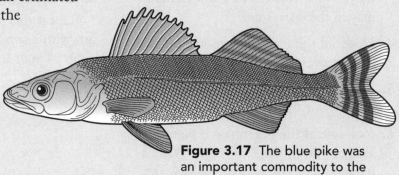

Figure 3.17 The blue pike was an important commodity to the fishing industry.

Lesson Review

1. What is biological diversity, and how can the removal or addition of a species change an ecosystem?

2. What is biomonitoring?

3. Why are bottom-dwelling invertebrates and insects used in most biomonitoring studies?

4. Briefly describe the Stream Conditions of Chester County Program.

5. Use the values in the text to calculate how many species, on average, are being lost to extinction every day.

6. Explain why sprawl can contribute to air and water pollution.

7. How can the extraction of natural resources contribute to habitat loss?

8. How did the use of the pesticide DDT affect birds?

9. List the various factors that led to the extinction of the North American passenger pigeon.

Chapter 4

Agriculture and Society

Figure 4.1 Urban sprawl continues to encroach upon fertile agricultural land.

Agriculture is a basic part of every society because everyone has to eat. Societies that can't feed themselves can't advance in other areas until the need for food is fulfilled. Over the last few thousand years, advances in agriculture have resulted in more food being grown on less land to meet the needs of a growing population. The societies that have done this most effectively have also created advanced civilizations and better standards of living for their citizens.

The advancement of agriculture in the United States has happened over a relatively short period of time—only about 200 years. In 1790, when the U.S. government took the first national census, 95 percent of people in the United States were farmers. Most farmers grew food only for their own needs. If they were lucky, there might be something left over to sell to others. According to Census 2000, only about 2 percent of people in the United States are farmers today. Yet today's farmers produce more food in greater varieties than at any other time in history.

U.S. farmers support a huge *food and fiber system*, producing enough food to feed the more than 280 million people of the United States, plus millions of other people around the world. With some of the most fertile soil on Earth, a favorable climate, and access to the most advanced farm machinery—but under 1 percent of the world's farm labor force—the United States produces much of the world's farm output. That output includes 25 percent of the world's beef and 15 percent of the world's supply of grain, milk, and eggs. More than one fourth of the world's food exports come from U.S. farms.

Pennsylvania is an important part of the U.S. food and fiber system. There are about 59,000 farms in Pennsylvania, with about 9 million acres of farmland under cultivation. Pennsylvania ranks 18th among the 50 states in annual income produced by its farms. The state is among the nation's leaders in milk production. Cattle are important in valleys in the southwestern part of Pennsylvania and along the Susquehanna River. Southeastern Pennsylvania has many poultry farms and is a leader in the production of eggs. Pennsylvania also ranks first in the nation in the production of mushrooms. Other important crops include apples and peaches, as well as cut flowers and houseplants raised in greenhouses.

Lesson 4.1
Food Production

When most people in the United States think of farms, they picture small family farms. In this type of farming operation, the number of acres farmed is fairly small and members of a family work the land, possibly with the help of some hired workers. The family lives on the land, which may have been passed down from generation to generation.

Much has changed in the last 200 years, although small farms have not disappeared. Small farms—which the U.S. Department of Agriculture (USDA) defines as farms that sell less than $250,000 worth of crops and livestock each year—still make up a majority of the farms in the United States. They raise everything from potatoes and peaches to cotton and cattle. However, the way of life found on small family farms is becoming less common. Although small farms still outnumber large farms in the United States, the bulk of the food produced in this country comes from large farms, often owned and run by huge corporations. Corporate farms now dominate the U.S. food and fiber system as

well as those of many developed countries around the world.

The use of modern technology has made U.S. farms the most efficient in the world, but technology has also made it much more expensive to farm competitively. Large corporations can afford to farm with the latest technology, which allows them to grow more food per acre and drives down the price of farm products. Because small farmers cannot compete with the large corporate farms, many of them have been forced to quit farming and sell their land. Corporations then buy more farmland. Since 1925, the number of farms in the United States has decreased from about 6.5 million to just over 2 million in 2000. At the same time, the average U.S. farm size has increased from about 143 acres to about 434 acres.

Food Production in Industrialized Countries

The key to the increase in productivity of farms in industrialized countries of North America and Europe is the *green revolution*. The green revolution is a modern farming method that uses scientifically produced varieties of grain (rice, wheat, corn) and fertilizers, pesticides, and water to increase crop yields. Until about 1950, farmers increased their yield, or the amount of food produced per acre, by increasing the number of acres planted. The methods of the green revolution have allowed farmers in industrialized nations to produce more food, not by planting more acres, but by coaxing the land to produce more on each acre. The green revolution also has helped developed nations increase their production, growing enough food to feed themselves and to export to other nations.

One tool that farmers use to coax extra productivity out of the land is irrigation. Farmers in industrialized countries have access to large amounts of water for crops, which often means sophisticated irrigation systems. In the United States, irrigation allows food to be produced on arid land that would otherwise be unsuitable for farming. Another way that farmers in industrialized countries increase their productivity is

Figure 4.2 Modern dairies use sophisticated computerized milking equipment that records and tracks production rates for individual cows.

by using the most modern laborsaving machinery to prepare their fields, plant and tend crops, and bring in harvests. The result is skyrocketing food production in industrialized countries. For example, U.S. farmers have more than doubled their crop production since the 1930s without increasing the amount of land under cultivation.

Raising livestock also takes place on a large scale with the aid of the latest technology. Chickens and eggs often come from indoor facilities that raise more than 100,000 chickens at a time. Machines give the animals food and water, and the animals often do not see the outside of the large buildings where they are raised.

The huge increase in the amount of food available in industrialized countries means that food is cheaper in these countries. Cheaper food means that more people can eat better while spending a smaller percentage of their income on food. As a result, people can spend that additional income on other items, raising their standard of living and providing jobs and income for people who make the additional items they can now afford.

Increased crop yields in industrialized countries also mean that those nations have surplus food and fiber to sell to other countries as exports. Industrialized countries that export food also gain revenue, but importing food drains the revenues of countries with food shortages.

However, modern, large-scale, industrialized agriculture, while increasing productivity, also

has some flaws. Concentrating animal production can create problems in handling manure, controlling flies, and suppressing odors. Over-reliance on chemical fertilizers and pesticides can cause pollution, disruptions of ecological balance, and in the case of pesticides, chemical pest resistance.

From Farm to Market

The relationship between farmers and the people who eat the food they produce has changed over time. Thousands of years ago, farming was local and often personal. People raised food to feed themselves and their families. Farm work was done entirely by hand. Then people learned to domesticate animals for food and to help with farm work. The use of animals such as oxen and horses to pull farm implements allowed people to cultivate larger areas of land and not only to provide food for their own families but also to have enough to trade to neighbors or to sell at local markets.

Today, few of us grow our own vegetables and fruits or raise our own animals for meat or other products. Modern agricultural technology allows a small percentage of the people of the world to farm and provide food and fiber for the rest. Most of us don't know the men and women who grow our food or when or where it was grown. In some cases, we can buy fresh fruits and vegetables from local farmers at roadside stands, at farmers' markets, or through farmers' co-ops. But in most cases, food goes through a long and complicated process in which fruits, vegetables, and livestock are sold to huge companies called food processors. They take the raw materials the farmers send them and, often through complicated processes, turn them into the frozen dinners, canned applesauce, powdered lemon drink, strawberry ice cream, curly macaroni, oven pizzas, potato chips, and toaster waffles found in stores.

After processing, the foods are specially packaged and then shipped to wholesalers who are often thousands of miles away from the farms where the foods were grown or raised. Wholesalers then sell the foods to supermarkets, delicatessens, and school cafeterias, where

Lab Study

Water from Dry Land: Water Harvesting

Irrigation brings needed water to thirsty crops in dry areas, but some irrigation systems are complex and expensive to build and maintain. Farmers in some desert areas of the Middle East use water-harvesting techniques to raise crops in arid areas. Water harvesting works on the principle that when desert soil is wet and compacted, the surface hardens and can serve as a channel that allows water to flow from a source to crops without being lost through seepage into the ground. In this lab activity, you will use clay to make a model of a water-harvesting system.

Materials		
clay	water	three $1\frac{1}{2}$-inch-high paper cups
large baking pan	measuring cup	

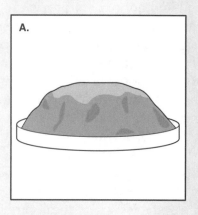

A.

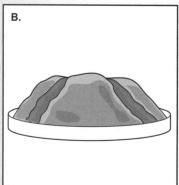

B.

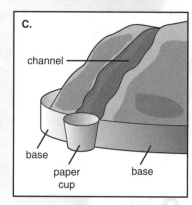

C.

channel

base

paper cup

base

Procedure
Part 1

1. Build a slightly sloping mound of clay about 6 inches tall and 10 inches wide in the pan.

2. Next, build a $1\frac{1}{2}$-inch-high base around the mound. (See diagram A above.)

3. Measure $\frac{1}{2}$ cup of water, and sprinkle it over the top of the mound to simulate rain. Be sure to sprinkle the water instead of pouring it.

4. Observe the flow of water. Record what happens to the water as it flows downhill.

Part 2

1. With your fingers, shape the top and sides of the mound so that water can be caught on top and sent flowing down three separate pathways along its sides. (See diagram B on page 96.)

2. At the end of each of the three pathways, cut a hole in the base surrounding the mound, as in diagram C. Place a paper cup in each hole, as in the diagram. Make sure that the clay mound comes to the top of each cup and that the pathways open to the top of the cups.

3. Measure $\frac{1}{2}$ cup of water, and sprinkle it over the top of the mound. Record what happens to the flow of water.

4. Pour the water that you collect in the three cups into the measuring cup. Record the amount you collect.

Conclusions

1. How do the results of Part 1 compare with the results of Part 2? Draw conclusions about how shaping the land allows you to collect previously wasted water.

2. Compare the amount of water collected in Part 2 with the amount of water that was poured over the mound at the start of this part of the activity. Infer what this suggests about the relationship between the amount of rainfall and the amount of rain that can be collected.

For Discussion

1. Make a generalization about whether water harvesting can replace irrigation on all types of farms. Determine the type of farm that could benefit most from water-harvesting methods. Identify the types of crops that might be grown on these farms.

2. Suppose that you are a farmer committed to using water harvesting to grow your crops. What must you know about the local climate and water needs of your crops before deciding what crops to plant? What would you do if the amount of rainfall in your area was not enough to support the crops you are considering?

Extension

Determine whether water harvesting is used in the area in which you live. If so, describe where and how it is used. If it is not used, discuss why it is not needed or not practical.

consumers finally eat it. The whole farm-to-market process that takes a food from field or feed lot to the consumer's table can take weeks, unlike hundreds of years ago when food was eaten where it was grown. At that time, food could not be packaged or frozen, so it was either eaten immediately or canned, dried, or cured to be eaten in the near future.

Food Production in Developing Countries

Agriculture in developing countries varies from place to place. Some farmers have large, modern farming operations similar to those in industrialized countries, but green revolution technologies are often too expensive for farmers in developing countries to use. They cannot afford the costly high-yield seed and expensive fertilizers, pesticides, and modern machinery that must be used with it. As a result, many of them still practice traditional subsistence farming on small plots of land. *Subsistence farming* is farming that just meets the farmer's survival needs; that is, farmers raise just enough to feed themselves and their families. As a result, crop yields in developing countries are much lower than those in industrialized countries. Because many of these countries have growing populations, they often do not raise enough food to feed their people and must import staples such as grains from industrialized nations such as the United States.

Figure 4.3 Slash-and-burn agriculture is one method of subsistence farming.

In traditional subsistence agriculture, farmers work their fields without modern machinery. They use human labor and draft animals such as oxen. Their farming methods and tools have often been used since ancient times. Subsistence farmers in tropical areas often practice shifting cultivation. In *shifting cultivation,* farmers clear a plot of land in the forest, plant crops on it for a few years until the soil is depleted, and then move on to clear a different field. Slash-and-burn agriculture is another type of subsistence farming. In *slash-and-burn agriculture,* farmers clear fields by cutting the trees and burning the vegetation where it lies on the ground. Farmers leave the ash, which contains nutrients from the burned vegetation, on the fields. Those nutrients then become available to crops, which farmers plant between the tree stumps.

Because most of the nutrients in tropical forest ecosystems are in the vegetation, tropical forest soils are not very fertile. When people cut tropical forests to plant crops, the soil quickly becomes depleted. Heavy tropical rains leach nutrients out of the soil quickly. The land also becomes hard as it bakes in the hot sun. As a result, farmers who use shifting cultivation or slash-and-burn agriculture must clear new fields every two to five years. They are constantly moving to clear still more fields as the old ones become too infertile to grow crops. This method works only in areas where the population is fairly small. In such cases, there is a minimum of forest disruption as new fields are cleared and old fields are left to grow back to forest. However, in many areas of the tropics where large numbers of people practice this form of agriculture, they can pose a huge threat to tropical forest ecosystems by deforesting large areas and leaving the bare soil open to erosion.

By contrast, some farmers in developing countries practice traditional intensive agriculture. They use more human and animal labor than subsistence farmers do. They also use more water, fertilizers, and pesticides on their fields. The aim of these farmers is not just to feed their families but to have some crops or livestock left over to sell. In developing countries, these farmers are a minority.

Agriculture Timeline

For hundreds of thousands of years, pre-historic people lived by hunting, fishing, and gathering wild plants. These hunter-gatherers moved constantly from place to place, often following migrating animal herds or edible plants in season.

Farming was a big step in the evolution of civilization. About 11,000 years ago people discovered that they didn't have to wander around gathering plants. They could actually plant seeds and grow plants. They also discovered that they could tame certain animals and use them for meat and to do work. This initial domestication of plants and animals probably began in the Middle East—in the Nile Valley of Egypt and in Mesopotamia—and subsequently spread to other areas. Agriculture developed independently somewhat later in northern and Southeast Asia and central Mexico and spread outward from these areas as well.

The domestication of animals such as goats, chickens, and pigs was important because it provided a steady supply of meat and milk for the first time. Later, animals such as horses and oxen were also domesticated and could be used by farmers for such work as pulling wagons or other implements. No longer did all work have to be done with human muscle. This allowed farmers to raise crops on more land and possibly to have some excess food to sell to others.

Farming allowed people to settle in one place because they no longer had to be constantly on the move looking for food. Small permanent settlements developed. Farming techniques improved as well. The first civilizations to use irrigation and oxen-pulled plows were those in Egypt and Mesopotamia. These innovations allowed farmers there to plant larger areas of land and grow more food than their immediate

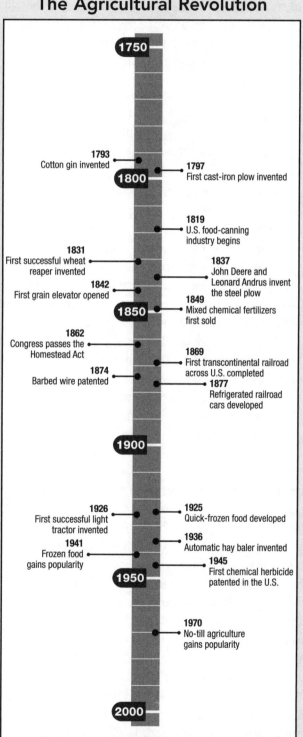

The Agricultural Revolution

1750

1793
Cotton gin invented

1797
First cast-iron plow invented

1800

1819
U.S. food-canning industry begins

1831
First successful wheat reaper invented

1837
John Deere and Leonard Andrus invent the steel plow

1842
First grain elevator opened

1849
Mixed chemical fertilizers first sold

1850

1862
Congress passes the Homestead Act

1869
First transcontinental railroad across U.S. completed

1874
Barbed wire patented

1877
Refrigerated railroad cars developed

1900

1926
First successful light tractor invented

1925
Quick-frozen food developed

1936
Automatic hay baler invented

1941
Frozen food gains popularity

1945
First chemical herbicide patented in the U.S.

1950

1970
No-till agriculture gains popularity

2000

families needed. Freed from the need to grow their own food, some people gave up farming and moved to growing towns and cities. They specialized in other skills, becoming carpenters, blacksmiths, weavers, bakers, potters, tailors, and teachers. This differentiation in work tasks helped civilizations develop.

By the A.D. 200s, the Roman Empire had developed from a small nucleus on the Italian peninsula into a powerful civilization that had conquered much of Europe, the Middle East, and North Africa. The Romans introduced the advanced farming techniques of the Middle East—such as the use of irrigation and the oxen-drawn plow—into Europe. The Romans also developed some new agriculture techniques of their own. For example, the Romans developed the technique of leaving some fields fallow, or unplanted, each year to help restore nutrients and break up pest life cycles. In their two-field system, half of the farm fields were planted each year, and the other half were left fallow. The Romans also pioneered the system of crop rotation, in which a crop that provided an important nutrient (such as legumes— peanuts, peas, beans, clover, and alfalfa—which put nitrogen into soil) is grown in rotation with crops that take the same nutrients out of the soil. Roman farmers used steep hillsides to grow crops by building terraces, or steps, into the hillsides. They also built huge irrigation canals to bring water to their crops.

During the Middle Ages, after the fall of the Roman Empire, many medieval farmers in Europe adopted a three-field crop rotation system, keeping one field out of three fallow each year and planting the other two. This system allowed medieval farmers to plant more land each year than the Romans could with their two-field system. Also during the Middle Ages, a new harness that allowed a horse to pull a plow was developed. Because a horse can pull a plow up to four times faster than an

ox can, farmers could get more work done in a shorter amount of time and plant more land. Farmers also developed several special breeds of livestock in Europe during this time. The Guernsey cow was developed in northwestern Europe in about 1100. The Guernsey, which gives especially rich milk, is still a major source of milk used to make butter today.

The European voyages of discovery that began in the 1400s also influenced the development of agriculture worldwide. Previously, crops and livestock had been developed in isolated regions. Adventurers and scientists began to find "new" crops in previously unexplored areas and transport them thousands of miles to other areas, where farmers began to grow them. The potato was unknown in Europe until Spanish explorers brought it from Peru in the 16th century. Potatoes eventually became a staple crop for European farmers and an important part of the diet in many European countries.

By the time the first European explorers and settlers arrived in North America, many Native Americans had developed advanced systems of agriculture. In various parts of the Americas, native farmers grew cocoa beans, corn, peanuts, peppers, rubber trees, squash, sweet potatoes, tobacco, and tomatoes. Europeans first learned of these crops from the Native Americans, who also taught the Europeans how to grow the crops. The Europeans added to the diversity of crops in North America as they brought their own seeds, livestock, tools, and farming methods to the regions they explored and settled.

During the early 1700s, the Agricultural Revolution began in Great Britain. It was the result of a number of discoveries and inventions that made farming more efficient and productive. By the mid-1800s, many of these innovations had spread throughout much of Europe and North America. As a result of the Agricultural Revolution, fewer people were

You Solve It! (continued)

needed to produce food than ever before. Farm families by the thousands moved to towns and cities in Europe and the United States starting in the 19th century.

Three developments brought about the Agricultural Revolution. First, crop-growing methods improved. For example, agriculture experts developed the four-field crop rotation system. Because of the rotation of crops, the system preserved soil nutrients while allowing farmers to grow food on all of their land each year. Second, there were many advances in livestock breeding that improved the quality of animals used for meat and allowed farmers to raise livestock more cheaply. Last, several important new farm machines were invented that allowed farms to grow more food using less labor.

Innovation in agriculture continued throughout the 19th and 20th centuries. As a result, in countries such as the United States, fewer farmers were needed to produce greater quantities of food.

Questions

1. Approximately how long ago did agriculture develop?

2. List four areas of the world where agriculture developed independently.

3. How did the development of better farming methods in ancient times help early civilizations develop?

4. Identify two agricultural techniques devised by the Romans.

5. What contribution did Native Americans make to European agriculture?

6. List the three developments that brought about the Agricultural Revolution in the 1700s and 1800s.

Lesson Review

1. How has the U.S. farm population changed over the past 200 years?

2. Identify three characteristics that make the U.S. food and fiber system successful.

3. List three of Pennsylvania's major agricultural products.

4. Discuss the state of the family farm in the United States today.

5. Define the green revolution.

6. How has the green revolution benefited farmers in developed countries?

7. How does the availability of large quantities of cheap food in developed countries affect the standard of living of the people there?

8. List three drawbacks of modern commercial farming.

9. Draw conclusions about why shifting cultivation and slash-and-burn agriculture are not good long-term agricultural systems.

10. Place the following events in the history of agriculture in proper sequence: the Agricultural Revolution occurs in England; the horse-drawn plow is first used; people domesticate animals; Native Americans show Europeans how to grow corn and tomatoes; farmers use oxen-pulled plows.

Lesson 4.2
The Food and Fiber System in the United States

Today's farm-to-market process is a long and complicated one that farmers even 50 years ago would not have recognized. However, it makes possible the great quantity and variety of food that is available to people in industrialized countries such as the United States.

The Farm-to-Market Process

Although details will vary, most food products pass through a complicated farm-to-market process with the following steps:

Production This is the first stage in the process, in which farmers produce the fruits, vegetables, grains, livestock, or clothing fiber. Hundreds of years ago, this was the only stage before the farmer's family or someone else consumed the food.

Food Processing *Food processing* transforms the raw foodstuffs from the farm into the food that you consume. Some farmers belong to cooperatives that collect the foodstuffs raised by members and sell them to food processors. In many cases, however, farmers have a contract to sell what they raise directly to a food processor, which often dictates the type of crop and the quantity it will buy. Farmers or ranchers who raise livestock sell their animals to meatpackers at markets.

In the simplest cases, fresh fruits, vegetables, and eggs are washed and sorted before heading to market. More often, however, food processors dry, can, freeze, pickle, shred, powder, or juice raw foods. They use basic plant and animal ingredients to make other foods. For example, sugarcane becomes granulated sugar, peanuts and soybeans become cooking oil, and berries become jam. Food processors also put raw ingredients together to make everything from cake mixes and pretzels to frozen spaghetti dinners and ice cream. In the process, they usually mix in additives such as colors, texturizers, preservatives, flavorings, and nutrients such as vitamins and minerals. Some processes improve food quality. For example, homogenization ensures that milk stays blended in the container and doesn't separate into liquid and fat solids.

Food processing plants also slaughter cattle, sheep, hogs, and chickens and prepare them for market. They make some of this meat into products such as hot dogs, sausage, and hamburger patties. Food processors also clean fish that are sold fresh or frozen.

Packaging This is the final step in food processing. Packaging protects foods from spoiling, spilling, or breaking. It includes attractive labels that help customers identify certain brands of processed foods, as well as words such as "Natural," "Fortified," "Low-Fat," and "No Preservatives" that may entice customers to buy particular products. The type of packaging depends on the needs of the product. Foam or cardboard egg containers protect fragile eggs. Plastic bags keep air away from foods such as meat and bread. Aerosol cans make it easy to use whipped cream, and squeeze bottles make mustard and ketchup handy and easy to dispense.

Transportation and Distribution Because most food is no longer consumed close to where it is grown, transportation plays an important role in the farm-to-market process. Trucks and trains (some refrigerated) move fresh foods from the farm to the food processing plant or, in some cases, to markets for sale directly to the consumers at farmers' markets. The transportation system is also necessary to move processed foods from the food processing plant to warehouses and markets. In some cases, very perishable or expensive food that must go long distances, such as fresh lobsters caught in Maine and sent to Montana, travels by air transport.

After processing, most food moves through the distribution process. Food processors sell large quantities of what they produce to wholesalers. The wholesaler stores the foods in a warehouse and then sells smaller quantities of each product to a retailer. The wholesaler might also sell foods to restaurants, bakeshops, school cafeterias, or other establishments.

Marketing Marketing is the advertising, buying, and selling of the products in the food and fiber system. Most consumers buy foods from retailers. Retailers include supermarkets, small grocery stores, delicatessens, greengrocers, butcher shops, and even vending machines.

Regulations The U.S. government regulates agriculture, especially in the areas of food safety, inspection, and grading. The USDA inspects all meat and many other types of food. The U.S. government also grades foods such as eggs, milk, meat, and grain to ensure that they meet certain standards. Some regulations protect the safety of plant and animal foodstuffs during production and processing, and others attempt to ensure the safety of people who work in factories and fields in the agriculture industry. Regulations also ensure the truthfulness of information on food labels, as well as the safety and honesty of packaging. Foods that come into the United States are inspected as well. If inspectors find disease or parasites or if the food does not meet U.S. standards, it cannot be sold in the United States. Other regulations ensure that farm production practices are safe for the environment. These regulations help reduce air and water pollution.

Research and Development Research and development in the agriculture industry is an ongoing process that strives to create new crop and livestock varieties; new food and fiber products; and additional methods for producing, processing, and storing foods. For example, if there's a new flavor of potato chip or ice cream on the supermarket shelf or a new type of packaging holding your favorite juice drink, scientists in research and development have created it because food processors think it will improve the basic product or make you more likely to buy it. Research and development is carried out primarily by universities, government agencies, and private companies.

Major Agricultural Regions of the United States

Why do pineapples grow in Hawaii, but not in Kansas? Why can you find large-scale cattle ranching in Wyoming, but not in Maine? Physical geography is the answer. Climate, soils, and landforms determine the types of plants that will grow in a certain region. Those factors help determine the types of crops farmers in that region are most likely to grow or the types of livestock they are most likely to raise. The crops that grow in the hot, wet climate of some parts of Hawaii won't grow in the hot, dry climate of Arizona. The thin, stony soils of the hills of Vermont won't support the same types of crops as the rich, dark soils of the flatlands of Illinois will.

The USDA recognizes ten U.S. farming regions, shown on the map below. The climate, soil, and landforms of each region influence the agricultural products it produces.

The Northeast The Northeast is a diverse geographic region that includes New England and the Mid-Atlantic. Cold winters and thin, stony soils limit agricultural production in the

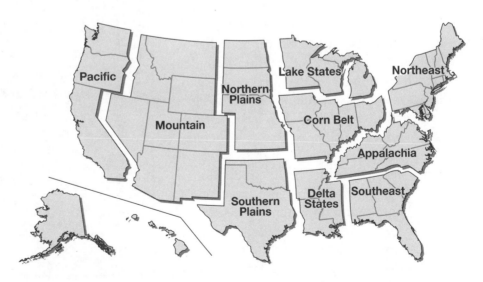

Figure 4.4 The USDA has divided the United States into ten different farming regions. Pennsylvania is part of the Northeast region.

northern part of the region. Nevertheless, with the region's ample rainfall and moderate climate, raising fruits and vegetables is important throughout southern New England and the Mid-Atlantic. An advantage of northeastern agriculture is that it is close to markets containing tens of millions of people. This means that fresh produce can be delivered quickly to the consumer. Pennsylvania, which is in this region, leads the nation in the production of mushrooms. Massachusetts is first in the production of cranberries, and New York is second only to Washington in apple production. Dairy farming is especially important in states such as Pennsylvania, Vermont, and New York. Raising poultry in large factory farm operations has become important in states such as Maryland, Delaware, and Pennsylvania. However, some of the best farm land in this area is being converted to sprawling suburban communities. Fishing in the nearby North Atlantic has been a leading industry in New England for hundreds of years, although over-fishing of that area now threatens the health of several important fish industries, such as cod and flounder.

The Lake States The northern part of this region has cold winters and poor soils that limit agriculture. However, other areas have excellent land for farming. The Great Lakes region has many dairy farms. States such as Minnesota and Wisconsin are leaders in the production of milk and dairy products such as butter and cheese. Forest products are important in Michigan, which is the nation's second-largest producer of Christmas trees. The area along Lake Michigan in Michigan's Lower Peninsula is a prime fruit-growing region, raising apples, blueberries, cantaloupes, cherries, peaches, and strawberries. Wisconsin leads the states in the production of beets, cabbages, snap beans, and sweet corn. Eggs and hogs are also important in this region, as are field corn, soybeans, wheat, and hay.

The Appalachian States Parts of this mountain region have productive farmland, but thin and rocky soils and eroded hillsides characterize much of the area. Products such as peanuts, cattle, hogs, and tobacco are grown here. Many dairy farms can also be found in the region.

The Southeast Much of this region has plentiful rainfall, mild summers, and cool winters. Main livestock products include beef cattle, chickens, and hogs. The Southeast also has many orchards and dairy farms. Georgia is known for its peaches, and the Carolinas are among the leaders in the production of tobacco. Florida's semitropical climate makes it a leading producer of hot-weather crops such as citrus fruit and sugarcane. Florida is also a major source of fresh fruits and vegetables that are shipped to the Northeast during winter months, when cold weather prevents farm production there. The coastal plain of this region produces peanuts, among other crops. The Southeast region also has cotton production areas. Forest products are important in states such as the Carolinas and Georgia. North Carolina leads the nation in the production of household wood furniture.

Figure 4.5 Florida is known for its oranges and other citrus fruits.

The Delta States Fertile farmland is abundant along the Mississippi River flood plain. The region also has plentiful rainfall and a mild climate. Major crops include chickens, rice, corn, and sugarcane. Livestock production is gaining importance. The region also has a Gulf of Mexico fishing industry that specializes in shellfish such as shrimp. Gulf fisheries are threatened, however, by fertilizer runoff from farmlands along the Mississippi River that have polluted areas of the Gulf of Mexico. The fertilizer has caused the growth of algal blooms, which remove oxygen from large areas of the Gulf, causing fish kills.

The Corn Belt As its name suggests, this is a great corn-growing area of the United States. About one half of the nation's crop comes from here. With fertile land and a favorable climate, the Corn Belt is one of the world's top producers of corn. The area is also ideal for raising soybeans. The Corn Belt is a major producer of hogs, cattle, and dairy products.

The Northern and Southern Plains The Plains are grasslands in which the amount of precipitation decreases from east to west. Crops that are essentially grasses, such as wheat, corn, barley, grain sorghum, and hay, do well here. Agriculture in both the Northern and Southern Plains is restricted by variations in climate across the region. Because the western part of the Plains is drier than the east, corn and wheat production gives way to raising cattle that forage on short-grass pastures and hay. Short summers and long, cold winters in the Northern Plains restrict agriculture there. However, the Plains region produces three fifths of the nation's spring and winter wheat. The southern part of the region also produces cotton.

The Mountain States The Rocky Mountains are cooler and wetter than the adjacent plains and deserts. Some high meadows are suited to raising cattle and sheep. Wheat is a major crop in the northern parts. Irrigation in some valleys in this region allows farmers to grow hay, sugar beets, potatoes, and several types of fruits and vegetables.

Figure 4.6 Vineyards are a common sight in California.

The Pacific Region This is a region of contrasts. The eastern parts of Washington and Oregon as well as central and southern California are dry, but because of large-scale irrigation projects that bring water to these areas, they are among the most productive agricultural areas of the United States. Farmers in Oregon and Washington raise wheat, fruit, and potatoes. California leads the nation in the production of fruits and vegetables, especially in its heavily irrigated Central Valley and Imperial Valley. California also leads the nation in the production of dairy products such as milk and cheese. Hawaii's rich volcanic soils and tropical climate make it ideal for raising crops such as pineapples and sugarcane. Alaska's frigid climate and short growing season limit agriculture severely. However, Alaska's farmers produce greenhouse and nursery products under glass in controlled environments. Alaska also has local dairy production.

Case Study

Pennsylvania's Lumber Industry

About 17 million acres of Pennsylvania, almost 60 percent of the state, are covered with hardwood forest. Pennsylvania's diverse forests include more than 70 tree species, such as red oaks, hickories, walnuts, poplars, birches, red maples, and sugar maples.

Pennsylvania is a leader in the production of hardwood lumber, producing approximately one billion board feet each year—enough to circle Earth seven times. Pennsylvania's softwood forests produce products such as pulpwood, which is used to make paper and building products.

Pennsylvania's timber and forest products industry is the fourth-largest manufacturing industry in the state, with one of the biggest forest products workforces in the United States. It is also the state's seventh-largest employer. The timber and forest products industry employs more than 88,000 people at more than 2,500 locations around the state, with an annual payroll approaching $3 billion.

The forest products industry has a large impact beyond just the Pennsylvanians who work in it. Private landowners receive about $380 million in revenue from timber sales to the timber and wood products industry. It is estimated that $17 worth of economic growth is generated through the manufacture of forest products for every dollar received by forest landowners.

Responsible management of forestland is important in Pennsylvania, so more than 2 million acres of Pennsylvania's forests have

Figure 4.7 Removing the bark is one of the first steps in processing timber.

been independently certified. Certification means that the forest is managed in an environmentally responsible manner. About one half of the certified hardwood forests within the United States are in Pennsylvania, and the state ranks first in the country in the amount of certified land within it.

Common tree species in Pennsylvania's certified forests include cherries, red oaks, white oaks, ashes, maples, beeches, poplars, and basswoods. A growing number of companies manufacturing finished wood products in Pennsylvania guarantee that their products were made from certified wood. Products include veneer, moldings, flooring, indoor furniture, and musical instruments. When a consumer buys a product made of certified wood, the consumer is supporting responsible forestry. For some people, it is important to support companies that use certified wood in their products.

The location of Pennsylvania also allows the state to lead the nation in the export of forest hardwood products. Forty percent of the population of the United States and 60 percent of the population of Canada lives within 500 miles of the state. In addition, Pennsylvania's extensive system of state and federal highways (the fourth largest in the United States) gives the state numerous links to markets in the region and across the continent. Water routes through its river and lake ports give the state access to the Atlantic Ocean, the Ohio and Mississippi River systems, and the Great Lakes.

Questions

1. What percentage of Pennsylvania is covered with forest?

2. How many Pennsylvanians are employed in the timber and forest products industry?

3. List three products of Pennsylvania's forests.

4. Define forest certification.

5. Describe how forest certification is good for Pennsylvania.

You Solve It!

The Price of Mushrooms

Pennsylvania leads the nation in the production of mushrooms. In 2001, sales of common mushrooms (*Agaricus* mushrooms) nationwide totaled 839 million pounds with an estimated revenue of $820 million. Pennsylvania mushrooms made up 53 percent of that total.

Farmers' Costs When you buy a package of mushrooms, only a part of that money goes to the farmer. If you buy a 16-ounce package of white button mushrooms for $2.50, the farmer receives only $.76. Some of that money pays for production costs, and the rest is profit.

Nonfarm Portion of Price The difference between what the farmer was paid and what you pay at the store includes the costs of transportation, distribution, and marketing.

At every step in the process, each company that handles the mushrooms also adds a little to cover its own profit.

Questions

1. What price was each farmer paid per pound of mushrooms sold?

2. What percentage of that price was profit? What was the farmer's cost per pound of mushrooms sold? How much profit (in dollars and cents) did the farmer make for each pound of mushrooms sold?

3. What percentage of the retail price went to the farmer? What percentage of that retail price did the farmer actually keep as profit?

Data Table		
Farmer's Cost	Percentage of Revenue	Cost per Pound
Wages	28	
Compost (growing medium)	23	
Spawn (fungus starter that produces mushrooms)	7	
Other (soil, fertilizer, disposal, packaging)	13	

Lesson Review

1. Sequence the following components of the farm-to-market process: distribution; production; processing; packaging.

2. List three aspects of the food and fiber system that our government regulates.

3. Identify the agricultural region in which Pennsylvania is located.

4. List three factors that help determine the crops that will grow in a region.

5. In which region is irrigation used to grow an abundance of crops? Draw conclusions about why this could become an environmental problem.

Lesson 4.3
Farming Methods

All agriculture depends on *soil*, the upper layer of land surface that all growing things use for physical support, water, and nutrients. The formation of soil begins with the weathering of surface rock. *Weathering* is the slow wearing away of rock by wind, water, and temperature fluctuations. Because soil is forming all the time, it is considered a renewable resource, but soil formation is a very slow process. In fact, it can take between 200 and 1,000 years to form just one inch of new soil, depending on the climate and parent rock. As a result, soils cannot easily be replaced and must be carefully conserved. In addition, soil is teeming with life. Fungi, bacteria, plants, insects, and vertebrates make up a diverse and healthy soil ecosystem. Crops benefit from a healthy soil.

Soil erosion is a major problem in agriculture. The loss of soil often means the loss of the ability of land to support crops. Some erosion happens naturally, as wind and running water remove topsoil, but people's actions also cause soil erosion. Activities such as logging, livestock grazing, and farming can speed soil erosion by removing vegetation that holds soil in place and exposing topsoil to wind and running water. Because soil is a farmer's most important resource, farmers have developed several soil conservation methods to prevent soil loss.

Preparing the Land

The way farmers prepare the soil for planting can make the difference between preserving fertile soil and losing it to erosion. In traditional agriculture, farmers use machinery such as plows to till, or break up, the surface of the soil and prepare it for planting. But tilling the soil exposes topsoil to erosion. To protect the topsoil, some farmers use conservation tillage methods. With *conservation tillage*, farmers disturb surface topsoil and vegetation as little as possible during planting. One method loosens the soil but does not completely turn it over. *No-till cultivation* is a process in which a machine drills holes in the topsoil for planting seeds without turning the soil over at all. Although no-till cultivation cuts down on soil erosion, it does have drawbacks. For example, it requires the use of pesticides to kill weeds that remain in the soil and could compete with crops.

In another type of conservation tillage, farmers use the leftover stubble from the previous crop to cover the soil surface between seeded areas. This serves two purposes. First, it helps prevent soil erosion by providing a cover that cuts down on windblown soil. Second, as the plant stubble decays, it creates humus that becomes part of the soil. *Humus* is a mixture of decomposed organic matter in topsoil that supplies nutrients to plants and helps retain soil moisture.

Planting the Land

Ideal farmland is flat, but many farmers don't have ideal conditions for planting crops. Farmers must plant crops on land that ranges from gently sloping to very steep. Precipitation that sends water cascading downhill in such places can easily strip away valuable topsoil. Farmers use soil conservation methods such as contour farming, strip cropping, and terracing to reduce soil erosion on sloping land.

Farmers who have slightly sloping fields can use contour farming. In *contour farming*, farmers plow their fields and plant crops across the slope of the land instead of up and down the slope. The ridges that this planting method forms across the slope help prevent water from running downhill and taking valuable soil with it. On land without a very steep slope, contour farming reduces erosion between 30 and 50 percent.

Some farmers use strip cropping on sloping land as well. *Strip cropping* is a planting method in which wide rows or strips of crops such as corn are planted alternately with rows of a grass or legume crop. The grass or legume crop grows as a relatively low ground cover that protects the surface of the soil from wind erosion. The fibrous roots of the cover crop also help hold the soil in place, providing additional protection. In addition, legumes restore the crucial nutrient nitrogen to the soil.

Figure 4.8 Contour farming (left), strip cropping (middle), and terracing (right) are effective errosion-control methods for sloping land.

Growing two different crops side-by-side in strip cropping also helps stop the spread of pests and plant diseases. Pests and diseases specific to just one type of crop cannot spread unchecked through a field that is planted with more than one crop.

On steeper hills, farmers often use terracing to reduce soil erosion. In *terracing,* farmers build a series of broad, flat ridges that run down a hillside like stairs. The ridge of each terrace helps retain water that would otherwise run unimpeded downhill. Terracing also provides level cropland in areas where the terrain might otherwise be too steep for planting.

Soil Enrichment

Another important part of soil conservation is maintaining and restoring nutrients to the soil. Without soil nutrients, crops cannot grow. The use of fertilizers and crop rotation can restore nutrients that years of farming the same land can remove from soil.

There are natural organic and artificial chemical fertilizers. Natural organic fertilizers are substances such as animal manure, green manure, and compost. Green manure is growing or freshly cut plants that farmers can plow under to return organic matter to the soil. Compost is partially decomposed organic plant and animal material that is used as a fertilizer.

Many farmers, especially in industrialized countries, also use artificial chemical fertilizers. These fertilizers contain essential nutrients such as nitrogen, phosphorus, and potassium, which crops drain from the soil during the growing season. These fertilizers help greatly increase crop yields, but they supply only two or three of the approximately 20 nutrients plants require. They also do not add humus to the soil. Runoff can wash chemical fertilizers from fields into surface water, where it can cause the growth of algae that robs the oxygen that is needed by fish from the water. Fertilizers can also pollute underground drinking water supplies.

Planting the same crops year after year can deplete the soil, but crop rotation cuts down on the drain of nutrients. *Crop rotation* is the changing of the crops planted in a field from year to year. For example, over a three-year period, a farmer might plant corn in the first year, wheat in the second, and clover in the third. Because each crop removes and replaces different soil nutrients, nutrient depletion is minimized.

The use of one soil conservation method does not rule out the use of others. In fact, farmers often use several soil conservation techniques to conserve topsoil and retain nutrients at sufficiently high levels to grow crops and provide enough food.

Farms and Human Nutrition

You can walk into a supermarket in Boston and buy grapes from Chile in the middle of winter. Italians can purchase apples grown in Washington, and people in Japan can buy beef raised in Texas. The great agricultural abundance of developed nations such as the United States as well as modern methods of food preservation and quick transportation allow people all over the world to enjoy foods grown thousands of miles away at any time of year, even out of season.

Modern farming practices, such as the use of high-yield varieties of seed, chemical fertilizers, modern pest-management techniques, and labor-saving machinery, have contributed to increasing both the amount and variety of foods that farmers can produce. For example, U.S. farmers have more than doubled their crop production since the 1940s without increasing the amount of land under cultivation. Today each U.S. farmer feeds and clothes about 140 people—105 of those in the United States and 35 in other countries.

To increase crop yields, farmers began planting just a few crops, especially grains such as wheat, corn, and rice, instead of planting a variety of crops. With the use of high-yield forms of these crops and large inputs of fertilizers, pesticides, and water, some farmers can now grow two or three crops per year on the same fields. In addition, with high-yield varieties producing up to five times the yields of traditional rice, wheat, and corn plants, the amount of food one farmer can produce in a developed nation dwarfs what that farmer could produce just a few decades ago.

Some developing countries adopted the modern farming methods of industrialized countries in the 1970s. As a result, their crop yields increased as well. For example, as a result of using high-yield grains, India doubled the amount of food it produced between 1970 and 1992, staving off famines during the 1970s and 1980s.

The world agricultural system produces enough food to supply the minimal nutritional requirements of everyone on the planet, but millions of people remain malnourished because they do not have access to that food. World population is increasing rapidly; experts estimate that agriculture will have to meet the nutritional needs of an additional 1.7 billion people over the next 20 years or so. Because most of the land that is suitable for agriculture is already under cultivation, that increase in food will have to come from getting the land that is now farmed to produce even more. Agriculture has been very successful in increasing crop yields over the past few decades, but there are limits on the capacity of the land to produce more and more food, especially in a manner that does not degrade the environment.

Although modern agriculture has increased the variety and quantity of foods available worldwide, it also has caused environmental problems. Farmland can destroy natural ecosystems. For example, people drain swamps and marshes and clear forests to create farms. As a result, wildlife habitat is destroyed. Chemical pesticides and fertilizers can pollute local soil and waters. Soil erosion and nutrient depletion can occur on farmlands that do not practice soil conservation. In addition, modern farming is extremely energy intensive. Large inputs of nonrenewable and polluting fossil fuels are needed to run machinery and carry on agricultural chemical production.

In response, farmers in many parts of the world have adopted farming practices that could limit the damage. These methods include planting trees and practicing other soil conservation measures to limit erosion as well as restricting the use of pesticides and other agricultural chemicals using an integrated pest management approach. (See Chapter 5.) But as the world's population continues to increase, the challenge of growing food for everyone on the same amount of farmland will increase as well.

Field Study

Do You Eat Locally?

If you live in Pennsylvania and drink orange juice, your juice has traveled a fair distance before getting to your table. In fact, you will find that many of the fruits and vegetables in your local market came from places far away from Pennsylvania. How many? In this field study, you will find out.

Procedure

1. Copy the table below onto a blank sheet of paper.

2. Visit a supermarket or greengrocer with a large produce section.

3. Observe a number of fruits and vegetables on sale. Record the specific names of the produce you observe in the first column of the table; for example, *Apple (McIntosh)* instead of just *Apple*. Add rows if you need more room.

4. In the second column, write the name of the state or country where the fruit or vegetable was grown.

5. Tabulate the percentage of the produce that was grown in Pennsylvania versus the percentage grown elsewhere. Then tabulate the percentage grown in the United States versus the percentage grown in other countries.

Locally Grown Food

Fruit or Vegetable	Where It's From

Conclusions

1. Determine whether most of the fruits and vegetables in your market are home-grown. Some information on where the fruits and vegetables were grown is available on fruit labels and store signs. You also may ask a produce clerk or manager about the origins of the produce you want to include in this activity.

2. Identify the fruits and vegetables that were grown in Pennsylvania.

3. Determine whether most of the fruits and vegetables you observed were grown in the United States or imported from another country.

4. Identify the states or foreign countries from which the produce from outside of Pennsylvania came.

5. Identify the fruit or vegetable that was shipped the greatest distance to get to your market. Calculate approximately how far it traveled.

For Discussion

1. Draw conclusions about why some produce comes from outside Pennsylvania.

2. Make generalizations about the advantages and disadvantages of importing produce from outside the state.

Food Safety

There are many possible sources of food contamination. They include bacterial contaminants such as *Salmonella, E. coli,* and *Campylobacter;* viruses; and chemicals. In most cases, exposure to foodborne contamination has mild results such as diarrhea and vomiting. Pathogens can create serious illness and, in some cases, cause death.

Foodborne illnesses usually follow the eating of foods that have been contaminated with bacteria during processing, improper storage, or improper handling. Sometimes the contamination occurs in a factory. In many cases, contamination occurs at home. Most raw poultry contains a number of potentially harmful bacteria when it is purchased at the supermarket, but thorough cooking at a sufficiently high temperature usually kills these bacteria. Improper cooking, or reusing utensils (such as knives that have touched raw chicken) without proper washing can spread the bacteria.

Although we know these dangers exist, we expect food to be safe when we buy it at a supermarket or eat it at a restaurant. For the most part, food in the United States is safe, largely because of government regulations. In the United States, the three agencies with the greatest responsibility for food safety are the Department of Agriculture (USDA), the Food and Drug Administration (FDA), and the Environmental Protection Agency (EPA).

The USDA helps ensure food safety by inspecting meat in slaughterhouses and processing plants. It grades meat and dairy products to indicate their quality. The USDA enforces regulations that help protect animals and plants from diseases and pests, and conducts research on increasing crop production, combating pests, fostering soil conservation, and educating people about good nutrition.

The FDA also has jurisdiction over some aspects of food safety, although it regulates drugs and cosmetics as well. The FDA is concerned with truthfulness in food labels, the safety of food packaging, and the maintenance of sanitary conditions in restaurants and other public eating places. The FDA also administers programs that help ensure the safety of dairy products and shellfish. The label listing nutrition facts that appears on all packaged foods is an FDA creation.

Chemical residues in foods, largely as a result of pesticides sprayed on fields, are another area of food safety concern. The EPA, as the agency that regulates the use of pesticides, has jurisdiction in this area. The EPA has the power to stop the use of pesticides that are dangerous to the environment, wildlife, or human health.

Even with so many protections of the food supply in the United States, problems still occur. The Centers for Disease Control and Prevention estimates that diseases carried by food send 325,000 people to the hospital each year, cause 76 million illnesses, and result in 5,000 fatalities.

As a result, it is necessary to be a wise consumer. Pay attention to container dates to ensure that you are getting fresh foods. Bacteria require warmth to grow, so be aware of how refrigerated or frozen items are stored in stores and at home. Examine packaging to make sure that it is undamaged. Be sure to wash all fresh fruits and vegetables before eating or cooking them. Pesticide residues or bacteria on the surface of produce can cause illness.

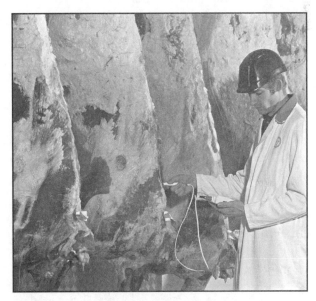

Figure 4.9 Meat-storage conditions in slaughterhouses and packaging plants are inspected and monitored by the USDA.

Food Poisoning

Although regulations are in place to safeguard the U.S. food supply, many cases of food poisoning occur each year. The following paragraphs describe some recent cases of food poisoning in the United States.

Case A

A group of people attended a company picnic on a warm summer day. Shortly after the picnic, about 400 of them became ill. The illness was traced to potato salad and turkey that was served at the picnic. When tested, the foods contained the *Salmonella enteritidis* bacteria. Poultry, milk, eggs, and foods made from eggs most often carry this bacterium. Symptoms of salmonella infection include diarrhea, abdominal pain, nausea, and fever. Symptoms usually last two to five days. People can best avoid infection by salmonella by properly refrigerating prepared foods and by thoroughly cooking poultry and other foods that could carry the bacteria.

Case B

A young woman decided to go on a healthy diet that consisted of mostly vegetables, fruit, and chicken. One day, she felt a tingling in her feet. A few hours later, she collapsed. Her condition deteriorated over the next few days, with constant pain, difficulty breathing, and partial paralysis. Over several months, she slowly recovered. Her illness was traced to chicken contaminated by the *Campylobacter* bacteria. She had cooked the chicken well, but she remembered using a cutting board on which she had chopped raw chicken to also chop vegetables for a raw salad she ate at the same meal. She did not wash the cutting board thoroughly between chopping the chicken and chopping the salad greens.

Case C

A young man went out to dinner and ordered tacos. He said they tasted strange. An hour later, he felt ill with stomach pains and diarrhea. His illness lasted for only a few days, but at one point the pain was so severe that he went to the hospital emergency room. Local health authorities tested for foodborne bacteria and found that he was infected with *E. coli*, a very dangerous and sometimes deadly bacterium often found in food. Some sleuthing determined that the bacteria had come not from the tacos but from a hamburger eaten at a backyard barbecue a few days earlier. The meat was contaminated at the food processing plant that had made the hamburger patties. The company voluntarily recalled 35 million pounds of ground beef that could have been tainted with the bacterium.

Questions

1. In Case A, identify the bacteria that were the source of the food poisoning. Which foods transmitted the bacteria to the people at the picnic?

2. Infer why the foods in Case A were contaminated with enough bacteria to cause the illness.

3. Identify the bacteria that caused food poisoning in Case B. Which food probably transmitted the bacteria?

You Solve It! *(continued)*

4. Given the way the foods were handled in Case B, draw conclusions about how the bacteria were transmitted to the person who became ill.

5. Identify the bacteria that caused the food poisoning in Case C. Which food transmitted the bacteria?

6. Infer how the way the food was handled at the barbecue in Case C could have aided in the growth and transmission of the bacteria.

7. Using the information in all three cases above, list three rules for handling and storing food that could decrease your chances of getting food poisoning.

Lesson Review

1. If soil is a renewable resource, why must people conserve it?

2. Define no-till cultivation. Describe why it is used.

3. Compare and contrast contour farming, strip cropping, and terracing.

4. List two positive and two negative aspects of using artificial chemical fertilizers.

5. How does crop rotation enrich soil?

6. Explain why the world's rising population presents a problem for agriculture.

7. List the three U.S. government agencies that regulate food safety.

8. Summarize the duties of the USDA in the area of food safety. Summarize the duties of the FDA.

9. In your opinion, why do food poisonings still occur, even though there are many food safety regulations?

Lesson 4.4
Agriculture and Technology

Throughout history, the story of agriculture has been the story of new inventions and advances in science that have allowed farmers to grow more food. Agriculture has come a long way from its primitive state thousands of years ago when farmers planted and harvested using human muscle alone, without even draft animals to help them. Today, farmers use computers, satellite technology, and genetically modified plants and livestock to maintain food production. Farmers will need this help as the world's population continues to grow and natural resources such as fertile soil and clean water become harder to maintain.

Some Important Agricultural Advances

In 1830, farmers in the United States needed between 250 and 300 labor hours to produce 100 bushels of wheat on about five acres of land. By 1987, a farmer needed just under three hours to produce the same amount of wheat on the same amount of land. This increased efficiency led to the situation we have today, in which a very small percentage of people in our society are needed to provide the food and fiber for everyone. The following scientific advances of the late 18th through early 20th centuries made farming easier and more efficient.

Cotton Gin (1793) Eli Whitney's cotton gin, which mechanically separated seeds, hulls, and other unwanted parts from cotton fiber, encouraged increased cotton production.

Productivity of Farmers in the United States	
Year	Needed to Produce 100 Bushels (5 Acres) of Wheat
1830	250–300 labor hours
1890	40–50 labor hours
1930	15–20 labor hours
1955	6–12 labor hours
1965	5 labor hours
1975	$3\frac{3}{4}$ labor hours
1987	3 labor hours

Figure 4.10 The invention and use of agricultural machinery has saved hundreds of labor hours.

Cast-Iron Plow (1797) The stronger cast-iron plow replaced the wooden plow, allowing farmers to till the soil better and faster.

Reaper (1831) Cyrus McCormick's reaper, a horse-drawn wheat harvesting machine, cut the time and labor needed to harvest wheat crops.

Steel Plow (1837) John Deere and Leonard Andrus began to manufacture steel plows, which made it possible for the first time to easily till the thick, sod-covered soils of the Midwest.

Chemical Fertilizers (1849) The first mixed chemical fertilizers were put on the market, allowing farmers to enrich depleted soils and increase crop production.

Transcontinental Railroad (1869) The completion of the first rail line across the United States spurred the completion of four more by

Figure 4.11 The McCormick reaper dramatically reduced the time required to harvest wheat.

the end of the 1800s. The railroads opened up new areas for agricultural production and trade.

Barbed Wire (1874) The invention of barbed wire gave farmers in treeless areas such as the prairies and Great Plains the ability to fence off their fields from roaming cattle.

Pasteurization (mid-1880s) Louis Pasteur discovered that controlled heating of foods such as milk and wine could preserve them longer by killing bacteria and other harmful microbes.

Tractor (1926) The development of the first successful light tractor allowed farmers to work the land faster, leading to an increase in farm production.

Biotechnology

Biotechnology is the management or manipulation of living organisms for the benefit of people. The most well-known form of biotechnology is genetic engineering. *Genetic engineering* allows scientists to alter the physical characteristics of plants and animals by transferring genes. A *gene* is the part of a cell that determines the characteristics that living things inherit from their parents. Genes determine everything from the color of a flower to the shape of a leaf to the texture of a person's hair.

Scientists can now identify the characteristics that some genes control. In agriculture, scientists are especially interested in genes that control characteristics that are desirable in plants and animals used for food. Scientists can then change the characteristics of those plants and animals by manipulating their genes. For example, carrots are high in vitamin A. By transplanting the gene that controls that characteristic of carrots into another plant that is not high in vitamin A, the vitamin A content of the second plant can be increased.

The government must approve the safety of these new foods before the producers sell them. However, because many genetically modified foods are fairly new, some people warn that their long-term effects on the environment and on human health are still unknown. They urge more testing before such foods are widely eaten or introduced into the farm environment.

Scientists are constantly looking for genes that control beneficial characteristics in plants. These characteristics include pest resistance, drought resistance, ability to tolerate salty water or soil, and enhanced vitamin and mineral content. Wild or newly discovered plants often contain the desired characteristics. The hope is that someday genetic engineering will allow farmers to grow food in marginal environments that do not support agriculture today and to produce foods that are healthier.

Farmers who raise livestock may use biotechnology to increase the number of offspring that cows have. In one method, scientists take an embryo from a cow's uterus and split it several times. This process produces several embryos that scientists implant in separate cows. The cows are selected for desired traits, such as high milk production.

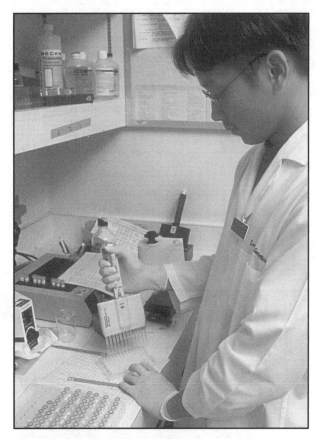

Figure 4.12 Scientists continue to research beneficial genetic characteristics using biotechnology and genetic engineering.

The Cost of Energy

Producing food involves many costs for farmers, including energy. Keeping the barn lights on or buying fuel to run machinery must be included in the farmer's budget.

Farmers have several choices in types of energy to use, including traditional fuels such as gasoline or diesel or alternative fuels such as ethanol.

As you can see in the table below, fuel types differ in cost. A machine that runs on gasoline has a different fuel cost than a similar machine that runs on natural gas, diesel, or ethanol.

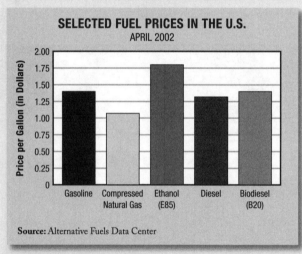

SELECTED FUEL PRICES IN THE U.S.
APRIL 2002

Price per Gallon (in Dollars)

Gasoline, Compressed Natural Gas, Ethanol (E85), Diesel, Biodiesel (B20)

Source: Alternative Fuels Data Center

Figure 4.13 The cost per gallon of different fuels does not illustrate the hidden costs of each.

Each fuel also has hidden costs and produces its own level of pollution. For example, compressed natural gas produces less soot and carbon dioxide than conventional diesel fuel does. Even if a dirtier fuel costs less per gallon than a cleaner fuel, what are the real costs in terms of pollution? Would it be better in the long run to pay more for the cleaner, more expensive fuel because it will be healthier for the farmer, the farm workers, and the environment? Or is the cost of the cleaner fuel so high that the farmer cannot afford to use it, regardless of its other benefits? These are issues farmers must consider when making a fuel choice.

Questions

1. Identify the fuel that would cost the farmer the most money to use. Identify the fuel that would cost the least.

2. Compare the costs of biodiesel and ethanol to that of diesel. Which fuel would you choose on the basis of cost per gallon alone?

3. Evaluate the total cost of gasoline versus ethanol—cost per gallon and pollution "costs"—to decide which fuel to use. Explain your reasoning.

Lesson Review

1. Describe the importance of the cotton gin, the steel plow, and pasteurization in the advancement of agriculture.

2. Do you think California would have developed as the nation's leading agricultural state without the transcontinental railroad? Explain your answer.

3. Define genetic engineering.

4. Summarize the way the manipulation of genes can improve crop plants.

5. Is it necessary for the government to regulate biotechnology? Explain your answer.

Chapter 5

Integrated Pest Management

Figure 5.1 Integrated pest management is an information-based approach to controlling pests. The Asian lady beetle is a natural predator, and the pyrethrum flower produces a natural pesticide.

If you have ever swatted flies away from a picnic lunch or discovered half-devoured lettuce leaves in your garden, you know something about pests. A *pest* is any organism that spreads disease, destroys property, competes with people for resources such as food, or is just a nuisance. We usually think of pests as insects or animals such as flies and mice, but weeds, fungi, and microorganisms such as bacteria and viruses can also be pests.

In undisturbed ecosystems, pests have natural enemies such as predators, parasites, and disease organisms to keep them in check. In fact, in most intact, naturally occurring ecosystems, these natural enemies can control 50 to 90 percent of the pest population. However, people have drastically altered most natural ecosystems, replacing diverse forest, meadow, and wetland habitats with orchards, tree farms, lawns, and farm fields that often contain just one or a very small number of plant types. This kind of planting supports a much smaller range of wildlife and microorganisms—including those that could keep pests in check—than does a natural, diverse ecosystem.

With natural pest controls gone, people have had to step in to reduce pest populations through artificial means. Since the 1940s, pest control has generally meant using synthetic chemical pesticides, including insecticides (insect control), herbicides (weed control), nematicides (roundworm control), fungicides (fungus control), and rodenticides (mouse and rat control).

Most common pesticides contain chemicals that can be harmful to human health and the environment. After the harmful nature of many pesticides became clear in the 1960s, an alarmed public was eager to decrease their use. But getting rid of pesticides completely was impractical because farmers had become dependent on them to protect crops and people had become dependent on them to protect their homes. Still, considering the potentially harmful effects, finding a way to control pests through alternative means and with smaller amounts of pesticides was desirable. As a result, *integrated pest management*, or *IPM*, became an important pest management tool. IPM uses a mix of methods such as traps, disease-resistant plants, and natural pest-killing substances, as well as the introduction of predators to control pests. Only when those methods prove ineffective do farmers, homeowners, and gardeners turn to synthetic chemical pesticides. In addition, IPM requires that a pest manager understand how a pest lives, what it likes to eat, what it doesn't like, what its enemies are, and so on. In other words, knowledge also is used as a pest management tool. Finally, IPM requires that pest control be economical and not harmful to the environment or human health.

Pennsylvania's Integrated Pest Management (PAIPM) program has been in place for about 20 years. Some of its main goals are to encourage the production of food and forestry products while decreasing the exposure of workers to harmful pesticides, to reduce air and groundwater contamination, to reduce or eliminate pesticide residues on crops, to cut the number of insecticide-resistant pests, to make pest control more cost-effective, and to maximize the use of natural organisms in pest control.

In addition to its main IPM program, Pennsylvania also has a school IPM program. The school program has two primary goals.

First, the state encourages the use of IPM to manage pests on school grounds. Under this program, preventive methods such as eliminating the pests' food, water, and shelter are tried first. If those methods are unsuccessful, the least toxic pesticides appropriate for targeted pests are used only in specific, limited areas—and only when other methods have not succeeded. The second goal is to teach Pennsylvania's students about the benefits, risks, and interdisciplinary nature of IPM.

Lesson 5.1
Pests Around the World

A pest is any organism that is in a place where you don't want it. However, an organism that is a pest in one situation can be beneficial in another. For example, honeybees are pests when they build a hive in a house and sting people who come too close to them, but they also play a critical role in fruit production by pollinating the flowers of many fruit trees. As the bees go from flower to flower sipping nectar, they transfer grains of pollen that stick to their bodies, allowing fertilization to occur. Fertilization (the uniting of a sperm cell from pollen with an egg cell in a flower) is necessary

Figure 5.2 The honeybee's critical role in pollen transfer and pollination makes it a very beneficial insect.

before fruit trees can produce seeds that become fruit. In fact, farmers import colonies of honeybees to their fields to pollinate the flowers of many fruit plants such as cranberries, apples, and cherries.

Leaf-cutter ants also can be considered pests because they destroy foliage, but they aid the growth of some plants. The leaf-cutter ant improves the germination success of the lobeira, a fast-growing

Figure 5.3 The hemlock woolly adelgid feeds on the plant sap at the base of the needles, causing the needles to fall off and the twigs to die. The pest will eventually kill the tree.

South American shrub, by taking lobeira fruit into its nest and then discarding the seeds onto nutrient-rich piles of waste (ant feces, seeds, and other waste it digs up) that it builds outside its nests.

Forest Pests

Forests are complex ecosystems in which millions of interconnected organisms, both pest and beneficial, exist in balance. In a healthy and diverse forest, natural enemies such as predator species hold pest populations in check. However, as much as 98 percent of the forests of the United States have been logged. The secondary forests, tree farms, farm fields, and pastures that have taken their place support a much less diverse array of plants and animals than did the original forest ecosystems. These less diverse forest environments are more vulnerable to invasion and attack by pests. Pollution further weakens forest trees, exposing them to pests and the diseases they spread.

For example, an insect pest called the balsam woolly adelgid and the effects of air pollution have combined to completely eliminate Fraser fir and northern bracted balsam fir trees from the highest peaks of areas of the southern Appalachians. The hemlock woolly adelgid is destroying the native hemlock forests of Pennsylvania and the Appalachian mountains. The Eastern hemlock is Pennsylvania's state tree, and hemlock woolly adelgid damage is now found in 35 of the 67 counties in Pennsylvania. The loss of these trees has transformed areas of closed canopy forest to more open canopy forest, causing a dwindling of breeding bird populations.

In Pennsylvania, several pests are common in woodlands. The gypsy moth caterpillar feeds on the leaves of oak and many other important tree species in the early summer. During some years, the caterpillars can completely defoliate some areas of forest in the state. Another pest is a fungus that causes black knot, a warty growth that targets the branches of cherry and plum trees. Trees become infected by windblown spores released from earlier galls, or diseased knots, that formed on the branches of uninfected trees. Black knot is controlled by cutting out and burning the galls during winter or early spring, before they break open. Another pest, the elm spanworm, hatches from eggs that lie dormant over the winter and feeds on tree leaves in late spring. The pest prefers trees such as red and sugar maples, hickory, basswood, and elm. State pest control experts must work to keep these pests in check through prevention and control programs in their areas.

Exotic Pests

Some destructive pests are native to the areas where they cause damage. There are also exotic pests. An *exotic pest* is an insect or other organism that is not native to an area and is introduced to that area by some means.

Today, most exotic pests enter a country as a result of world trade. The U.S. Department of Agriculture's Animal and Plant Health Inspection Service (APHIS) is responsible for patrolling U.S. ports and inspecting imported goods for exotic pests. Between 1985 and 1998, inspectors made almost 7,000 seizures of exotic pests found on wood items alone. These items were entering the United States from other nations with which the United States trades. Inspectors found these pests in a number of items, including logs, wood chips, unseasoned lumber, crates, cable spools, and wood packing material. Exotic pests also have been found on live plants and among seeds.

When exotic organisms enter a new country, they often become pests because their natural enemies did not travel with them. Trees are especially vulnerable to exotic organisms because the natural enemies that would ordinarily prey on exotic pests and keep the pests in check are absent. In the United States and Canada, exotic pests have introduced devastating tree diseases such as white pine blister rust, chestnut blight, and Dutch elm disease. Some of the exotic insects that are now damaging North American trees and forests are the European gypsy moth, the balsam woolly adelgid, the pine shoot moth, and the Asian long-horned beetle.

The gypsy moth arrived in North America from Eurasia in 1868 or 1869. Gypsy moth infestations were first noticed in the Boston area. In 1890 the government first attempted to eliminate the pest and its rapid infestation, but failed. Since then, the insect has continued to spread slowly west across the United States. The gypsy moth eats the leaves of hundreds of North American tree species but is most often found among stands of oak and aspen. Gypsy moths can be found throughout the contiguous United States; however, they are concentrated in New England and the mid-Atlantic. The pest is also established in parts of the Midwest, primarily Michigan, and parts of Ontario, Canada.

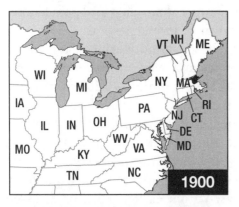

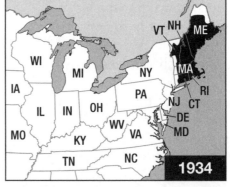

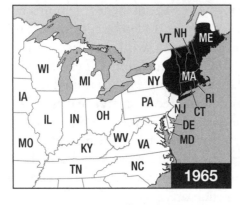

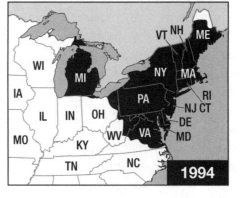

Figure 5.4 The gypsy moth spread across the northeastern United States during the last century, defoliating many forests.

The gypsy moth first appeared in Pennsylvania in 1932, in Luzerne County. Since then, it has infested every county in the state. The heaviest areas of defoliation from the gypsy moth are in the central and southern parts of the state. However, the overall level of infestation decreased between 2000 and 2001 because the gypsy moth contracted fungal and viral diseases (natural pest control organisms) that helped decrease the populations. Still, even with a decrease in the total gypsy moth population, the total cost for Pennsylvania to fight just this one pest in 2002 was more than $1 million. To minimize the damage from gypsy moths in some areas, the Department of Conservation and Natural Resources sprays the kurstaki strain of the natural insecticide *Bacillus thuringiensis* (a strain known as *Btk*) on woodland areas. *Btk* is not harmful to people but kills the gypsy moth caterpillars.

Another exotic pest, the Asian long-horned beetle, was first spotted in New York in 1996 and in Illinois in 1998. It is thought to have arrived in the United States from China, housed in crates and pallets. The beetle is a serious threat to maple trees and other hardwoods. More than 5,000 trees have been cut down and destroyed in Chicago and New York City during the last few years in an attempt to eliminate further infestation by the beetles.

Parasitic fungi introduced to the United States from abroad cause some of the most destructive forest diseases, such as Dutch elm disease, chestnut blight, and white pine blister rust.

Dutch elm disease is a severe disease caused by a fungus. The native elm bark beetle and the European bark beetle carry this fungus, which can kill a large elm tree in just four to eight weeks. The disease was first observed in the Netherlands in 1919 and then in the United States in 1930 near New York City. It has since spread to elm trees throughout the United States and has killed more than two thirds of the elm trees in the country.

The chestnut blight was introduced from China in the early 1900s on Asian chestnut trees imported by the Bronx Zoo. Since then, it has wiped out almost all large American chestnut trees from New England to Georgia. Aside from the sentimental loss of these trees, the blight has negatively impacted an important food source of animals in eastern forest ecosystems by eliminating nuts important to the diet of black bears, turkeys, and other animals.

Birds can also be exotic pests. Starlings are common sights near farms and orchards. Starlings came to the United States from Europe in the late 1800s and have since continued to migrate steadily across the country. Starlings are considered pests because they compete with livestock for food, transmit diseases, pollute livestock food and water, eat fruits from trees and vines, and compete with other birds for nesting sites and food sources. Although most people consider starlings themselves to be pests, starlings do eat other pests such as grubs and insects.

The Asian lady beetle, a native of Japan, was intentionally introduced to the United States in the 1970s and 1980s by the Department of Agriculture. The beetle was released to control aphids and other soft insects. Recently though, a population increase and spread of the beetle has made them a serious nuisance to homeowners. As a pest, they overwhelm homes from September to April and spend the winter in attics, ceilings, walls, and other living areas. Thousands of lady beetles can be found congregating in a house. Although the beetles are essentially harmless to humans, if they are disturbed they do produce an offensive yellow chemical that can stain walls and furniture.

Many other countries also experience problems because of the introduction of exotic pests. The introduction of the European wood wasp has damaged forests in Uruguay and Brazil, and exotic bark beetles have caused damage in Australia and China. Pine wilt disease, carried by the pine wood nematode, has damaged many trees after being introduced into Japan, South Korea, Taiwan, China, and Portugal. The pine wood nematode is found naturally throughout many areas of North America, but it is an exotic pest in Japan. Experts believe that it was introduced into Japan in the early 1900s when it hitched a ride on pine logs from North America.

The European brown spruce long-horned beetle entered Canada around 1990 and has infested thousands of red spruce trees in an area of Halifax, Nova Scotia, since then. The Canadian Forestry Service discovered the beetle for the first time in spring 2000. The beetle also threatens other types of spruce trees, as well as fir, pine, and larch trees and is a threat to red spruce forests throughout the eastern United States.

Organic Farming

Organic produce is grown naturally, without the use of synthetic fertilizers and pesticides. Organic livestock production prohibits the use of antibiotics and hormones. During the 1990s, the organic farming market exploded into a booming segment of U.S. agriculture as consumers sought healthier and safer food sources. Sales of organic foods continued to grow between 20 and 25 percent per year through much of the 1990s. By the year 2000, organic food sales in the United States were estimated to have totaled almost $8 billion.

Fresh fruits and vegetables accounted for 42 percent of organic food sales in 2000. Organic fresh produce is followed by packaged groceries (15 percent of sales), dairy foods (11 percent), bulk and frozen foods (8 percent), soy-based foods (6 percent), beverages (5 percent), meats (3 percent), and candy and snack foods (2 percent).

Interview Organic Farmers

Contact a farmer who grows organic fruits and vegetables. If you do not know any organic farmers in your area, ask the reference librarian at your local library to help you find the names of organic farming associations in Pennsylvania. Write or call one of these farmers to ask for an interview in person or by phone. You can also visit a local farmers' market and look for people selling organic produce. Ask the farmer whether you can set up an interview.

Write your interview questions in advance. Ask the farmer what he or she grows. Have the farmer describe the benefits and drawbacks of organic farming. Ask about the pests that

Figure 5.5 Fresh produce is plentiful in markets across the United States; however, the majority of produce in most markets is not grown organically.

You Solve It! (continued)

attack their crops and how they control them without the use of pesticides. Ask whether they use IPM methods to protect their crops.

Examine Organic Produce

Determine where organic fruits and vegetables are sold in your community. Visit local supermarkets and farmers' markets. Observe the organic produce on sale.

Use what you have learned to answer the questions below.

Questions

1. Are there organic farmers in or near your community? If so, what fruits or vegetables do they grow?

2. Describe a benefit of organic farming mentioned by the farmer you interviewed. Describe a drawback.

3. Which pests plague local organic farmers? How do they control them?

4. Does the farmer you interviewed use IPM for pest control? Explain your answer.

5. Identify places in your community where you can buy organic produce.

6. List several types of organic produce you can purchase.

7. Contrast the prices of organic produce and nonorganic produce. Infer what accounts for the difference in price.

8. Compare and contrast the appearances of organic and nonorganic produce. Infer what accounts for the difference in appearance.

9. Would you prefer to eat organic produce? Explain your answer.

10. Explain how you would persuade the manager of a local market to begin selling organic produce.

Lesson Review

1. Define the word *pest*, and give an example.

2. Draw conclusions about how replacing a natural pine forest ecosystem with a single-species pine farm would affect the ability of natural predators to keep down pests.

3. Define *integrated pest management*.

4. List the two main goals of the Pennsylvania school IPM program.

5. Contrast the honeybee's role as a pest and its role as a beneficial organism.

6. Explain why exotic pests are often more troublesome than native pests in an ecosystem.

7. Describe the problems caused by one exotic pest in the United States.

8. Explain why organisms that are pests in the United States may not be pests in the countries of their origin.

Case Study

Exotic Plants in Pennsylvania

Invasive plants are a threat to both the wildlife habitats and native species of Pennsylvania because, with no pests to control them, they grow quickly and displace native plants. Many of these invasive plants were innocently introduced as landscaping plants because of their beauty. Invasive plants common to Pennsylvania include mile-a-minute weed, purple loosestrife, tree of heaven, autumn olive, Japanese knotweed, phragmites, Canada thistle, and Japanese stiltgrass.

Mile-a-minute weed is an exotic plant that was introduced into south-central Pennsylvania from eastern Asia in the 1930s. Since that time, the mile-a-minute weed has spread throughout much of Pennsylvania as well as Delaware, Maryland, New Jersey, New York, Ohio, Virginia, and West Virginia.

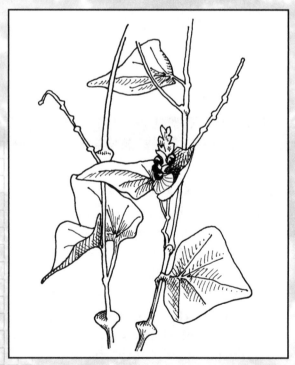

Figure 5.6 Hand-pull mile-a-minute weed if you see it, or mow it to prevent it from flowering and spreading seeds.

The weed is especially troublesome because it grows so quickly—up to 6 inches per day and 25 feet in a growing season. It has long, viney stems and light blue-green triangular leaves from 1 to 2.5 inches across. Each plant produces 50 to 100 seeds, which drop around it or are carried to other areas by water, birds, rodents, or people. The mile-a-minute weed often invades sunny, open areas with moist soil and abundant organic matter. It is common on roadsides, at the edges of woods, in places where forest trees have been cleared, and in damp areas such as low meadows and stream banks.

The mile-a-minute weed is a threat to Pennsylvania forests because it interferes with the regrowth of trees in areas where forest trees have been cleared. The weed grows over and smothers developing saplings and seedlings that would otherwise form the foundation of new forest. In fact, the weed overgrows large areas, forming a dense canopy that covers anything less than 10 feet tall.

Experts do not believe that mile-a-minute weed can be totally eradicated in Pennsylvania, but several methods are in use to control it. Hand-pulling removes small infestations of the weed, and mowing and cutting help prevent the weed from flowering. In keeping with IPM principles, herbicides are used as a last resort to control large areas of mile-a-minute weed growth.

Purple loosestrife is an aquatic plant that was introduced into Pennsylvania from Europe in the 1800s. It invades wetland areas, choking waterways and displacing native wetland plant species. When purple loosestrife becomes dominant in an area, most native wildlife disappears because other plants that wildlife use for food and shelter have been crowded out. The bog turtle, an endangered species in Pennsylvania and a federally listed threatened species, is one native wetland animal that is severely threatened by this change in habitat. Waterfowl such as ducks avoid wetlands dominated by purple loosestrife. Songbirds cannot find food in such areas because they cannot eat loosestrife's small, hard seeds. The weed now infests about half of Pennsylvania's wetlands and is spreading quickly. As purple loosestrife continues to take over Pennsylvania's wetlands, it encroaches on the natural habitat of many wetland creatures.

Purple loosestrife is an upright, bushy plant with beautiful purple flowers. It can grow to seven feet tall. The weed has spread rapidly because it is very efficient in the way it reproduces. Each year, the plant can produce over one million tiny seeds that can be spread easily by water, wind, and the feathers and fur of birds and other animals. People also spread the weed unknowingly by carrying its seeds on muddy boots or on boats and other vehicles that have been in areas where loosestrife is plentiful. Uninformed gardeners have also spread purple loosestrife into new areas of the state by planting it in their gardens.

Because purple loosestrife has no natural enemies to stop it from spreading, the weed is now established throughout the United States. Pennsylvania has declared loosestrife a noxious weed, targeting it for elimination. The Pennsylvania Department of Agriculture recommends prevention as the best method of fighting loosestrife's spread. The department asks the public to be aware of the appearance of the weed, to avoid planting it, and to remove small patches of it by hand when it appears in new areas. Members of the public can help by rinsing equipment, clothing, and footwear when moving from areas infested with purple loosestrife to areas where the plant has not yet taken hold.

It is sometimes necessary to apply pesticides to control larger populations of purple loosestrife. However, in keeping with the Pennsylvania IPM program, authorities are now experimenting with the release of loosestrife-eating insects to destroy the weed and slow its infestation rate.

Figure 5.7 You can help control purple loosestrife by hand-pulling small patches of it and rinsing clothing, equipment, and shoes when leaving infested areas.

Lesson 5.2

IPM in Practice

IPM is the modern, ecological approach to managing pests in agriculture, forests, homes, or wherever pests are a problem. IPM is a scientific approach to pest management that is based on a series of specific decision-making steps. IPM steps integrate knowledge of pest identity and biology with population sampling information so that if pest management actions are needed, they can be taken at the right time, are worthwhile, and are done safely. IPM also uses a mix of many different tools to manage pests instead of relying on a single tactic. These tools may include pest traps, disease-resistant plants, predators and parasites, physical barriers such as window screens, and other tools. Preventive measures that avoid pest problems are favored over intervening after a pest problem has gotten out of hand.

The Six Steps of IPM

There are six basic steps involved in any IPM decision.

1. Properly identify pest damage and responsible pests. In the case of insects, the vast majority are not pests. There are an estimated 10 million species of insects in the world, but only about 3,500 species are considered to be key pests. Cases of mistaken pest identity may result in ineffective and wasteful actions. For instance, if plant damage caused by overwatering is mistaken for a fungal infection, a fungicide spray may be used needlessly, and the plant will still die.

2. Learn pest and host life cycles and biology. At the time you see a pest, it may be too late to do more than spray it with a pesticide. However, there is often another stage of the pest's life cycle that is susceptible to preventive actions. For example, weeds reproducing from last year's seed can be prevented with mulches. Knowing the biology of a pest allows the pest manager to take advantage of the pest's weaknesses and interfere with its life cycle.

3. Monitor or sample the environment for pest populations. Preventive actions must be taken at the correct time if they are to be effective. For this reason, as soon as a pest has been correctly identified, monitoring must be started before the pest becomes a problem. For example, in school cafeterias where cockroaches may be expected to appear, sticky traps are set out before school starts. Traps are checked at regular intervals so that any cockroach infestation can be observed before it becomes a problem. Some questions that can be answered by monitoring include the following.

- Are pest organisms, indications of pest damage, or both present?
- What is the distribution of the pest? Is it all over or only in certain spots?
- Are the numbers of pests increasing or decreasing?

4. Establish action threshold (economic, health, or aesthetic). In some cases, a certain number of pests can be tolerated. For example, soybeans are quite tolerant of defoliation, so if there are only a few caterpillars in a field and their population is not increasing dramatically, there is no need to do anything. However, there is a point at which something must be done. For the farmer, that point is the one at which the cost of damage by the pest is more than the cost of controlling the pest. This is an action threshold based on economics. Whenever human health is a consideration, such as when there is a threat of malaria, thresholds are very low, meaning that only a few pests are necessary to start a pest management activity. Personal tolerances also vary. Some people do not like any dandelions in their yard and spend much time and money getting rid of them. Other people do not mind them and leave them alone.

5. Choose an appropriate combination of management tactics. For any pest situation, there are several options to consider. The next section on IPM tactics explains these options in more detail.

6. Evaluate and record results. After the appropriate control options have been chosen and applied, the IPM manager must evaluate the success of those control methods. This success is based on the answers to specific questions. Did the actions have the desired effect? Was the pest prevented or managed to the IPM manager's satisfaction? Was the method itself satisfactory? Were there any unintended side effects? What will be done in the future for this pest situation? After these questions are answered, the results should be recorded for future reference.

IPM Tactics

The goals of using multiple tactics are to effectively keep pests below levels that cause harm and to avoid outbreaks. Multiple methods keep pest populations off balance and avoid development of resistance to pesticides. The methods that are the least toxic yet still effective are used before more toxic methods whenever possible. Because IPM is based on managing pests, not eradicating them, IPM uses pesticides as sparingly as possible, a practice popular with those who are concerned about the health risks associated with pesticide use. IPM exhausts other pest management methods such as using disease-resistant plants, biological controls, multicropping, and biorational pesticides before turning to conventional pesticides.

There are hundreds of tactics or practices that can be used against pests, each with its own benefits and risks. These tactics can be grouped into several categories.

1. Cultural Methods

Cultural pest control methods suppress pest problems by minimizing the conditions they need for life (water, shelter, food). These methods include choosing plants that are adapted to local growing conditions, planting them in the right place, and giving proper attention to their nutritional and water needs. Strong plants resist diseases, outgrow weeds, and are less likely to succumb to insects.

An example of a cultural method is multicropping. *Multicropping* is the practice of

Figure 5.8 This field is multicropped with sunflowers, corn, and blue hubbard squash.

growing many crops together in the same field. Multicropping can require more labor, planning, and expense than growing many fields of the same crop. But when the same crops cover a large area, it is easier for pests to take hold and spread. Planting fields with several crops means that pests that feed on one crop will not overrun the entire area. Multicropped fields can also host both pests and the predators that can help keep them in check.

Multicropping is not new to agricultural practice. Native American tribes have used this method for thousands of years, planting food crops such as corn, beans, and squash together.

Insects often locate their host plants using their sense of smell. As a result, some multicropped fields are planted with strong-smelling plants. These plants act as decoys and mask the presence of the plants that are being protected from pests. Sometimes, cabbages are protected against flea beetles by planting tomatoes alongside them.

Multicropping can also protect against pests by providing a physical barrier to protect crops. A cover crop of clover will prevent the cabbage root fly from laying its eggs in a field, for instance.

The diversity of multicropping can help decrease the presence of insect pests by supporting beneficial insects that prey on those pests. For example, planting white and red clover with cabbage reduces both cabbage aphid and cabbageworm pests by increasing the number of ground beetles, which are cabbage aphid and cabbageworm predators.

2. Physical Methods

Physical methods prevent pest access to the host or area, or, if the pests are already present, remove them by some means. This could mean physically barring the pest, trapping it, vacuuming, mowing, or tilling, depending on the pest and the situation.

In many homes a variety of physical methods are used. Window screens prevent insect entry, steel wool stuffed in wall openings prevents the entry of squirrels into an attic, and vacuuming reduces dust mites and flea larvae in carpets.

3. Genetic Methods

Genetic methods use pest-resistant plant varieties developed by classical plant breeding. Recently, this category has been expanded to include genetically engineered pest resistance, such as *Bt* corn or potatoes. These crops have been genetically engineered to carry the *Bt* gene. When insect pests feed on these modified plants, the *Bt* gene will cause the pests to die. There are also special uses of genetic techniques on pests themselves, such as sterile male insect releases.

Many plants have developed natural defense mechanisms to ward off pests, including physical adaptations, natural chemical resistance, and a tolerance to pest damage and defoliation. These natural defenses are called *host plant resistance*. Using this to their advantage, plant breeders have produced many varieties of food and grain crop plants that pests are not attracted to or that can tolerate a pest attack without a loss in food yield.

4. Biological Methods

Biological control of pests involves using other living things that are enemies of the pest to be controlled. There are several main types of biological control of insect, weed, and disease pests. These include parasitoids, predators, pathogens, and weed feeders. Biological control does not expose people to dangerous chemicals, but it does work more slowly than chemical pesticides, often allowing pests to continue to feed or lay eggs as the pests deteriorate.

Parasitoids A *parasitoid* is an insect that develops on or within an insect host, ultimately killing the host. The parasitoid, which is smaller than the host, lays eggs or larvae in, on, or near the host. The immature parasitoid then feeds on the body fluids or organs of the host as it develops into an adult. In some species only one parasitoid will develop in a host, but others may lay eggs that develop into hundreds of larvae (young insects). Beneficial parasitoids include wasps and flies. For example, a wasp may lay its eggs inside an aphid, an insect that feeds on and destroys garden plants. As the wasps develop on or inside the aphid, the aphid is killed.

Predators Insect and plant pests have predators. A *predator* is a natural enemy that feeds on the insect or pest. These predators can be

Figure 5.9 The golden orb weaver spider spins a sticky web to capture aphids, flies, grasshoppers, wasps, and bees. A female can capture and eat prey twice her size.

introduced in areas where there are pests to control their populations. Some predators attack specific prey, but others attack a wide range of prey. Predators of insects and mites include beetles, lacewings, flies, midges, spiders, wasps, and predatory mites. Predators, which are usually larger than their prey, consume many prey during their lifetime. Although many predators are useful natural enemies of pests, predators can also attack beneficial insects and plants.

Pathogens A *pathogen* is a disease-causing organism that infects insects, plants, humans, and other animals. Some pathogens, including bacteria, viruses, fungi, and protozoa, can attack pests and be a tool for the pest manager. Some pathogens can be spread artificially when incorporated into sprays. These are called microbial insecticides or bio-insecticides. The majority of insect pathogens are specific to certain insects and certain stages of their life cycle, so they do not generally affect beneficial insects, other wildlife, or people. Pathogens kill pests, reduce their ability to reproduce, slow the growth of pests, or shorten their lifespan. One drawback is that they act more slowly than some other biological controls.

Weed Feeders A *weed feeder* is an arthropod (such as an insect), other animal, or pathogen that feeds on weed pests. Insects control weeds by eating flowers, seeds, leaves, stems, and roots. They also transmit pathogens that infect the plants. Weed feeders can be extremely effective, and their use offers several advantages. Weed-feeding natural enemies are highly specific and ecologically sensitive enemies. Weed feeders tend to reproduce quickly to establish themselves within the population of the target weed. However, in some cases, the weed feeder species has failed to establish itself in a new area and has not been successful in controlling plant pests.

Biological control can be carried out using three strategies: 1) conserving and encouraging naturally occurring biocontrol organisms by protecting them and their natural environment; 2) increasing the numbers of naturally occurring species by purchasing and releasing more of the same species; and 3) finding and introducing new biocontrol species specific to pests. These new biocontrol species are usually found in the part of the world where the pest originally came from.

5. Chemical Methods

There are many chemicals that are used in pest management situations, but not all are alike in their range of action, toxicity, or persistence in the environment. These chemicals are generally referred to as pesticides. Pesticides can be classified according to use.

Conventional Pesticides The most widely used method of pest control remains the synthetic chemical pesticides. About 100,000 pesticides are in common use worldwide, with 2.5 million tons applied to farm fields each year. Although widely used, conventional pesticides remain a mixed blessing. For decades these pesticides have prevented the deaths of millions of people from insect-transmitted diseases such as malaria and typhus. They have increased food supplies and lowered food costs by preventing loss of food crops to pests. Much of this success is because conventional synthetic pesticides work more quickly than many alternative pest control methods. However, most synthetic pesticides contain potent poisons. Long-term exposure to even low levels of some pesticides has been connected with health problems such as birth defects, nervous system disorders, and cancers. Some pesticides tend to remain in the environment long after they are applied and can accumulate in the tissues of living organisms. In addition, they often kill beneficial organisms that are not the direct target of pest control.

Conventional Household Pesticides Pesticides are common items around the house. Combined with other methods, pesticides keep homes free of pests such as roaches and ants. They keep pets free of fleas and ticks. They protect houses from termites. Repellents applied to skin keep away biting mosquitoes, which can carry disease. They also prevent the spoiling of gardens by insect pests and weeds.

Nevertheless, pesticides are poisons that people live with in their homes every day. Pesticides that are sprayed in homes can

Lab Study

Active Ingredients in Pesticides

Before using a pesticide, always read the label. The label is your guide to using the pesticide as safely as possible.

Materials

copies of pesticide labels

notebook

pencil

table from the next page

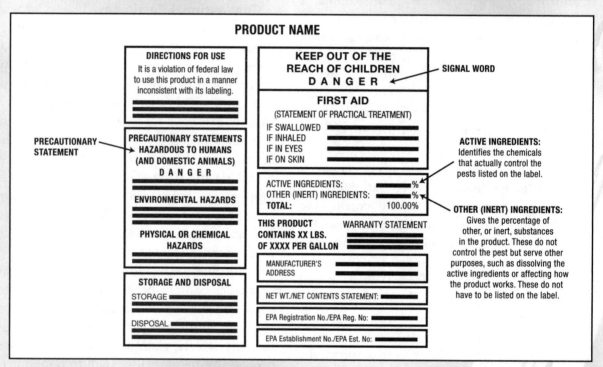

Figure 5.10 Pesticide labels contain important safety and usage information.

Procedure

1. With members of your group, observe the pesticide product labels that your teacher has provided.

2. Record the name of each pesticide and its use in the chart.

3. Find the active ingredient(s) in each pesticide. List them in the chart.

4. List the health and environmental hazards associated with each active ingredient in the chart. You will find some of these data on the label, but you may have to do research to find additional information.

5. Record the pesticide's "signal word" on the chart.

Conclusions

1. List the pests that these pesticides control.

2. What can you conclude about the safety of the active ingredients in these pesticides? Are any of them harmful to people, wildlife, or the environment? In what ways?

3. Place the pesticide labels in order from least dangerous to most dangerous. Explain how you reached this conclusion.

For Discussion

1. How can the risks associated with the use of these pesticides be minimized?

2. Would you use any of these pesticides? Explain your answer.

3. Use what you learned in this lab to explain why the use of conventional pesticides is the pest control method of last resort.

4. Explain why the U.S. government requires the information that you see on pesticide labels.

Extension

Take a look at the pesticides around your house. Carefully read the labels that detail how these products should be used and stored. Be sure to wash your hands well with soap and water if you handle the pesticide containers. Evaluate whether you and your family have been following instructions closely enough to use the pesticide safely. Discuss your findings with others in class.

Data Table					
Pesticide Name	Pesticide Use	Active Ingredients	Health Hazards	Environmental Hazards	Signal Word

accumulate residues in carpets, on furniture, and in house dust. Some pesticide residues remain in carpets for up to a year. They also can be blown or tracked in from lawns and gardens. As a result, pesticide exposure in some homes can be very high.

One potentially dangerous class of pesticides, the organophosphates, has been common around the home for many years. Three of the most common organophosphate insecticides are malathion (mal-uh-THY-uhn), diazinon (dy-AZ-ih-nahn), and chlorpyrifos (klor-PEER-uh-fahs). Malathion is a general-purpose insect killer used in insect sprays and garden sprays. Diazinon can be found in ant and roach sprays, lawn and garden insecticide sprays, and flea collars. Chlorpyrifos is used in ant, roach, and flea sprays; termite treatments; wasp and hornet sprays; lawn and turf sprays; flea collars; and pet shampoos. Organophosphates kill insects by disrupting the function of their brains and nervous systems. Early childhood exposure to this class of chemicals may also disrupt the neurological development of children. In response to these potential dangers, the EPA, whose job it is to regulate pesticide use, has recently restricted the use of these pesticides, especially in places where children might be exposed.

Conventional Agricultural Pesticides The bounty of fresh fruits and vegetables in the produce section of the supermarket is remarkable—and dependent at least in part on the use of conventional pesticides on food crops. Some of the same organophosphate pesticides mentioned above have been routinely sprayed on food. Although the use of these organophosphates is regulated by the EPA, chemicals such as malathion, diazinon, and chlorpyrifos are still used on fruits and vegetables such as apples, grapes, peaches, oranges, pears, peas, and tomatoes.

Although the pesticides deter pests from feeding, they often do not break down quickly and disappear. They can persist for long periods of time as residue on fruits and vegetables. The safe exposure level for pesticides is set by the EPA.

Figure 5.11 This helicopter is spraying a conventional agricultural pesticide over a tree farm in Pennsylvania.

As with other synthetic pesticides, conventional agricultural pesticides can have many negative side effects. Farm workers can suffer from continued exposure to some pesticides and become sick. Pesticides can leach into soil, ultimately ending up in surface water and groundwater. In some farm areas, about 45 percent of the groundwater and more than 80 percent of streams and fish sampled have detectable amounts of at least one pesticide. Atrazine, one of the most widely used herbicides in the United States, is present in more than half of the stream samples taken in agricultural areas. It has seeped into drinking water supplies throughout the United States, especially in areas of the Midwest where it is applied to corn. Some studies associate atrazine with an increased incidence of cancer. However, strict regulations have been enforced in recent years to decrease use of and exposure to this chemical.

Because of the clear benefits of conventional pesticides (effectiveness against pests, ease of use, and low cost), they remain one of the pest control tools available to those using IPM. However, the health risks associated with use of and exposure to conventional pesticides has made them the pest control method of last resort.

Biorational Pesticides

A *biorational pesticide* is a naturally occurring compound or a chemical such as a toxin or growth regulator derived from a living organism. A biorational pesticide may be the synthesized form of a naturally occurring chemical including pheromones and insect growth regulators. They are generally considered more environmentally friendly than are synthetic chemical pesticides. Biorational pesticides are based on the physiology or biochemistry of a pest. They work by disrupting specific, unique aspects of a pest's metabolism or life cycle. Because these aspects are unique to the pest, the chemicals usually have limited or no impact on other species. This makes biorational pesticides much more specific and more environmentally considerate. Examples of

biorational pest control agents include compost teas for disease control, synthetic growth hormones, chitin inhibitors (chitin makes the hard outer shell on insects), and molt-accelerating hormones.

A *natural pesticide* is one that is made of natural (not synthesized) ingredients such as minerals mined from the earth (kaolin clay, diatomaceous earth), bacterial extracts, or plant extracts. Many natural pesticides can be considered biorational because they pose less of a health and environmental risk than do synthetic chemical pesticides. These often break down rapidly when exposed to heat, light, and water. However, some natural pesticides can be environmentally harmful and would not be considered biorational.

Microbial Pesticides The naturally occurring bacterium *Bacillus thuringiensis*, or *Bt*, is used to produce the most commonly used microbial pesticide, a type of biorational pesticide. The *Bt* toxin destroys the lining of the pest's intestinal tract, making it impossible for the pest to continue to eat. Many different strains of *Bt* are found naturally in soil and produce toxins that affect different insects. For instance, for gypsy moth caterpillars and hornworms, the kurstaki strain of *Bt (Btk)* is fatal. Another strain kills the Colorado potato beetle. No matter which strain of *Bt* is used, the pest must eat *Bt* to be harmed by it. This selectivity is one of the primary advantages of this type of natural pesticide.

Insecticidal Soap Although they have been used for more than 1,000 years, insecticidal soaps are currently gaining new popularity because they are considered harmless to humans, mammals, and bees. Insecticidal soaps are made from the salts of fatty acids, the principal components of the fats and oils found in animals and plants. Insecticidal soaps work well on soft-bodied pests such as aphids, leafhoppers, spider mites, caterpillars, and flies. The biggest advantage of insecticidal soaps is their safety to people and harmlessness to beneficial insect species. Insecticidal soaps kill pests quickly but work only on contact and have no residual effects.

Common Natural Insecticides

Pesticide	How It Is Applied	What It Does
Insecticidal bar soap or soft soap	mixed with water and applied to pests	kills aphids, flies, caterpillars
Garlic and onion	grown along the edges of garden and crop beds	protects some plants from aphids, caterpillars, and cabbage worms
Gynandropsis gynandra (chisaka, esaka, spiderweed)	plant is burned; ashes are mixed with water and sprayed on vegetables	kills aphids
Lantana canmara	lay leaves and branches of the plant over potatoes in storage	protects potatoes from the potato moth during storage
Neem	oil is sprayed on plant leaves	protects against fungi and nematodes
Pyrethrum	extract (pyrethrin) is sprayed directly on plants	kills garden pests such as aphids, white flies, spider mites, mealy bugs, and some types of slugs
Rotenone	applied directly to plants	used against garden insects, cattle grubs, and lice
Ryania	extract is applied directly to plants	kills caterpillars, leaf beetles, and thrips
Tomato	use prunings of healthy plants around cabbage plants	smell keeps away cabbage worm and cabbage butterfly, preventing the laying of eggs
Wood ash	spread around plants	alkaline ash irritates cutworms and keeps them in check

Source: "Natural Pesticides," at http://www.dainet.de/infop/magazine/mirror/nat-pest.htm

Figure 5.12 Natural pesticides offer a wide range of pest control. Natural products may take longer to be effective, but they have fewer negative effects on the environment.

Botanical Insecticides Botanical insecticides are made from natural, living plants. One of the most common and effective botanical insecticides is pyrethrum, a flower extract. Many insecticidal products contain a variant of the extracted active ingredient, pyrethrin, which comes from the flower. The pesticide is very deadly to insects but is safe for most mammals and breaks down quickly in the environment.

Rotenone is the most toxic of the natural pesticides. People have used it to kill insects since 1848. Rotenone comes from the ground-up roots of a plant native to South America. It is used primarily to control leaf-feeding caterpillars and beetles, such as cabbageworms and the Colorado potato beetle. It is a contact and stomach poison to insects, which stop feeding shortly after exposure. Rotenone also breaks down quickly in the environment, but it can be toxic to humans.

Ryania is the powdered extract from the roots and stems of the shrub *Ryania speciusa*. It affects insects such as caterpillars, leaf beetles, and thrips when eaten or on contact. It has a minimal effect on beneficial insects and is fairly nontoxic to mammals.

Neem The neem tree is grown in Africa and Asia and has provided important pharmaceutical remedies in India for hundreds of years. Neem oil, harvested from the tree's seeds, is an extremely effective natural pesticide that repels pests and curtails their feeding. The oil is sprayed directly on the leaves of the host plants and will kill the pest only if the oil touches it. However, neem also alters the hormones that allow many insects to mature, killing them as they molt or emerge from eggs. Neem insecticides are most effective at controlling leaf-chewing beetles and caterpillars, but some insects, such as aphids, are less susceptible to it. Another advantage of neem oil is that it is very safe for humans. Neem oil is highly selective, targeting only insects.

Water Spray A high-pressure spray from a hose is a surprisingly effective pest control method with no negative health or environmental effects. A spray of water on garden plants can wash away mites, aphids, and other insect pests.

6. Regulatory Control

Regulatory control refers to the role played by government agencies in trying to stop the entry or spread of pests into an area or into the country via inspection, quarantine, destruction of infested material, and other methods. The

Figure 5.13 Pests can be removed from plants using a method as simple as a spray of water.

EPA, USDA, and U.S. Customs Service are some of the government agencies that try to stop the spread of pests in the United States.

Lesson Review

1. Describe how organophosphate pesticides kill pests. List three organophosphate pesticides.

2. Why is the use of some chemical pesticides on food crops potentially harmful?

3. List three important pieces of information on a pesticide label.

4. Explain the importance of reading pesticide labels.

5. Draw conclusions about why it would be important for a farmer to know the active ingredient in a pesticide he or she uses.

6. List two types of biological control, and summarize how they work.

7. Briefly explain the six steps involved in every IPM decision.

8. List three natural pesticides. Draw conclusions about why natural pesticides are becoming more popular.

9. If you had garden pests that needed to be controlled, would you be more likely to use biological controls, natural pesticides, or conventional synthetic pesticides to get the job done? Explain your answer.

Lesson 5.3
Effects of IPM on the Environment and Society

Because the primary goal of IPM is to reduce pests to acceptable levels rather than to eradicate them, IPM methods commonly involve less pesticide use than do conventional pest control methods. This practice results in fewer negative impacts on the natural environment. Before using IPM, farmers, gardeners, and public health officials must weigh both its positive and negative aspects.

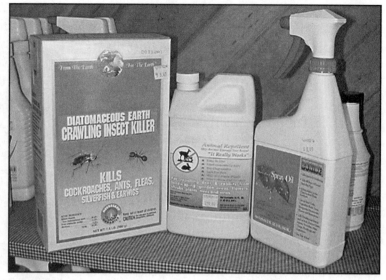

Figure 5.14 Natural pesticides are often highly selective and usually pose little or no risk to humans or animals.

Benefits of IPM

Safer for People and the Environment Because IPM uses pesticides only when other methods have failed and uses them as sparingly as possible, farmers using IPM typically reduce their chemical pesticide use by one third or more. As a consequence, IPM limits the volume of toxic ingredients entering the natural environment.

Less Pesticide Residue on Food The EPA considers pesticide residue on food one of the most serious environmental health threats in terms of the risk of cancer. When pesticides are used in IPM programs, they are applied more sparingly than in conventional pest eradication programs. As a result, there is less danger that pesticide residue will remain on foods.

Less Chance of Pesticide Resistance When pesticides are used on a pest population over a period of time, the pests can develop a resistance (a type of immunity) to them, making the pesticides ineffective. Today, about 1,000 kinds of insects, plant pathogens, and weeds have developed enough immunity to common pesticides that the chemicals no longer kill them. Because IPM uses a smaller number of pesticide applications at lower doses, use of IPM approaches makes it less likely that pests will develop immunity.

Less Damage to Nontarget Organisms Some pesticides target specific pests, but broad-spectrum pesticides kill target pests as well as other organisms, some of which are beneficial to the environment. The restricted use of pesticides in IPM means that fewer organisms that are not targets of the IPM program will be harmed.

Lower Costs for Farmers IPM can reduce the amount of money that farmers spend on pesticides because fewer types of pesticides are used and those that are used are applied in smaller amounts. During the 1990s, an IPM program in Pennsylvania reduced the use of soil insecticides, saving farmers about $23 million. In New Jersey's IPM program, eggplant growers saw pesticide costs drop from $500 to $1,500 per acre to $300 to $400 per acre. This reduction in pesticide costs may be partially offset by increased management costs. IPM requires more management activities such as monitoring, trapping, and using special planting techniques. Because natural, environmentally conscious methods of IPM have increased management costs, farmers must weigh the potential losses because of insect damage with the savings associated with using fewer pesticides.

Preserves Nutrients in Soil Planting one type of crop over large areas year after year tends to drain the soil of the nutrients required by that crop. Planting methods such as multicropping or strip cropping demand less of the soil's nutrients. Rotating crops each season—for example, planting a field of corn one year and soybeans the next—helps replenish the nutrients in the soil.

Drawbacks of IPM

There are very few drawbacks to IPM. However, some precautions should be taken.

May Alter Local Ecosystems Introducing natural predators, parasitoids, and pathogens to kill pests changes the balance of local ecosystems. In most cases, the introduced organisms do not have great negative impact. However, biological controls can cause unpredicted ecological effects or become pests themselves when they are placed in the environment. For example, Asian lady beetles were introduced to control aphids and scales, but they became pests themselves when they invaded houses to spend the winter.

Can Contaminate Environment IPM lessens the use of pesticides but does not eliminate it. Many of the current pesticides are very potent, even in small concentrations. Even minimal use of such a pesticide could result in the poisoning of surface water and groundwater, soil, or air.

Does Not Eliminate All Pests Although IPM methods are extremely effective, IPM does not attempt to eradicate all pests. Some pests will always be found in gardens or farm fields, but with IPM methods they remain at levels that are controllable and do not cause economic hardship. These levels may be acceptable when dealing with pests that attack farms or garden fruits and vegetables. In the case of a pest that carries a deadly disease, however, such as the mosquito that spreads the West Nile virus, IPM methods that do not eradicate all pests where people live may not be the best method of pest control. In those cases in which public health is involved, spraying with chemicals to eradicate all pests may be a more acceptable method.

Figure 5.15 This truck is spraying for mosquitoes in an effort to control the West Nile virus and other mosquito-borne diseases. The National Park Service has posted signs (inset) in many areas encouraging people to take precautions against the West Nile virus.

Field Study

Identifying Pests and IPM Solutions

Pests are everywhere, and chances are that you will spot them, or evidence of their presence, if you know where to look. In this field study, you will observe pests around you and propose solutions for controlling them.

Materials		
notebook	pencil	hand lens

Procedure

1. Choose a place to observe pests. Consider locations such as your backyard or garden, a local park, a forest or field, or even the grounds at school.

2. Identify organisms—animals or plants—that you believe to be pests.

3. If you cannot observe the actual pests, look for evidence of their presence. For example, partially eaten cabbage leaves in a garden would point to a pest in the area, even if you don't observe a pest actually eating the leaves.

4. Observe the effect the pests have had on the natural environment or on nearby structures. Record that information in the table.

5. Determine whether the pests you observe are destructive enough to warrant an IPM program to control them. If so, write a brief program for control of one of the pests in this area. Be sure to include your reasons for calling for the program, the outcome you expect, and the steps you would take to put your program into effect.

Figure 5.16 Corn sap beetles feed on damaged corn ears, laying their eggs in the decaying material.

Conclusions

1. Draw conclusions about whether there are pests in the area you observed. Why did you come to this conclusion?

2. Determine whether the pests have caused damage in the area you observed.

3. How can IPM be used to control this pest problem? Explain your answer.

For Discussion

1. Compare your IPM plan with those of others in class. How are they alike? How are they different?

2. Which pest control method did class members rely on the most? Discuss why this was the case.

3. Did any of the plans rely heavily on the application of conventional pesticides? Discuss why this was done.

4. Would using a no-pest-control plan be an option for the area you observed? Explain your answer.

Extension

Come up with a pest control plan for a fairly small, contained area in your yard or inside your home. Implement the plan. After several weeks, report to the class on your results.

Data Table			
Pest	Evidence of Pest	Effect on Environment or Structures	Should the Pest Be Controlled?

Managing Pests in Your Community

The Pennsylvania IPM program supports several methods of pest control. The "Pyramid of IPM Tactics" for plants, buildings, and animals/humans shows the relative importance of pest control tactics in Pennsylvania. The bottom of each pyramid shows the methods that should be considered first. The top of the pyramid shows the IPM methods that are used as a last resort.

Your community has probably created a plan to control local pests. Interview officials in the city Department of Health, Department of Environmental Protection, or Department of Public Works to learn which methods are used. Use what you learn from city officials as well as the information in the appropriate pyramid to fill in the table provided by your teacher.

Questions

1. Describe the role of "prevention" in the pyramid of IPM tactics used in Pennsylvania. List three methods of prevention used to control plant pests.

2. Explain where biological controls fit into Pennsylvania's IPM hierarchy. List two biological controls for animal pests.

3. How do conventional pesticides fit into the IPM hierarchy of tactics? Why is this the case?

4. Describe how the general characteristics of pest control methods change as you move up any of the IPM tactics pyramids.

5. Place the following pest control methods in the sequence in which they would be used to control pests inside buildings: boric acid, nematodes, traps, building design, antimicrobial disinfectants.

Data Table				
Pest	Control Method Used	Were Methods Below This on the Pyramid Tried First?	Does Pest Control Program Follow PAIPM Rules?	What Changes Could Be Made?

You Solve It! *(continued)*

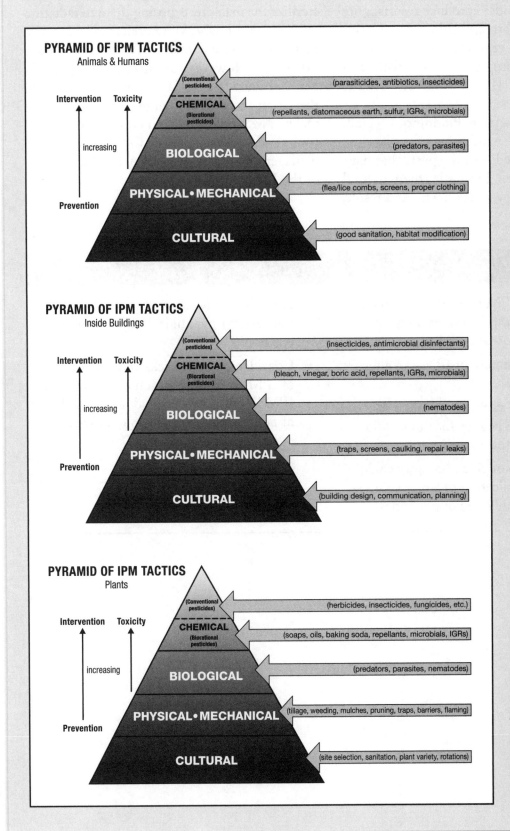

Figure 5.17 These pyramids show how IPM is based on preventive and less toxic methods of pest management, only increasing in intervention and toxicity when required.

May Lose More Crops Methods other than the use of chemical pesticides—removal of the source of pest infestation or the use of natural predators or parasitoids—produce results more slowly. As a result, farmers and gardeners may lose more fruits and vegetables to pests before their pest control program takes effect. The benefits of using IPM, however, usually overcome these losses.

Can Require Intensive Planning Overall, using IPM methods requires careful planning and extensive knowledge of the pests that have infested an area, their life cycle, their natural enemies, and how they attack hosts. As a result, IPM can be time-consuming and complex to implement. For example, one IPM method is sterilization of male insect pests. Scientists sterilize the males by exposing them to radiation or chemicals in labs. When released, the sterile males mate with females that fail to produce offspring. However, sterilization requires a detailed knowledge of the mating behavior of the target insect and a large number of sterile males. Nevertheless, the increased amount of time and effort needed for planning and management is usually offset by the benefits of the IPM approach.

Lesson Review

1. Explain why IPM reduces the amount of toxic chemicals introduced into the environment for pest control.

2. Explain how the use of IPM can alter local ecosystems.

3. Eradicating all pests is not a goal of IPM. Describe how eradication could be harmful to the ecosystem.

4. Explain how pesticide immunity could lead to the application of larger volumes and more deadly types of pesticides.

5. Describe the position of pesticide use in the PAIPM pyramids. Why is it in this position?

6. Consider the drawbacks and benefits of IPM. Form an opinion about whether IPM is, on balance, a good or bad method of pest control. Explain your answer.

Chapter 6

Ecosystems
and Their
Interactions

The Great Lakes are the largest group of freshwater lakes in the world, stretching almost 1,000 miles from one end to the other and holding one fifth of the world's supply of liquid fresh water. The Great Lakes system contains a wealth of species of fish and other aquatic species. You may wonder what the harm could be in adding just one more species. Ecologists know that's an unwise question to ask. Natural systems—lakes, rivers, forests—have a way of achieving balance when people do not intervene.

However, in 1988, human actions intervened in the Great Lakes accidentally with the introduction of the zebra mussel, an aquatic shelled animal smaller than an adult thumb. The mussel probably reached North America in or on a boat from Europe, where it is common. The mussel was discovered in Lake St. Clair, a connecting waterway between Lakes Huron and Erie. By 1990, zebra mussels had established themselves throughout the Great Lakes system, including the waters of Lake Erie that border the northwest tip of Pennsylvania. By 1994, the mussels were living in bodies of water in or adjacent to states as far south as Louisiana and as far west as Oklahoma. Scientists think boaters and fishers unknowingly carried the mussel from infested waters.

Figure 6.1 The zebra mussel population in Lake Erie has grown so large that the mussels are crowding out the native clams and clogging water pipes. The mussels attach themselves to driftwood, intake valves and other pipes, clams, and other debris.

Ecologists quickly realized that the little mussel could have a great impact on life in the freshwater systems it was colonizing. One impact seemed positive. Zebra mussels pass large amounts of water through their bodies, cleansing the water of some pollutants as they filter out food particles. As a result, the growing zebra mussel population in Lake Erie has helped make the lake's waters four to six times clearer than it was before the mussels established themselves. The clearer waters of the lake have allowed light to penetrate deeper into its waters than in previous years, encouraging the growth of aquatic plants.

Unfortunately, zebra mussels also have a downside. Aside from growing in clumps that clog the intake pipes of power plants and drinking water facilities, zebra mussels have been known to interfere with the feeding, growth, and reproduction of mussels native to the Great Lakes. In fact, some studies have shown that in areas of the Great Lakes system where zebra mussels have the highest densities, the number of native mussels has declined—crowded out by the exotic invaders. The mussels are also implicated in the disappearance of clams from parts of western Lake Erie. Large numbers of zebra mussels can also pick the waters clean of much of the phytoplankton and zooplankton (tiny plants and animals) that are the foundation of the web of life in aquatic ecosystems, leaving little food for other species. Some waterfowl and fish feed on zebra mussels; however, they cannot eat enough of the mussels to control their population.

The case of the zebra mussel invasion of the Great Lakes shows that just a small change in the natural environment—even a small change that's strictly accidental—can have a huge and unforeseen impact. So, when you ask what the harm is in adding one new species to an ecosystem, now you know that it depends on the species. As you learn about ecosystems, you will discover that it's not very hard to throw these systems out of balance.

Lesson 6.1
Ecosystems

Earth is one of nine planets in the solar system, but it's the only planet with a *biosphere*, a layer of soil, water, and air that sustains life.

If you travel around the United States, or even just around Pennsylvania, you will notice that the biosphere differs from place to place. The plants and animals in the marshes at the edge of eastern Pennsylvania's Delaware River look nothing like the plants and animals of western Pennsylvania's Allegheny National Forest. No one would mistake any part of Pennsylvania for the desert Southwest or the tropical forests of Hawaii. That's because a different type of ecosystem dominates each of these areas. An *ecosystem* consists of a group of living organisms that interact with one another and the nonliving physical environment as one unit.

There are many types of terrestrial, or land, ecosystems. There are ecosystems of the forest, desert, and grasslands. The plants and animals found in an ecosystem depend primarily on the local climate and soils in an area.

Forest ecosystems are common in Pennsylvania, covering more than half of the state. Of the many forests in Pennsylvania, oak-hickory is the most common type of forest ecosystem, covering 47 percent of the forested area in the central and southern parts of the state. Oak and hickory trees are the largest and most important plants in this ecosystem. The ecosystem also contains many animals, insects, and microorganisms. The second most common forest ecosystem in Pennsylvania is the northern hardwood forest, which covers 38 percent of the state. The northern hardwood forest, with its birch, sugar maple, beech, and black cherry trees, is common in the northern and northwestern parts of Pennsylvania.

There are also many aquatic ecosystems. Freshwater ecosystems include ponds, lakes, rivers, streams, and wetlands. Marine or salt-water ecosystems include estuaries, coastal marshes, coral reefs, and the open ocean.

Each ecosystem has a hierarchy of living things. The most basic level is the organism. An *organism* is any form of life, from a tiny bacterium to a bear. Organisms can be grouped into species. A *species* is a group of organisms that are alike in several ways, including appearance and genetic makeup, and that can breed with one another to produce healthy offspring. A *population* is a group of individuals of the same species found in a given area or located in the same area at a given time. For example, a group of white-tailed deer in an oak-hickory forest in southeastern Pennsylvania would be a population.

However, the population of deer doesn't live in isolation in the forest. The deer might eat the leaves and fruit of berry bushes, which are also eaten by populations of mice. The mice also interact with the populations of snakes and birds that prey on them.

The deer, mice, bushes, snakes, and birds are all part of the forest community. A *community* consists of the populations of living organisms that interact with one another in an ecosystem.

Ecosystems vary in size. They can be small areas such as a tiny pond or a small mountain meadow, or they can be large areas such as a forest, desert, or grassland. Within ecosystems, communities and their populations of plants and animals change over time in size, age, and distribution, depending on the environmental conditions around them.

Each population or individual organism in a species has specific needs in terms of food, water, temperature, light, and so on. These needs are met within its habitat. A *habitat* is the place where a particular species lives and from which it obtains what it needs for survival. A habitat can be as large as the Atlantic Ocean or Lake Erie, or as small as a rotting log in a hardwood forest in northwestern Pennsylvania.

Biotic Factors in an Ecosystem

Ecosystems have both living and nonliving components. As you learned in Chapter 1, *biotic factors* are the living parts of an ecosystem. Biotic factors include plants, animals, fungi, and microorganisms. In Pennsylvania's oak-hickory forest, the biotic factors include white oak trees, shagbark hickory trees, white-tailed deer, raccoons, bacteria, and fungi such as mushrooms.

These biotic factors interact with one another. For example, deer interact with each other to reproduce. They also interact with other living species in the ecosystem, including those they depend on for food as well as those that use them as prey.

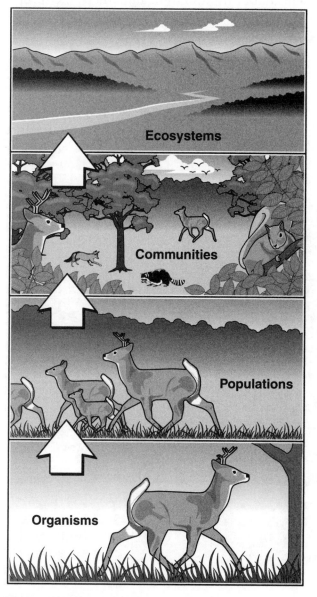

Figure 6.2 Every ecosystem is based on a hierarchy of living things.

Abiotic Factors in an Ecosystem

The biotic factors in an ecosystem also interact with and affect abiotic factors. *Abiotic factors* are the nonliving physical and chemical parts of an ecosystem. Although they are nonliving, they influence and support the biotic parts of the ecosystem.

On land, abiotic factors include surface water and groundwater, air, wind, soil nutrients, temperature, precipitation, and energy from the sun as well as the altitude and latitude of the ecosystem. In aquatic ecosystems, abiotic factors include currents, salinity, temperature, penetration of sunlight in water, and the concentration of nutrients in the water. The living parts of an ecosystem depend on the abiotic factors for survival. For example, the trees of the oak-hickory forest could not live and produce food without water, solar energy, and nutrients from the soil.

Each species survives best within a certain range of environmental conditions—a specific range of temperature, soil, water pH, latitude, and amount of precipitation. The conditions that define the physical limits within which an organism can survive are tolerance limits. In the Delaware Bay estuary, an area where salt water from the Atlantic Ocean and fresh water from the Delaware River meet, the concentration of salt in the water helps determine which aquatic species can survive there. A freshwater fish that thrives in the ecosystem of the Delaware River might be killed by the concentration of salt farther downstream in the bay or the ocean. As a result of this limitation and others, the species of fish in the Delaware River ecosystem and the ocean are different.

An abiotic factor such as shade can be important in a forest. In Pennsylvania's northern hardwood forest, beech trees survive best in shade, and black cherry trees prefer open areas in bright sunlight. As a result, in a mature area of forest with many trees and shrubs creating a

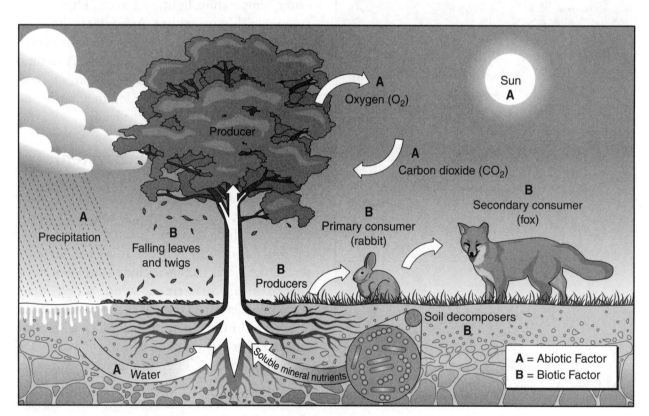

Figure 6.3 Abiotic and biotic factors work together to sustain the organisms living in an ecosystem.

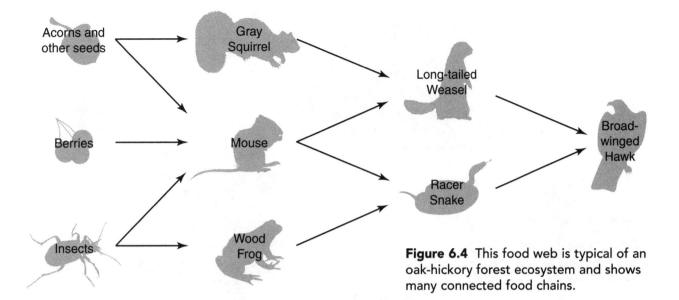

Figure 6.4 This food web is typical of an oak-hickory forest ecosystem and shows many connected food chains.

shady canopy, the lack of sunlight will inhibit the growth of young black cherry trees.

The actions of people can change abiotic factors and disrupt ecosystems in ways that expand the ability of some species to survive in an ecosystem while placing additional limitations on the ability of other species to live. Constructing a dam across a river, for example, changes the conditions of the river downstream in several ways. Dams block the flow of nutrient-rich sediments, which pile up behind the dam wall. Deprived of these essential nutrients, many of the plants and animals downstream suffer. Dams can also have devastating effects when they block fish, such as salmon, from heading upstream to spawn, or reproduce. The dams effectively eliminate the ability of these fish to survive in such rivers. Because dams restrict the flow of rivers—creating low water levels when water is diverted and high levels when operators send extra water downstream—they can alter the temperature of water below them. As a result, some organisms, such as certain species of fish, may no longer be able to survive there.

The concentration of toxic substances in air, water, and soil is also an important abiotic factor that affects ecosystems. Electric power plants that burn fossil fuels release pollutants such as sulfur dioxide and nitrogen oxides into the air. These pollutants form weak acids in the atmosphere that fall on forests and surface water as rain and other forms of precipitation. Among other effects, acid rain can change the chemical composition of soils, creating conditions in which some plants find it difficult to survive.

Matter and Energy in an Ecosystem

There is a lot of activity in an oak-hickory forest ecosystem. Squirrels and mice scamper across the forest floor. Birds soar overhead and land on tree branches. Shrubs and trees grow toward the sun. Deer graze on tender shoots as they wander among the trees. Insects and worms tunnel in the soil. Sustaining all of this activity requires food and energy. Nutrients and energy flow through ecosystems in food chains and food webs. A *food chain* is the transfer of energy from one organism to another. As each organism eats or is eaten by another organism, that energy is transferred. A simple food chain for an oak-hickory forest ecosystem might start with the sun shining on a berry bush. The bush produces berries; the mouse eats the berries; and the snake eats the mouse.

But nature is never that simple. The mouse eats berries, but it eats other foods, too. The snake eats mice, but other animals in the forest, such as the weasel, eat mice as well. A food web gives a more complete picture of the true flow of nutrients and energy through an ecosystem.

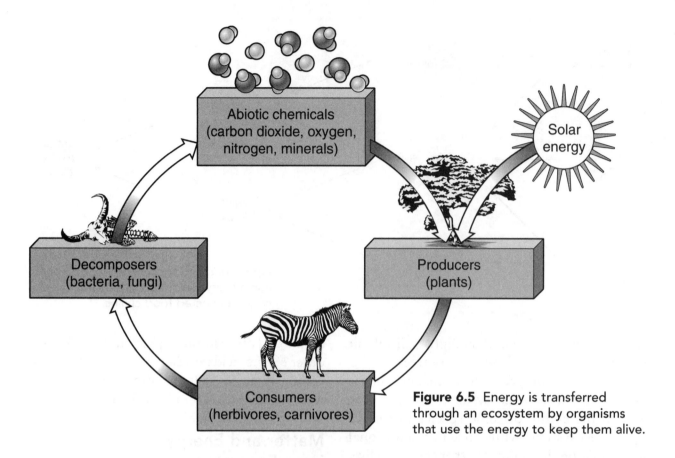

Figure 6.5 Energy is transferred through an ecosystem by organisms that use the energy to keep them alive.

A *food web* is a network that shows many connected food chains. The food web on the previous page shows a more complete picture of some of the organisms that eat one another in the oak-hickory forest. Of course, there are hundreds of organisms in the forest, and a complete food web would be many times this size.

Regardless of the different plants and animals that compose them, all energy in food webs begins with the sun. The sun provides the energy to drive the process of photosynthesis, in which green plants use water and nutrients from the soil and carbon dioxide from the air to produce food in the form of the simple sugar glucose. Because green plants are the only organisms in an ecosystem that can produce their own food, ecologists call them producers. A *producer* uses elements from the environment to make its own food. The cells of producers also convert solar energy to chemical energy and store it in their cells.

As you move through an ecosystem food chain, the next group of organisms are consumers.

A *consumer* is an organism that gets its energy and nutrients by feeding on other organisms. Many different animals play the role of the consumer. Some animals eat only plants and are called *herbivores*. Herbivores are the *primary consumers*—those that feed on plants for food and energy—in a food chain. In the oak-hickory forest ecosystem, the white-tailed deer is a primary consumer. A *secondary consumer* feeds on primary consumers in an ecosystem. A secondary consumer can be a carnivore or an omnivore. A *carnivore* eats meat, or other animals. An *omnivore* eats both plants and animals and can be a primary or secondary (or higher) consumer. In the oak-hickory forest ecosystem, the snake, weasel, and frog are secondary consumers. A *tertiary consumer* (sometimes called a higher-level consumer) eats secondary consumers and primary consumers. In an oak-hickory forest ecosystem, a chipmunk would be a primary consumer, eating the acorns from the oak tree. A black rat snake may come along and eat the chipmunk. The snake would be the secondary consumer. Later, a broad-winged hawk searching for food in the forest may catch and eat the black rat snake. The hawk, then, would be the tertiary or higher-level consumer.

Ecosystems also have scavengers and decomposers. A *scavenger* feeds on dead organisms. In the oak-hickory forest, scavengers could include flies, crows, and some types of ants. A *decomposer* is usually a type of bacteria or fungus that breaks down dead organisms and wastes. Decomposers complete the nutrient cycle in an ecosystem by returning the nutrients in living organisms to the soil so that plants can use them again.

Each organism in an ecosystem also belongs to a certain trophic level. A *trophic level* contains all organisms in a feeding level that are the same number of steps away from the sun, the source of energy in all terrestrial ecosystems and most aquatic systems.

As you move up from one trophic level to another in an ecosystem, there is a 90 percent loss of energy (as heat). That means that only 10 percent of the energy is passed along from one trophic level to the next. Organisms use that energy for the internal processes that keep them alive. Because of the huge loss of energy between trophic levels, food chains and food webs usually have no more than four or five trophic levels. Too little energy is left to support organisms feeding at higher trophic levels. An *energy pyramid* is made up of the trophic levels in a food web and the amount of energy that moves from one level up to the next.

Soil—An Integral Part of Many Ecosystems

Soil is a major component of terrestrial ecosystems, including the oak-hickory forest. As you know, soil is a renewable resource that is forming all the time as the result of the weathering and

erosion of rock on Earth's surface. But because soil forms so slowly, often taking hundreds or even thousands of years to accumulate just an inch or two of topsoil, it is a precious resource that must be carefully conserved.

Soils differ from place to place, depending on the parent rock from which they form as well as the local weather and climate. Each type of soil has a particular soil profile, or arrangement of different layers that comprise it. Each layer is called a *soil horizon*.

Geological processes can change the amount and quality of soil in an ecosystem. Water flowing downhill on sloping land can erode topsoil as water picks up particles of soil and carries them downhill. The constant removal of soil from slopes is natural wherever there is

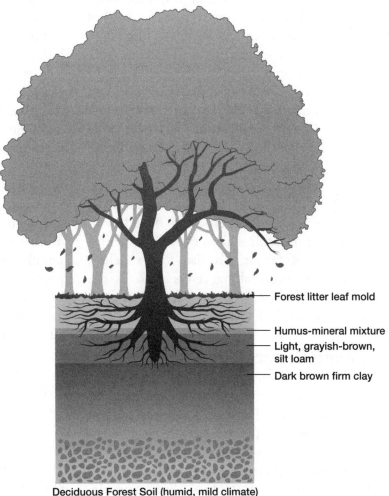

— Forest litter leaf mold

— Humus-mineral mixture
— Light, grayish-brown, silt loam
— Dark brown firm clay

Deciduous Forest Soil (humid, mild climate)

Figure 6.6 This is a typical soil profile found in a deciduous forest.

precipitation. In humid climate ecosystems, the rate of soil erosion and the rate of formation of new soil are often close enough to maintain the soil in a relatively constant condition. However, in some cases erosion removes soil faster than it can form. This often occurs when people disturb the natural environment of an ecosystem by cutting forests or plowing under grasslands. Without vegetation to hold the soil in place, erosion accelerates. Topsoil, which contains the nutrients and moisture needed by plants in the ecosystem, can be washed away, making the soil less able to support trees and other plant life. An ecosystem with fewer producers supports fewer consumers.

Natural ecological processes can deposit soil as well. When water that carries soil slows down as it reaches the bottom of a slope or level land, it no longer has the energy to carry its load of sediment. It then deposits, or drops, this load, creating areas of sedimentation or deposition. Thick, fertile soils develop in some areas of sedimentation. The Mississippi River carries a load of sediment as it flows within its channel. In times of flood, it spreads beyond its channel onto the adjacent flatlands of its flood plain. As the floodwaters recede and the current slows, the river retreats to its channel and the water drops its load of sediment. The sediment is nutrient-rich soil. This deposition of sediment creates areas of fertile soil on river flood plains. Deposition of fertile soil also forms deltas. Soil in these areas along rivers such as the Mississippi is among the most fertile land for farming in the United States.

Carrying Capacity of an Ecosystem

Populations cannot grow indefinitely. They change in size when individuals are born or move into an area. Populations decrease when individuals die or leave an area through emigration. Various factors affect these processes.

Population decreases and increases are influenced by many factors. For example, adequate rainfall and good weather conditions can increase the production of acorns, which in turn, can help more turkeys survive the winter, resulting in increased winter survival and an increase in the possibility of reproduction. Therefore, weather conditions, habitat quality, species survival, and reproduction all affect population growth. However, a poor acorn crop and a hard winter can cause major losses of turkeys in the winter. As a result, the turkey population is weakened and more susceptible to starvation, disease, and weather conditions. Disease, poor weather conditions, and poor habitat quality are factors that influence a decrease in population.

Populations would continue to increase if they had all of the resources they require in unlimited amounts, but there are always factors that limit their increase. The factor that is most important in controlling population growth is called the *limiting factor*. In a terrestrial ecosystem, there can be a number of limiting factors, such as temperature range, availability of water or light, and fertility of soil. Because of these limiting factors, each ecosystem has a finite capacity for growth connected to its carrying capacity. The *carrying capacity* of an ecosystem is the number of individuals of a species that it can support. The population of any ecosystem is the result of the balance achieved between factors that encourage growth and those that inhibit it.

If factors that increase growth are stronger or more numerous than those that inhibit growth, populations will grow. A young and growing population that has not yet reached resource limitations grows exponentially. It begins slowly and then increases more rapidly as the population increases and more individuals reproduce. A line graph that shows exponential growth forms a J-shaped curve.

Exponential growth cannot sustain itself indefinitely. Sooner or later, the population reaches the ecosystem's carrying capacity. An S-shaped curve shows that the population grows slowly at first and then increases more and more quickly. As it does, growth levels off and stabilizes.

In a forest ecosystem, for example, a population of raccoons might increase exponentially as long as food, water, and space for them are abundant. As the population gets larger, the rate of growth decreases until the population level stabilizes around the forest's carrying capacity for raccoons.

In a stable ecosystem, the population of a species fluctuates around the carrying capacity for that species. But suppose that disease or overhunting removes most rodent predators from the forest. The rodent population, if otherwise healthy, might explode. As the rodent population continues to grow, limitations such as shortages of food, water, and space would develop because of increasingly scarce resources. If the population briefly exceeds the carrying capacity of the ecosystem because of its rapid growth, the rodent population would crash because, for example, many individuals would not be able to find food and other resources.

Natural disasters that destroy habitats or food supplies can also limit population growth. For example, when tornadoes struck a part of the Allegheny National Forest in 1985, thousands of acres of forest were destroyed. The growth of populations that depended on this area of forest for food and shelter would have been limited while the forest regenerated itself.

At times, a large population can degrade the resources of an ecosystem so much that the carrying capacity could decrease. For instance, in Pennsylvania and many other eastern states, the deer population in forests has grown tremendously. Because they are eating so many young shrubs and tree seedlings, they are causing dramatic changes in forest ecosystems. These changes can affect the survival of other species that depend on forest plants. In most cases, when a population briefly overshoots its carrying capacity, one of two things can then happen. Either some of the population will migrate to other areas where the resources exist to support them, or the population will die back to a point at which it fits the new carrying capacity of the area. In the case of deer in the forests of Pennsylvania, the deer would most likely disrupt the forest ecosystem and displace

many species before the deer population would die back.

Because of modern technology, people have increased the carrying capacity of many areas of the world beyond their natural limits as well. As you know, farmland can produce more food today than it could 50 years ago because of the use of high-yield seeds, pesticides, and herbicides. Huge dams, aqueducts, canals, and irrigation projects allow millions of people to live in deserts that would otherwise be unable to support large populations. However, there are limitations to how much the carrying capacity of the natural environment can be increased and how long such increases can be sustained.

Habitats and Niches

Each organism lives in a certain habitat and functions in a certain way within an ecosystem. Each ecosystem has many habitats. Habitats in a forest ecosystem might include tree branches, rotting logs, soil, holes in tree trunks, or spaces under rocks.

A *niche* is the role an organism plays within an ecosystem. A niche includes the food an organism eats and how it obtains that food. For example, is the organism a predator or prey species? The niche also includes the specific part of the ecosystem the organism inhabits and the times of year at which the organism is present. The scarlet tanager is a songbird that spends its summers in the treetops of Pennsylvania forests and then migrates to Central and South America for winter. The time of day at which a species is active is also part of its niche. Owls are night predators, and hawks are day predators.

No two species can occupy the same niche in one ecosystem. If they did for a short time, competition for food, water, and space would cause one species to eliminate the other. However some species that live in the same habitat have developed very specialized niches that help them live together. For instance, three species of warblers (a type of bird) feed on the insects that live in a certain type of conifer tree. One species of warbler feeds in branches near the top of the tree. The second species looks for

Lab Study

Temperature and Photosynthesis in *Elodea*

As you learned, all organisms survive within certain environmental limits. In this activity, you will determine the minimum and maximum water temperature in which an *Elodea* plant can survive, according to its rate of photosynthesis.

Materials

4 flexible straws	0.5% sodium bicarbonate solution	test tube rack
4 one-hole stoppers		4 beakers full of water
4 test tubes	beaker of hot water	stopwatch or clock with a second hand
4 thermometers	beaker of ice water	
	Elodea plants	

Procedure

1. Work in groups of four, with each student completing steps 2 through 8 at the same time.

2. Put the curved end of a flexible straw into a hole in one of the stoppers. The end of the straw should be flush with the bottom of the stopper.

3. Fill the test tube with the sodium bicarbonate solution.

4. Place a thermometer in the test tube. Use the hot-water bath or the ice-water bath to adjust the temperature of the solution. Each member of the group should adjust the temperature of liquid in his or her test tube to match one of the temperatures in the table on the next page.

5. When the temperature is right, remove the thermometer and put a sprig of *Elodea* into the test tube. Put the stopper into the test tube.

6. All group members should put their test tubes in a rack near a sunny window.

7. Hold the free end of the straw below the surface of the water in a beaker.

8. Using a stopwatch or a clock with a second hand, count the number of bubbles released by the *Elodea* plant in one minute. Record this number in a chart.

9. Repeat this measurement two more times, and calculate the average number of bubbles produced in one minute.

Conclusions

1. As a group, prepare a bar graph that shows the average number of bubbles produced per minute at each of the four temperatures.

Figure 6.7 Use this illustration to set up your experiment.

2. What is the relationship of water temperature to the rate of photosynthesis of the *Elodea* plant?

3. Could water temperature restrict the areas in which *Elodea* could grow? Explain your answer.

For Discussion

1. Summarize the importance of photosynthesis for green plants in an aquatic environment.

2. What types of environmental conditions might alter the water temperature of an aquatic ecosystem? Include both natural and human-made conditions.

Extensions

Design an experiment to determine whether the amount of dissolved carbon dioxide in an aquatic environment could be a limiting factor for an *Elodea* population.

Data Table	
Student	**Temperature of Test Tube (°C)**
1	10°
2	20°
3	30°
4	40°

insects in the middle branches of the tree. The third species always feeds in the branches at the base of the tree. These different niches allow the three types of birds to live successfully within the same habitat.

Many species actually modify their environments to meet their needs. Some plants send out toxins into surrounding soil to prevent other plants from taking root near them. Beavers use twigs, branches, and rocks to build dams across streams. The dams create calm ponds in which the beavers build lodges of twigs and branches for shelter.

Ecologists find it useful to understand the niches of as many species as possible. This knowledge is vital in conserving species that are threatened or endangered. For example, the Eastern wood rat is threatened in Pennsylvania. Biologists do not fully understand why. In order to help conserve the wood rat, biologists are working to understand the type of habitat it requires, as well as its niche, to ensure that all of its needs would be met in another area—and that it would not be competing directly with another organism.

Knowing the niches of species is also useful when determining the impact of human actions

Figure 6.8 When beavers build dams across streams, the dams create calm waters where beavers can build lodges for shelter.

on the environment. What happens, for example, when an exotic plant is planted in a field? In many instances, the people who plant the exotic plant do not know its niche. Exotic species often occupy the same niches as native species but are better able to compete with them because the exotic species have no natural enemies in the new ecosystem that they invade. As a result, the exotic plant often becomes a pest as it chokes out native plants.

Homeostasis in an Ecosystem

Changes occur in ecosystems all the time. Trees die, and new trees grow in their place. Young animals are born as older ones die or are killed. Water deposits soil in some places and washes it away in others. Seasons come and go. Trees grow using nutrients from the soil. Then storms knock down the trees, which decompose and return to the soil.

Regardless of the constant changes that occur within an ecosystem, the ecosystem will remain essentially the same, as long as there are not huge disturbances. So, an oak-hickory forest remains an oak-hickory forest, and a saltwater marsh remains a saltwater marsh. The natural stability in an ecosystem that keeps it from undergoing radical change is *homeostasis*. Homeostasis helps an ecosystem resist transformation—and helps it recover when stresses are so great that they cause serious problems.

Ecosystems maintain homeostasis, in part, because the organisms within them have the ability to resist change. The body of a healthy deer, frog, beetle—even a blueberry bush—constantly maintains internal processes that use energy and cycle the water and nutrients it needs to stay alive. Populations within ecosystems also resist change. As you have learned, the populations of species in an ecosystem fluctuate around the ecosystem's carrying capacity—rising when resources are abundant and falling when they become scarcer in a continuous cycle. The many resources in an ecosystem that are needed by living things, such as nutrients in the soil, water, and essential compounds in the air,

are cycled constantly as well. As you will see in Lesson 6.2, for example, plants use carbon dioxide from the air to make food and store energy, and then animals return the carbon dioxide to the air after they eat the plants.

Healthy ecosystems maintain this delicate balance, but stresses that can cause change happen all the time. Some are natural, such as floods, storms, or wildfires. When these changes occur, the ecosystem has the ability to bounce back relatively quickly. Hurricane Agnes roared through forests in western Pennsylvania in 1972, blowing down trees and killing or displacing forest animals. But before long, tree seedlings were sprouting from the ground, and animals that had survived were again having young. The ecosystem was on its way to repairing itself. Would a forest fire mean the end of forests in a particular area? That's not likely. Some seeds would survive the fire, and some would blow in from other areas and take root to allow new plants to grow. Some animals and insects that burrow underground would survive, and animals from outside the burned area would eventually recolonize the land. Again, the forest would repair itself.

However, if the change to an ecosystem is too extreme or the ecosystem is unhealthy, it may not have the ability to repair itself. Human activities often cause dramatic changes in ecosystems, from which they may not recover. As you will learn in Chapter 7, this can happen when important species are killed off or removed. It can also happen when pollution or other activities disrupt the natural processes that keep the ecosystem going.

Biomes

A *biome* is a geographic region of Earth that is inhabited by a community of distinct types of plant and associated animal species. Biomes are largely defined by climate, especially average annual temperature and precipitation. The soils of biomes also differ. There are forest, grassland, desert, highland, and ice cap biomes on land. The organisms in a biome are adapted to that biome's particular environmental conditions.

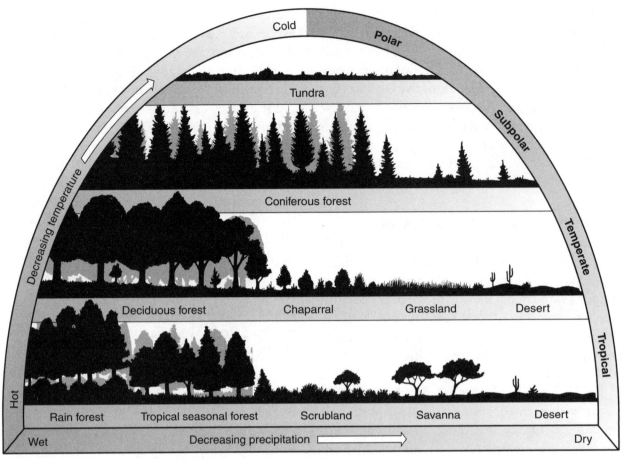

Figure 6.9 Biomes are determined by average temperature and precipitation.

Biomes are huge areas on Earth that contain many ecosystems. The biome that includes Pennsylvania covers much of the eastern third of the United States. It contains the oak-hickory ecosystem and many others.

Because climate largely defines biomes, latitude and altitude are important in defining these regions as well. Latitude influences climate because average temperatures become colder as you move from the equator toward the poles. Temperatures also become colder as you move higher in altitude above sea level, as when you go up a mountain. In fact, each additional 300 feet in altitude on a highland is about equivalent to a 62-mile change in latitude.

The same biome often occurs in several places on Earth. For example, the desert biome is in northern Africa as well as southwestern North America. Although they may have different

species of plants and animals, they have similar characteristics and niches that are suited to the desert. The same is true of widely separated tropical rain forest biomes, grassland biomes, and so on.

There are also aquatic biomes. Some are freshwater biomes. Others are marine or saltwater biomes. Water biomes vary with factors such as depth of the water (which controls temperature), amount of sunlight that penetrates the water, concentration of dissolved oxygen in the water, and presence of nutrients.

Land Biomes

Forests Forest biomes cover areas with relatively high average yearly rainfall. Depending on the average yearly temperature, tropical, temperate, or boreal forests will form.

Tropical Rain Forest Tropical rain forests cover large areas on both sides of the equator in central South America, Africa, Southeast Asia, and northern Australia. Tropical rain forests are warm year-round and have almost daily heavy rainfall. The largest of these rain forests is the Amazon of South America. The lush vegetation of the tropical rain forest grows in distinct layers. Plants in the lowest layer of the tropical forest must adapt to limited ability to absorb sunlight under a dense forest canopy. For example, lianas, which are climbing vines, wind around the trunks of trees until their leaves reach the sunlight of the top layer of the forest, called the upper canopy. Because tropical forest soils are not fertile, some trees have roots that spread out laterally in the poor soil and absorb nutrients from decomposed vegetation near the surface, where matter decomposes. The most impressive feature of these forests is their great species diversity. Although they cover only about 2 percent of Earth's land surface, they contain up to 80 percent of Earth's land species. Characteristic animal species of the South American rain forest include monkeys, alligators, sloths, and colorful birds such as macaws.

Tropical Deciduous Forest and Tropical Scrub Forest Tropical rain forests give way to tropical deciduous forests and tropical scrub forests as you move away from the equator and as rainfall becomes less steady and intense. Tropical deciduous forests have rainfall during one wet season. The forests' deciduous trees lose their leaves during the dry season. A *deciduous* tree survives during a cold or dry season by dropping its leaves. Tropical deciduous trees are less lush and diverse than those of the tropical rain forest. Tropical scrub forests contain deciduous trees and evergreen trees that are relatively small. These forests occur in the tropical forest areas with the longest dry seasons.

Temperate Deciduous Forest Temperate deciduous forests are found in moist areas with long, warm summers and cold winters. Precipitation falls throughout the year. All of Pennsylvania is within this biome. A few species of trees dominate forests here. They include broadleaf deciduous trees such as oaks, hickories, maples, beeches, and sycamores. Trees of this forest biome are primarily deciduous. Their leaves turn brilliant shades of red, purple, orange, and gold in fall; drop off; and then grow back in spring. Many of the large predators of the temperate deciduous forest were killed or displaced long ago. These predators include wolves and mountain lions. Today, dominant animal species include bears, deer, squirrels, rabbits, raccoons, and opossums.

Temperate Coniferous Forest Some ecologists also recognize areas of temperate coniferous forest in mid-latitude coastal areas that have mild winters and heavy rainfall. A *coniferous forest* is one in which coniferous, or cone-bearing, trees dominate. These tree species include pines, firs, and spruces. In North America, the coastal areas of Oregon, Washington, and British Columbia (Canada) contain areas of temperate coniferous forest.

Boreal Forest The northernmost forested areas contain the boreal forest, or taiga. Evergreen conifers are the dominant tree species in these forests. In contrast with broadleaf trees such as oaks or hickories, these trees have thin, needle-shaped leaves with a waxy coating. The leaf structure offers protection against cold and holds in moisture. Boreal forests grow in areas where there are long, cold, dry winters and short, warm summers. There is little diversity in these forests because of the harsh climate and poor soil. Animals that are common in this biome include elk, moose, wolves, and squirrels.

Grasslands

Grassland biomes generally receive less rainfall than forest biomes but more than desert biomes. Some stands of trees grow along the courses of streams and rivers, but this biome is dominated by grass. A combination of periodic drought and seasonal fires helps maintain natural grasslands and keeps trees and shrubs from establishing themselves in large numbers. There are three major types of grasslands: tropical, temperate, and polar. The latitude and resulting temperature determine which of these three types of biomes develops in an area.

Savanna Grasslands of the tropics and subtropics are often called savanna. They have warm temperatures all year, but they have a distinct wet season and a long, dry season. Some of the world's largest areas of savanna are in southern Africa, central South America, and interior Australia. In Africa, herbivores such as giraffes, zebras, elephants, antelopes, and gazelles inhabit the savanna, and each occupies a specific niche within the grassland, which minimizes competition. For example, giraffes eat leaves and stems from the tops of trees, and zebras eat grasses and stems on the ground.

Temperate Grassland Temperate grasslands cover much of the interior of North America. In the United States, they include the tall-grass prairie of the Midwest and the short-grass areas of the western Plains. Similar grasslands cover interior areas of Eurasia, South America, and Africa. Winters are very cold, and summers are hot and dry. These areas have fertile soil, formed in large part by the decay of the upper parts of the grasses that die off each year. The Corn Belt and vast wheat-growing areas of the United States are located in areas of temperate grassland. Temperate grasslands contain a wealth of small animals such as prairie dogs, jackrabbits, squirrels, coyotes, wolves, bobcats, and snakes. Some animals, such as prairie dogs, live in burrows. Bison were a dominant species of the North American grasslands until the late 1800s, when they were hunted nearly to extinction. In North America, very little of this natural grassland remains because it has been replaced by farm fields and both urban and suburban development. However,

Figure 6.10 Caribou feed on the grasses, mosses, lichens, and short shrubs found in the tundra.

there are now efforts to preserve the natural grassland that remains.

Tundra Polar grasslands are also known as tundra. These areas are treeless plains that are cold all year and have very little precipitation. Most precipitation in tundra biomes is snow. Plants in this biome grow very close to the ground to retain moisture and stay out of the path of cold winds. Many plants have thick, leathery, wax-coated leaves to retain heat and moisture. Common tundra plants are short grasses, mosses, lichens, and short shrubs that are adapted to cold, ice, and constant wind. Because of the cold, decomposers work slowly in this biome, resulting in poor soils. The animals of this biome are mostly plant-eaters—hares, squirrels, and lemmings—that escape the cold by burrowing underground or withstand it through adaptations such as thick fur and compact bodies to minimize heat loss.

Desert and Chaparral

About 30 percent of Earth's land surface is desert. A *desert* is an area that typically gets less than 10 inches of rain each year. Although most people think of deserts as scorching hot places, they can be hot or cold, depending on their location.

Desert There are tropical, temperate, and cold deserts. Tropical deserts have high temperatures all year and very low average annual precipitation—often less than one inch that falls during one brief part of the year. The southern Sahara is a tropical desert, as is the Atacama Desert of South America. The Atacama may be the driest spot on Earth, with some areas going decades without precipitation. These deserts have few plants. Common physical features include sand dunes and rock formations. Temperate deserts, such as the Mojave in the western United States, have hot summers and cool winters. They also have more annual precipitation than other types of deserts. Temperate deserts contain plants (cacti and succulents) and animals (lizards and snakes) that are specially adapted to living in a dry environment. Cold deserts have cold winters

and warm or hot summers. The Gobi Desert of China is a cold desert. Much of Antarctica is also classified by many as a cold desert because of its very low average annual precipitation.

Desert plants and animals have special adaptations that allow them to live in a harsh environment. Many plants store any available water. The saguaro cactus in the Southwest United States has fleshy stems that can expand during rare periods of heavy precipitation to hold extra water. Succulents have thick, wax-coated leaves that cut down on moisture loss. Other plants, such as the creosote bush, have extensive root systems that are very efficient at drawing whatever moisture is available from the soil and crowding out other plants that might compete for limited resources. Animals in the desert often burrow underground to escape the intense heat of the day.

Chaparral Chaparral occurs in areas with mild, rainy winters and hot, dry summers. Well-known areas of chaparral are in southern California and lands around the edges of the Mediterranean Sea in southern Europe and northwestern Africa. The plants of the chaparral are primarily hardy evergreen shrubs with hard, leathery leaves. After hot, dry summers, areas of chaparral are prone to late summer or fall wildfires. The fires actually help maintain the ecosystem. Much of the plant life has seeds that need fire to open and sprout, and some plants have stored nutrients that the heat of fire releases.

Highland and Ice Cap

Elevation is the major influence on the climate of highlands. Because temperature drops with altitude, the tops of some high mountains remain snow-covered even when low-latitude areas with fairly warm climates surround them.

Mountain Highland biomes occur in mountainous areas. Because temperature drops with elevation, the climate in these biomes shifts as one climbs up a mountain. Precipitation levels also change, depending on location on the windward or leeward side of a mountain. For example, moisture-filled clouds roll east toward the Washington Cascades from the Pacific Ocean.

Figure 6.11 In addition to temperature and precipitation, latitude and altitude also determine biomes.

Rising to cross the mountain range, the clouds cool and dump a great deal of rain on the windward or western side of the mountains. By the time the system crosses to the eastern or leeward side of the mountains, it is fairly dry. The eastern side of the mountains has a much drier and warmer climate as a result. Because of temperature and precipitation differences, different ecosystems exist as one climbs a mountain, similar to the range of ecosystems one finds when moving from the equator toward the poles.

Ice Cap This biome occurs in polar areas that are always cold and where snow builds up from year to year into enormous ice sheets that cover the land surface. Ice cap areas are primarily in Antarctica and the interior of Greenland.

Aquatic Biomes

Freshwater Freshwater biomes include streams, rivers, lakes, ponds, and wetlands that occur inland. Their waters generally contain a concentration of salt that is very low—less than 1 percent of their volume. Pennsylvania contains all of these freshwater biomes. Freshwater biomes cover a much smaller area than do marine biomes, but almost 41 percent of the world's fish species live in them.

Marine Marine biomes are saltwater biomes that are part of the world's oceans and cover most of Earth. Marine biomes include coastal biomes and those of the open ocean. Coastal biomes include estuaries and coastal salt marshes. These areas, in shallow waters between the coast and the continental shelf, are rich in nutrients. They are the breeding grounds for many aquatic animal species and waterfowl. In fact, coastal marine biomes contain 90 percent of marine species. Pennsylvania does not have an ocean coastline, but the southeastern corner of the state borders the Delaware River, near the point where it widens into Delaware Bay, an important east coast estuary. The largest marine biome is the open ocean. Although it is large, the open ocean contains only about 10 percent of marine species. Most species of the open ocean are in the upper zones, where sunlight can penetrate.

A Pond Ecosystem

Ponds are small, shallow bodies of fresh water that are usually enclosed. Some small streams may enter ponds, but waterways generally don't flow out of them. Because ponds are shallow, sunlight usually penetrates from the surface down to the bottom. This allows plants to grow on pond bottoms as well as around their edges. Many of these plants grow up through the pond's surface. The animals in a pond differ, depending on the pond's location and depth and the type of soil in the area.

Pennsylvania has many ponds. The illustration below shows some parts of an ecosystem that could exist in a small pond in Pennsylvania. Use what you have learned about ecosystems to finish the table on the next page. Remember that some organisms can be both primary consumers and higher-level consumers, depending on the food they consume at a given time.

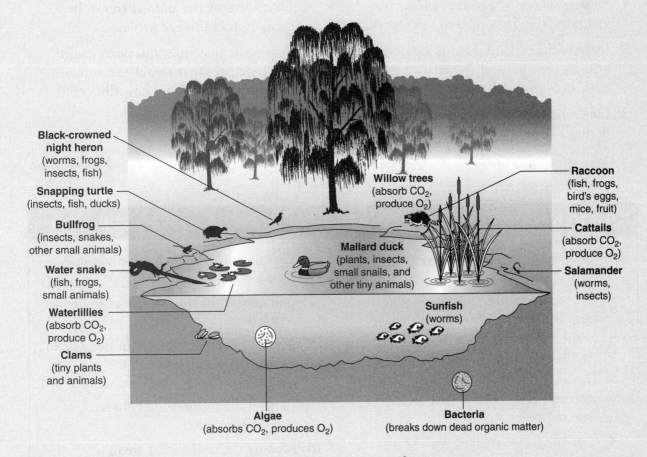

Black-crowned night heron (worms, frogs, insects, fish)

Snapping turtle (insects, fish, ducks)

Bullfrog (insects, snakes, other small animals)

Water snake (fish, frogs, small animals)

Waterlillies (absorb CO$_2$, produce O$_2$)

Clams (tiny plants and animals)

Willow trees (absorb CO$_2$, produce O$_2$)

Mallard duck (plants, insects, small snails, and other tiny animals)

Raccoon (fish, frogs, bird's eggs, mice, fruit)

Cattails (absorb CO$_2$, produce O$_2$)

Salamander (worms, insects)

Sunfish (worms)

Algae (absorbs CO$_2$, produces O$_2$)

Bacteria (breaks down dead organic matter)

Figure 6.12 Every organism in a pond ecosystem serves a specific purpose.

You Solve It! (continued)

A Pond Ecosystem			
Producers	Primary Consumers	Secondary or Tertiary Consumers	Decomposers

Questions

1. Determine why waterlilies, willow trees, and cattails are important to this ecosystem.

2. Identify the mallard duck as a producer, primary consumer, or secondary consumer in this ecosystem. Explain your answer.

3. Infer what would happen to this ecosystem during a time of extreme drought.

4. Describe how the animals shown here could impact this ecosystem.

5. Sediments that enter this pond could cause changes that would end with a forest ecosystem. Infer how this could happen.

Lesson Review

1. Define an ecosystem, and identify one ecosystem in Pennsylvania.

2. Put these terms in the correct sequence, from the smallest group of life-forms to the largest: biome, organism, population, ecosystem, community.

3. Explain the way biotic factors interact with and depend on abiotic factors in an ecosystem.

4. Can an ecosystem exist without producers? Explain your answer.

5. Contrast food chains and food webs.

6. Explain why a food chain would not have ten trophic levels.

7. Summarize the importance of soil in an ecosystem.

8. Make a generalization about the way an increase in population and the carrying capacity of an ecosystem are related.

9. Explain the relationship between habitat and niche.

10. Identify the factors that are most important in determining land biomes.

11. List the factors that are most important in determining aquatic biomes.

Lesson 6.2

Cycles in an Ecosystem

Earth is a closed system, like a large terrarium. The planet has all of the water, oxygen, carbon, and other elements that it ever has had—or ever will have. Matter continuously cycles throughout the parts of ecosystems, from abiotic factors to biotic factors and back again.

There are several major cycles in an ecosystem, including the water cycle and atmospheric cycles, such as the carbon cycle and the nitrogen cycle. Carbon, nitrogen, and water are all substances that are essential to living things, making the processes that recycle them important. But human activities have been impacting these cycles. The ultimate result of this interference is still unknown, but there are signs of potentially harmful effects.

The Water Cycle

Some people might call Earth the water planet. Water covers about 70 percent of its surface. More importantly, most living things are primarily water (your body is 65 percent water) and cannot exist without it. Earth's water supply is finite, which means that the same water that exists on Earth now was here when the dinosaurs disappeared 65 million years ago. The molecules of water that hit your back as you shower could have been in Thomas Jefferson's teacup at Monticello 200 years ago or part of the Nile River of Egypt thousands of years before that.

The oceans are the greatest reservoirs of water on the planet. With energy from sunlight, water evaporates from oceans (and other surface water) and rises into the atmosphere as a gas called water vapor. In the atmosphere, water vapor cools and condenses into liquid form as cloud droplets. If the cloud droplets continue to grow, they can become precipitation, which returns to Earth, often falling directly back into the ocean or other surface water. Some falls on land, where it seeps directly into soil or washes over the surface and enters bodies of water, such as lakes and rivers, as runoff. Water that

seeps into the soil becomes groundwater. Some reservoirs of groundwater, called aquifers, provide much of the drinking water in the United States. Plants also take up water from the soil through their roots. This water can return directly to the atmosphere through transpiration. Transpiration is the process by which plant leaves give off water to the atmosphere.

Plants contain a great deal of water. Animals take in this water when they eat either plants or other animals that have eaten plants. When a plant or animal dies and decays, decomposition releases water back into the soil, water, or air.

Sooner or later, all water returns to the ocean. This can take a very short time—maybe just hours for water to evaporate from the ocean, form clouds, and then fall back into the ocean as rain. In the case of precipitation such as snow that becomes part of a glacier or polar ice cap, the process of its return to the ocean can take thousands of years.

Although water constantly cycles through the environment, human activities can pollute it. If pollution is severe enough, water becomes virtually unusable by people and other living things. Because less than 1 percent of Earth's abundant water is fresh water that people can use for drinking, bathing, cooking, and growing food, water conservation has become an important part of water use planning.

The Carbon Cycle

Carbon is considered the building block of life. Without carbon, the organic compounds that living things need for food and that store the energy that keeps life going would not be able to survive. Carbon is essential for DNA, proteins, fats, and carbohydrates, among other substances. Carbon in the form of carbon dioxide is also a greenhouse gas that helps maintain heat in Earth's atmosphere. The ocean, the atmosphere, and rocks all store large amounts of carbon. When carbon leaves these reservoirs, it cycles through the environment in several connected ways.

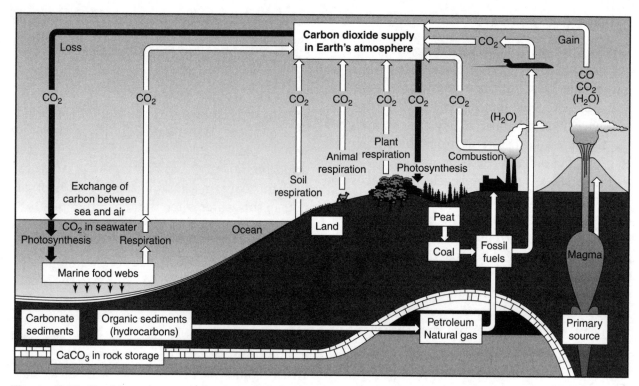

Figure 6.13 Earth's carbon supply constantly cycles through the land, water, air, and organisms.

In one part of the carbon cycle, carbon moves between the atmosphere, oceans, and living organisms. Through photosynthesis, plants use carbon dioxide from the atmosphere and ocean to make glucose and other organic chemicals (chemicals that contain carbon). As consumer organisms eat both plants and animals that eat plants, carbon moves through the food webs of ecosystems. Some carbon returns to the air and oceans directly through the respiration of living things. For example, you return carbon dioxide to the air when you exhale. The decomposition of living organisms also returns carbon to the soil, water, and air in the form of carbon dioxide. Depending on the number of trophic levels carbon moves through in this part of the cycle, the time for completion of the cycle varies.

Other parts of the carbon cycle take much longer to complete. For instance, carbon travels from living organisms to rocks and then back into the air or water where living organisms use it again. Shells of marine animals, which contain carbon, fall to the bottom of the sea when the animals die. They pile up, are covered by sediment, are compacted, and form rock, such as limestone. Over millions of years, what was once seafloor can become dry land. Erosion on land dissolves carbon-containing minerals, such as limestone, returning carbon to the air and water, for example, as carbon dioxide.

A third carbon pathway involves the formation and burning of fossil fuels. Oil and natural gas form from the remains of dead organisms that were primarily composed of carbon and hydrogen. Buried by layers of sediment on the ocean floor, the remains are compacted and go through chemical changes that turn them into petroleum. This process takes millions of years. When people remove the oil and gas from the ground and burn it as a fuel, the combustion releases carbon dioxide into the atmosphere, where it becomes available again for photosynthesis and cycling through living things.

People are now altering the carbon cycle through deforestation and burning of fossil fuels. Deforestation increases the carbon concentration in the air because it removes trees that use carbon dioxide from the air for photosynthesis. Fewer trees means that less carbon dioxide is absorbed from the atmosphere. Burning fossil fuels in power plants and motor vehicles releases carbon as a by-product of combustion. The concentration of carbon dioxide in the atmosphere has been rising fairly steadily during the last few decades, contributing to the phenomenon called global warming.

The Nitrogen Cycle

Nitrogen is another important element in organic compounds such as proteins, DNA, amino acids, and chlorophyll. Nitrogen is also the most abundant gas in Earth's atmosphere. It cycles from the atmosphere through living organisms and back to the atmosphere again. However, when you breathe in nitrogen, it does not enter into chemical reactions that allow your cells to use it. So people, and most other consumers in ecosystems, get nitrogen from food.

Although plants and animals cannot use simple nitrogen molecules (N_2), they can take up and use nitrate (NO_3-). Nitrate is formed when nitrogen from the air combines with oxygen in a process called fixation. Nitrogen-fixing bacteria live in root nodules on a group of plants called legumes. Legumes include plants such as clover, peas, soybeans, and alfalfa. The bacteria can convert gaseous nitrogen from the atmosphere into ammonia. Then the ammonia is converted into nitrate. Plants use the ammonia, nitrate, and other nutrients absorbed from the soil to make nitrogen-containing compounds essential to life, such as proteins. Animals can take in nitrogen only by eating plants. Like carbon, nitrogen moves through the various trophic levels of an ecosystem as animals eat plants and other animals eat those animals.

During decomposition, bacteria breaks down organic compounds, such as proteins, into

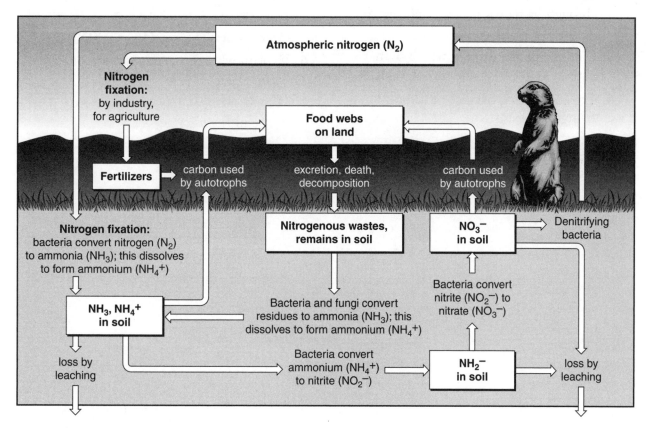

Figure 6.14 Nitrogen is an essential nutrient that must be combined with hydrogen or oxygen to be used by plants.

simple nitrogen-containing compounds, such as ammonia. Denitrifying bacteria act on the ammonia, breaking it down into nitrogen and hydrogen. These bacteria release nitrogen gas back into the soil and atmosphere to finish the cycle.

In addition to land plants such as legumes, some aquatic bacteria can also fix nitrogen for use by plants in aquatic ecosystems. Lightning flashing through the atmosphere can also change nitrogen into nitrate.

Just as human activities are altering the carbon cycle, they are altering the nitrogen cycle as well by increasing the rate of nitrogen fixation. The amount of nitrogen cycling through living things has doubled since the 1950s. This is largely the result of activities such as the use of nitrogen-containing chemical fertilizer, the burning of fossil fuels that release nitrogen compounds during combustion, and the destruction of forests and wetlands that also release nitrogen through vegetation decay. The added nitrogen in the environment is partly responsible for problems such as acid rain, pollution of water systems in agricultural areas, and formation of algae blooms. These blooms rob water bodies of oxygen as they decompose, causing aquatic organisms to die.

Lesson Review

1. Explain the sequence of events in the cycle that moves carbon from the soil, through living organisms, and then directly back into soil.

2. Summarize the ways in which human activity is affecting the carbon cycle.

3. Explain the importance of carbon for living organisms.

4. Will Earth ever run out of water? Explain your answer.

5. Describe the role of plants in the water cycle. Describe the role of the sun.

6. Explain why nitrogen is important to living things.

7. Why is nitrogen fixation a necessary part of the nitrogen cycle?

Nutrient Cycling in an Ecosystem

The soil in each ecosystem contains nutrients. These nutrients—nitrogen, phosphorus, potassium—are taken up by plants, make their way through the ecosystem food web, and then return to the soil after the death and decay of plants and animals. Of course, not every bit of these nutrients enters plants. When it rains, for example, some nutrients leave the ecosystem as runoff.

The graphs at right show the amount of nitrate that a forest ecosystem loses as a result of runoff at various stages in its history. At each stage, the forest is in a different condition.

Use the graphs and your knowledge of ecosystems, nutrient cycles, and human activities in forests to answer the questions below.

Questions

1. Infer which graph shows the loss of nitrate in a forest ecosystem in which many trees are being cut down. Explain your answer.

2. Infer which graph shows a forest ecosystem that was heavily logged several years before but in which the plant community is growing back. Explain your answer.

3. Infer which graph shows nitrate loss in an intact, stable forest ecosystem. Explain your answer.

4. Describe how the graph that shows nutrient loss in a stable forest ecosystem could be different if the area experienced drought for a long period.

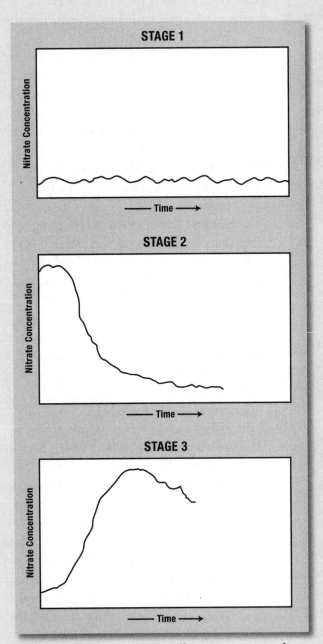

Figure 6.15 Forests lose different amounts of nitrate as a result of runoff at various stages in their history.

Case Study

The East Side Project

The Allegheny National Forest is a 513,257-acre forest preserve in the northwestern part of Pennsylvania. For the last several years, there has been heated disagreement about how to manage the land within the forest.

With a management plan called the East Side Project, the U.S. Forest Service seeks to manage the forest with several goals in mind. Those goals include sustaining the forest ecosystem, providing a variety of wildlife habitats, and providing quality wood products.

The Forest Service proposes cutting down more than 8,000 acres of the forest. This proposal, among others, caused a disagreement between Forest Service officials and members of several environmental and conservation groups. The Forest Service says it is acting to make the forest healthier. Environmental groups say the Forest Service is interfering in the natural development of the forest ecosystem.

However, people have been interfering in the Allegheny for years. Most of the Allegheny is second-growth forest, meaning that it is forest that has regrown after the original forest was cut down. The original trees in the area were primarily American beeches, eastern hemlocks, and smaller numbers of sugar maples, red maples, white pines, and black cherries. Some of the most extensive logging of virgin growth (the original forest cover) occurred between the late 1800s and the early 1900s. The second-growth forest that exists in much of the Allegheny National Forest today dates from regeneration after that logging.

When an ecosystem is disturbed, it does not necessarily grow back the same way. The second-growth forest that grew back in the area that is now the Allegheny National Forest is not identical to the original forest. Because the logging in the early part of the twentieth century involved clear-cutting (removing every tree), shade-loving trees did not take hold when the forest first began to grow back. Most of the species that began to grow were those that thrive in bright sunlight, such as black cherries and red maples. The huge population of deer in the forest, which increased a great deal during the twentieth century, has also had an impact on the way the forest has regenerated itself. The deer browse on the forest floor, eating young, tender tree shoots before they can develop into trees. Because of the absence of native tree species in some areas, their space on the forest floor has been filled by other species of grasses and bushes that cast shade on the forest floor and further inhibit the survival of tree seedlings.

The Forest Service has stated that parts of the ecosystem of the Allegheny National Forest are not healthy. According to the Forest Service, too many of the trees are dead or dying, and the condition of many areas of the forest will prevent natural tree regrowth. The Forest Service would like to clear the present forest in some areas—healthy and unhealthy trees alike—to allow the regrowth of a healthier forest. The processes that would allow this include clear-cutting, applying herbicides in some areas to kill plants that shade the forest floor, fencing off areas of seedlings to prevent deer from eating them, planting trees of selected species (not necessarily those that were dominant originally), and applying fertilizers to help newly planted seedlings grow faster.

Environmentalists believe that the Forest Service is interfering in the development of the forest in unnecessary and harmful ways. They believe that clear-cutting the forest is harmful because it removes all trees and plants

Possible Management Plans					
Activity	Alt. 1	Alt. 2	Alt. 3	Alt. 4	Alt. 5
Potential Disturbed Areas	1,197 a	633 a	798 a	802 a	0 a
Herbicide/Fertilizer Treatment	337 a	0 a	287 a	193 a	0 a
Fencing	29 a	0 a	25 a	12 a	0 a
Vegetation Removal for Roads	101 a	62 a	24 a	64 a	0 a
Returned by Decommissioning	31 a	23 a	9 a	23 a	0 a
Pit Expansion and Development	40 a	33 a	30 a	40 a	0 a

in the area and destroys wildlife habitat. Clear-cutting the present forest would also stop the natural process of regeneration. Black cherry trees, the most valuable timber trees in this forest ecosystem, became much more plentiful after the area was first clear-cut in the early twentieth century. Although they made up less than 1 percent of the virgin forest, they cover almost 30 percent of some areas of the forest today. Some environmentalists claim that the management practices of the Forest Service are effectively stopping regrowth of the forest from going forward naturally in order to keep profitable cherry trees dominant in some areas. If the forest were allowed to develop naturally, beech, maple, and hemlock trees would eventually crowd out the cherry trees.

The environmental coalition filed a lawsuit to stop the East Side Project timber cutting and sale. The outcome of the suit could determine the future development of the forest.

Questions

1. Summarize the arguments for and against the East Side Project timber cutting and sale.

2. Is the forest today the same as the natural ecosystem that existed before cutting began in the 1800s? Explain your answer.

3. What role have both people and deer played in the development of this ecosystem?

4. Some scientists think that acid rain is responsible for the large number of dying trees in some areas of the forest. The forest plan does not address acid rain. Is this a problem? Why or why not?

5. Look at the table above that shows five alternatives for managing land included in the East Side Project and the acreage that each would impact. Identify the alternatives that would have the least and greatest effect on the area on the basis of that acreage. Explain your answers.

6. Do you see a compromise that could be reached? If so, explain your compromise. If not, explain why you do not think a compromise is possible.

Lesson 6.3
Ecological Succession

You move into a new home across the street from a farmer's pasture. Soon after you move in, the owner sells the farm. The new owners decide not to use the pasture. They let it return to its natural state. As the years pass, the open pastureland becomes crowded with wildflowers, weeds, and small shrubs. Eventually, small seedlings take root, and trees begin to grow. You graduate from high school and return to your home year after year for holidays and special occasions. After a few more years, you can look across the street to a lot full of young trees and shrubs.

What you've witnessed over all those years is an ecological process called succession. *Ecological succession* is a process in which the communities of an ecosystem change over time.

Stages of Succession

There are a couple of types of ecological succession. *Primary succession* occurs in places where an ecosystem has never existed. For example, in 1963, a new volcanic island named Surtsey emerged from the North Atlantic near Iceland. The surface of the tiny island was initially barren volcanic rock and ash. The process of primary succession soon began, as seeds washing ashore or carried by the wind

reached the island and resulted in the first plants taking root on the island.

The stages of succession follow a certain pattern. The species that appear in the earliest stages are those that tend to be smaller, grow faster, require fewer resources, and thrive in an environment where there is little competition from other species. These are pioneer species. A *pioneer species* is a hardy species that is one of the first to establish itself at the start of the process of succession. Pioneer species often include mosses and lichens.

Pioneer species prepare the way for the species that come after them in later stages of succession. When a pioneer community colonizes an area of mostly bare rock, the pioneer species break down rock to form soil. As they die and decay, they add nutrients to the soil. When other species begin to take hold in the area, they compete with and push out the pioneer species, continuing the process of succession. At each stage, competition among species causes a change in the dominant community in an area.

In later stages of succession, larger, slower-growing species replace the earlier, faster-growing species. Because these species live longer, they reproduce many times during their lifetime, giving them an advantage over species that were dominant in earlier stages of succession. As the ecosystem ages, its communities also become more diverse.

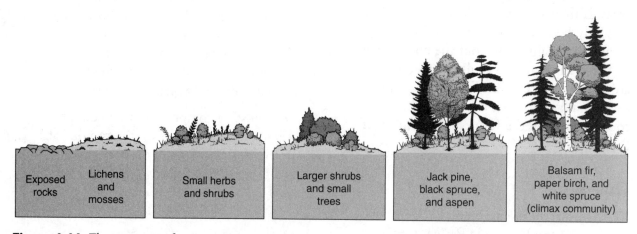

Figure 6.16 The process of primary succession happens in an area where no ecosystem existed before. Over time, bare, exposed rock is covered with a fully grown forest community.

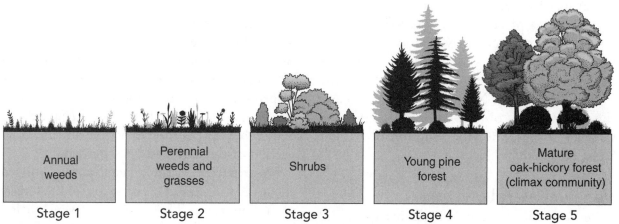

| Annual weeds | Perennial weeds and grasses | Shrubs | Young pine forest | Mature oak-hickory forest (climax community) |
| Stage 1 | Stage 2 | Stage 3 | Stage 4 | Stage 5 |

Figure 6.17 Secondary succession reconstructs an ecosystem after the original community has been disturbed or destroyed.

The process of succession continues until the ecosystem species form a climax community. A *climax community* is one that forms in the last stage of succession. If undisturbed by natural disasters such as fire and flood or by human activity, the ecosystem of a climax community will stay the same. The oak-hickory forest of Pennsylvania is a climax community, as is the beech, hemlock, and maple forest of northern Pennsylvania.

Catastrophic events, such as volcanic eruptions or tornadoes, can interrupt the process of succession at any stage. If there is a great deal of destruction, the process may have to start again from the beginning.

Secondary Succession

Secondary succession is the process that begins in an ecosystem when something has disturbed or destroyed the natural community. Secondary succession occurs in abandoned farmlands, burned or cut forests, heavily polluted streams, and areas that have been inundated by flood-waters. Secondary succession also occurs in areas where the land is being reconstructed after having been heavily mined. This occurs in many areas in Pennsylvania. The mined land is reconstructed to approximate the original contour, using the same type of topsoil and vegetation originally found on that land. As long as soil is still in the area, new vegetation quickly begins to recolonize the area.

The diagram on this page shows the stages in secondary succession that lead to a climax community of oak-hickory forest. In order to plant a field of crops, farmers cut down the original cover of oak-hickory forest. When farmers abandon a field, several stages of succession over about 150 years result in the return of the climax forest community.

Stage 1 After a farm field is abandoned, quick-growing annual weeds cover the field.

Stage 2 Perennial weeds and grasses take hold among the annual weeds, eventually crowding most of them out. Perennials are plants that die back in winter but sprout anew each spring.

Stage 3 At the next stage, shrubs dominate the ecosystem. The perennials paved the way for the shrubs, which were able to outcompete the smaller plants.

Stage 4 This stage is dominated by pine forest. The reasons for pine tree domination of shrubs include the fact that the taller pine trees can shade shrubs and deprive them of sunlight. Pine trees are also more effective at spreading their seeds than are shrubs.

Stage 5 In the last stage of secondary succession, the pines are crowded out and oak-hickory forest is dominant in the ecosystem. These trees make up the dominant species of the climax community. This oak-hickory community will remain dominant unless some natural or human-made disturbance disrupts the ecosystem.

Natural disasters often interrupt cycles such as the stages of secondary succession. These disasters can include volcanic eruptions, tornadoes, hurricanes, and floods. This was the case with natural disasters such as the fires at Yellowstone National Park in 1988 and the destruction of forests in Washington's Cascade Range after the eruption of Mount Saint Helens in 1980.

Renewal at Yellowstone

Yellowstone National Park occupies 2.2 million acres, primarily in the northwest corner of Wyoming. In 1988, the Yellowstone ecosystem included large stands of lodgepole pine that had not burned extensively for more than two centuries. That summer, lightning strikes started several dozen fires, which is normal for the park. But the combination of the driest summer in 100 years, high temperatures, and brisk winds helped spread the fires rapidly. The fires burned out of control through much of August and September. By the time they were out, about 36 percent of the park had been burned.

Many people in the general public worried about the widespread "destruction" of the forests of Yellowstone. These worries were fueled by regular media stories. However, ecologists were not particularly worried because they understood that fire is one of the natural cycles

Figure 6.18 Since the 1988 fires in Yellowstone, the ecosystem has begun repairing itself. This lodgepole pine forest is already growing grasses, small shrubs, and lodgepole saplings as part of the process of secondary succession.

of the Yellowstone ecosystem. The 1988 fires set into motion a process of secondary succession at Yellowstone that occurs naturally every 250–300 years.

After the fires were out, grasses began to poke through the ashes. Small shrubs followed and wildlife returned. In some cases, the wildlife never left. Some small burrowing animals such as mice and squirrels merely emerged from their underground homes after the fires were out. The fires did kill some animals that live aboveground in the forest but not as many as people might think. Fire is another method of natural selection—weak, injured, or sick animals are more likely to succumb to a fire. However, most of the park's large animals—bison, elk, and bears—survived because they were able to flee the burning areas. They returned quickly, along with some smaller animals. Primary consumers were especially well suited to the regenerating landscape of young grasses and the tender shoots of shrubs and trees.

More than a decade after the fires, the signs of continued succession and renewal are everywhere. Among the tall, dead trunks of burned trees, small shrubs and young lodgepole pine saplings are growing. Lodgepole pines are actually adapted to survive fire. Some of the cones of these trees burn up in fire, but others need the heat of fire to open and spread their seeds. These cones were able to help reseed the lodgepole pine forest.

If no other serious fires occur, secondary succession will continue at Yellowstone. In another 150–200 years, a dense lodgepole pine forest will again cover the landscape.

Mount Saint Helens Comeback

Volcanic eruptions are natural events that often cause devastation and can also set the process of secondary succession in motion. After a period of quiet that had lasted more than 100 years, Mount Saint Helens erupted in May 1980. When the mountain blew, a burning hot cloud of gases, ash, and rock roared down its slope, singeing and flattening thousands of acres of surrounding forest. In addition, a huge mudflow containing soil plus snow and ice melted by hot ash and gases rushed down a river in the area, inundating forests and farm fields. Thousands of animals—bears, elk, deer, birds, and more—died, along with millions of fish and several dozen people.

Succession began soon after the eruption. Surprisingly, just the next year, scientists found a few hardy insects and spiders living on the barren plains from which all other life had been wiped clean. Dead insects that had been killed by the eruption and had fallen to the ground served as their food.

During the first year after the blast, plants were dispersed by the wind and colonized barren surfaces. Millions of wind-borne seeds drifted over the area, with many taking root. In some places, patches of plants that had been shielded from the blast by unmelted snow or high ridges also survived. These plants thrived again, too. Seeds from the surviving plants were spread farther by wind and flowing water. Conifers also began to reestablish themselves.

By 1990, secondary succession had brought some plant life back to about one fifth of the barren area around the volcano. During the years that followed, several species of birds—horned larks, rock wrens, meadowlarks, and red-winged blackbirds—became more common in the area. By the late 1990s, populations of toads, frogs, and salamanders had begun to increase in many lakes and ponds in the blasted area. The eruption of Mount Saint Helens occurred in May, when snow still covered much of the area. Some aquatic animals survived the blast because they were protected by the cold water and ice-covered surfaces of ponds, lakes, or streams. Many terrestrial populations did not have this protection. Today, grasses and young trees are beginning to reestablish themselves. Barring an event like another huge eruption, the plants and animals of the forest ecosystem that once surrounded the volcanic mountain will return.

Field Study

Secondary Succession in a Schoolyard

Secondary succession begins when a community of pioneer species colonizes disturbed ground. Over time, many species come and go until a complex community forms. In this activity, you will observe the beginnings of succession on a schoolyard, in a park, in your backyard, or in a field.

Materials		
area of bare soil	string	plain sheet of white paper
meter stick	garden spade or shovel	pencil
4 wooden stakes	rake	table on page 177

Procedure

1. Choose a small area near your home or school that you can clear and observe over a two-month period.

2. Use the meter stick to measure a one-meter square portion of the area you select. Use the stakes and string to mark this plot of land.

3. Pull up any weeds or small plants growing in the plot.

4. Use the spade or shovel to turn the soil over to remove any stray bits of vegetation.

5. Break up clumps of dirt with the rake, and then smooth out the surface of the soil. Do not pack it down.

6. Draw a map of your plot and the area around it. Include the locations of items nearby, such as trees, large rocks, bodies of water, buildings, or parking lots.

7. Observe your plot once or twice a week for two months. Record the types and estimated number of each plant species that you find growing in the plot each week.

8. As each new species appears, describe it and draw conclusions about its effect on the plot.

Conclusions

1. Identify the pioneer species that colonized your plot.

2. Identify the biotic and abiotic factors that impacted the colonization of your plot.

3. How does your plot compare with the area surrounding it? Is it a mature or an immature ecosystem? Explain your answer.

Data Table

Type of Plant	Number Observed	How Plant Affects Area

4. After two months have passed, does the pioneer community look as if an intermediate community is replacing it? If so, identify species that make up the intermediate community.

For Discussion

1. Could natural events create the type of disruption that you caused when you cleared the plot of land for this activity? Could other human activities cause it? Explain your answer.

2. Consider the following statement: Farmers keep an ecosystem at an early stage of succession. In your opinion, is this true? Why or why not?

Extensions

1. Study the maps, observations, and conclusions of your classmates. How do their results compare with yours? How can you account for differences in the sequences of appearances of species, the types of species, and the number of species that colonized their plots?

2. Write a report on the succession that occurred after the eruption of Mount Saint Helens. What were the pioneer species? What types of plants would you expect to colonize the area in the future?

Effects of Human Activities on Ecosystems

Coal mining began in Pennsylvania in the 1700s and is still an important economic activity in the state. The state is among the leading coal producers in the United States and is the only state that mines anthracite coal. Anthracite is the most valued type of coal because of its high energy content and the fact that it burns more cleanly than other types of coal.

The effects of hundreds of years of coal mining in Pennsylvania are mixed. Coal mining has provided jobs and an economic boost to many areas of the state. Pennsylvania's coal mines have also provided an important natural resource for the iron, steel, and electric power industries. But the acid and other toxic compounds that leak from abandoned mines have polluted more than 2,400 miles of the state's streams, seeping into soil and contaminating groundwater supplies. Many people consider this the state's biggest environmental problem.

Acid mine drainage is a toxic discharge that forms when the mineral pyrite, which occurs in most coal seams, is exposed to air and water during mining. Acid mine drainage makes water more acidic and coats stream bottoms with iron hydroxide. Acidic streams can become unsuitable for many native species. Aquatic species are often tolerant of water within only a narrow pH range. When pollution creates a more acidic environment, many species cannot survive, which disrupts aquatic ecosystems.

Although much work remains, Pennsylvania has passed many laws since the late 1980s to curb the worst effects of acid mine drainage. The state has also spent tens of millions of dollars to build more than a dozen facilities to treat acid mine drainage discharges. The Pennsylvania Department of Environmental Protection is now forbidden to issue a mining permit for any operation that could cause acid mine drainage.

Questions

1. What causes acid mine drainage?

2. Explain how acid mine drainage harms ecosystems.

3. Has Pennsylvania responded to the effects of acid mine drainage? Explain.

Lesson Review

1. Define ecological succession.

2. Contrast primary and secondary succession.

3. Contrast pioneer and climax communities in ecosystems.

4. Put the following stages in secondary succession to an oak-hickory forest in the correct order: climax oak-hickory forest; abandoned farm field; pine forest; weeds and grasses are dominant; shrubs become dominant.

5. List three natural disasters that can set secondary succession in motion.

6. List two ways in which new plant life can take root on newly barren ground.

7. Infer how Earth's surface would be different if the process of secondary succession did not occur.

Chapter 7

Threatened, Endangered, and Extinct Species

Figure 7.1 Dinosaurs have been extinct for 65 million years, yet fossils and skeletal remains provide evidence of their existence.

Just how many species are on Earth? So far, scientists have identified about 1.75 million of them. There could be as many as 100 million or more species on the planet, but no one really knows for sure.

Species appear and disappear all the time. Some, like the dinosaurs, vanish suddenly. A catastrophe—perhaps the impact of a gigantic object from space—may have helped wipe out the dinosaurs 65 million years ago. Although people were not around to record the event, the dinosaurs left behind fossil evidence that they were here.

Unlike the dinosaurs, most species disappear without notice. In fact, scientists estimate that 99.9 percent of all the species that have ever lived on Earth are now extinct. An *extinct* species is one that no longer exists. Although extinction is a natural process, human activity—such as releasing pollution—has accelerated the rate of extinction of species, which will affect world ecosystems in ways that we cannot possibly foresee.

As you will recall from Chapter 6, each species in an ecosystem has a particular niche, or role to play. When human actions prematurely remove a species from an ecosystem, they eliminate what that organism does to keep the ecosystem functioning. Remember that we have not identified most of the species on Earth, and we don't know the niches of many of the species that we have identified.

When we lose species, we also can lose key elements that keep Earth's natural systems operating and balanced. We might lose animals that help cycle nutrients through our environment or plants that provide us with food and release oxygen into the air. We also might lose organisms that could supply new medicines and foods. Important drugs such as the antibiotics penicillin and tetracycline come from plants or microorganisms, as do many medicines that fight cancer. Scientists have investigated only a small percentage of the hundreds of thousands of plant species that could possibly be used as medicines.

Every day ecologists are learning more about how ecosystems work. This knowledge could help us avoid making destructive changes that might lead to species extinction. It also could help us find ways to repair the damage to the planet that has already been done.

Lesson 7.1
Biodiversity

As you travel around the world, around the United States, or even just around Pennsylvania, you see a tremendous number of different plants and animals. That's biodiversity. *Biodiversity* refers to the great variety of organisms on Earth.

Figure 7.2 The different colors and markings of these kittens show how genetic diversity within a population can occur.

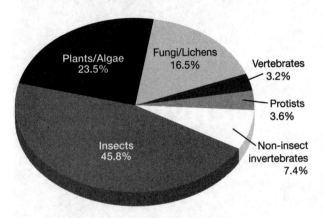

Pennsylvania Biodiversity
Estimated Species Richness of Major Groups

Plants/Algae 23.5%
Fungi/Lichens 16.5%
Vertebrates 3.2%
Protists 3.6%
Non-insect invertebrates 7.4%
Insects 45.8%

Figure 7.3 Pennsylvania's biodiversity is dominated by insect species. Mammals are included in the vertebrate category.

Scientists study biodiversity on three major levels: genetic, species, and ecosystem. In addition to the many different species that live on Earth, biodiversity involves genetic variation *within* a particular species. You can see genetic diversity clearly in human beings. All humans belong to the same species, but how many of us look exactly alike? Because of genetic diversity within the human population, physical traits such as people's height, hair color, eye color, and susceptibility to disease vary greatly. Biodiversity also involves the diversity of ecosystems. As you learned in Chapter 6, there is a great variety of ecosystems on Earth, containing different communities of living organisms that interact with the physical environment in many ways.

Scientists estimate that there are more than 20,000 different species in Pennsylvania alone. (See graph above.) In addition to the more commonly known animals, other organisms such as insects, plants, fungi, and lichens make up a large part of the biodiversity of the state. These are often the types of organisms we know the least about, especially in terms of their niches in ecosystems. Scientists in Pennsylvania are working to maintain the state's biodiversity by listing and monitoring as many Pennsylvania species as possible. An important step in conserving species and maintaining biodiversity is finding out what role each species plays in an ecosystem.

Interactions Among Organisms in an Ecosystem

Biodiversity is the foundation of ecosystem stability. The tremendous number of species with all their different roles (niches) helps an ecosystem resist disturbances and also recover when natural disasters or human interference disrupt it.

Each organism in an ecosystem plays its particular role. As you learned in Chapter 6, there is a relationship in each ecosystem among producers, consumers, and decomposers. All of the consumers (including the scavengers) depend on the producers for food, either directly (herbivores) or indirectly (carnivores). The decomposers depend on both the producers and consumers for food.

Over the last few hundred years, many large predators, such as mountain lions and wolves, have disappeared from Pennsylvania's ecosystems. In past centuries, people killed many of these animals, not realizing the positive role they played in the natural environment.

The predator-prey relationship helps keep an ecosystem in balance. In predator-prey relationships, an organism of one species (the predator) eats a living organism of a different species (the prey). Examples of predator-prey relationships include polar bears that eat fish, lions that eat zebras, red foxes that eat rabbits, and robins that eat worms. As the prey population increases, the ecosystem can support more predators. Predators feed on prey, and as the prey population decreases, the lack of sufficient numbers of prey to feed the predators causes the predator population to decrease. This cycle continues, keeping both predator and prey populations from becoming too large for the area's carrying capacity.

Predators can also be important in maintaining the health of an ecosystem. Often the weakest and the sickest individuals are easiest for predators to kill, so predator populations help keep the prey populations stronger and healthier by getting rid of their least fit members.

Other relationships in an ecosystem can also help promote stability. *Symbiosis* is a relationship in which organisms live closely together over a long period of time. Symbiosis can be parasitic, mutualistic, or commensalistic.

Parasitism is a relationship in which one species, the parasite, feeds on a second organism, the host. The parasite harms the host by living in or on it. Examples of parasitic relationships include ticks or mosquitoes that live off the blood of hosts. Bacteria that cause diseases are parasites, as are plants such as mistletoe, which grows on the trunks or branches of various types of trees. Parasitism promotes ecosystem stability in several ways, such as preventing the populations of some organisms from becoming too numerous.

In *mutualism,* both species involved in the symbiotic relationship benefit. Bees and flowers have a mutualistic relationship. Bees obtain food by feeding on the nectar of flowers. As bees feed, grains of pollen (the male reproductive cells of plants) stick to their bodies. Bees spread the pollen grains as they travel from flower to flower. This pollination of flowers is a necessary step in the reproduction of the plants.

In the plant world, lichens are also mutualistic. The lichen is actually two organisms—an alga and a fungus—that grow together. The algae undergo photosynthesis and provide food for the fungi as well as themselves. The fungi gather the water and minerals that they need and share these with the algae.

In another peculiar mutualistic relationship, oxpecker birds ride around on the backs of animals such as elephants and rhinoceroses, picking parasites off the large animals' backs. In return for the food, the birds clean the animals and sometimes warn them of approaching danger by letting out loud calls.

In the last type of symbiotic relationship, *commensalism,* one organism benefits while the other is not affected. In the tropical rain forest, the thick canopy of treetops provides too much shade for some plants to grow underneath. Plants such as the white orchid establish roots

Lab Study

Population Growth in an Aquarium

As duckweed grows, some leaves split off and form new plants. Over time, the population of duckweed can grow quite large. To illustrate a model of population growth, you will observe the growth of duckweed plants in an aquarium.

Materials		
10 duckweed plants	water	notebook
10-gallon aquarium	single-pump aerator for the aquarium	pencil

Note *Leave the aquarium light on during the whole activity. Also remember to maintain the water level in the aquarium by replacing water that is lost through evaporation.*

Procedure

1. With your partner, estimate and record the amount of time (in days, weeks, or months) that you think it will take for the duckweed to begin to reproduce.

2. Estimate the amount of time it will take for the duckweed population to double.

3. Draw a data table in your notebook such as the one on the opposite page, with columns for "Day" and "Population Size of Duckweed."

4. Every other day, count the number of duckweed plants in the aquarium. Record your data in the table. Continue this for five or six months or until the surface of the aquarium is completely covered.

5. When there are too many plants to count, create a method for estimating the percentage of the surface covered by duckweed. Follow these steps:

   a. Calculate the surface area of the aquarium in square inches.

   b. Count the number of plants in one square inch. Do this ten times, and then divide by ten to find the average number of plants per square inch.

   c. Estimate the percentage of the surface the plants cover.

   d. Estimate the population by multiplying the number of square inches by the average number of plants per square inch.

6. When the duckweed covers the surface and you have finished collecting data, draw a graph of population size versus time, using the data from your table.

Population Size of Duckweed		
Date	Population Size	Population Change Since Last Count

Conclusion

What is the shape of your graph? Determine why the graph has this shape.

For Discussion

1. If the growth of all organisms on Earth produced the same growth pattern shown by the duckweed, would the world be overpopulated with plants and animals? Explain your answer.

2. List some factors that might limit the growth of the duckweed population in a natural setting.

3. Explain why Earth's human population has grown exponentially, following the curve that you learned about in Chapter 6.

Adapted by permission from the National Association of Biology Teachers. The original activity, "Using Lemna to Study Geometric Population Growth, The American Biology Teacher" by Larry DeBuhr, appears in vol. 53, no. 4, April 1991, pp. 229–232.

high in tree branches, growing through the high canopy to reach sunlight. The orchid gets moisture from the air and precipitation and the nutrients it needs from waste that falls from the upper limbs of the trees. The tree on which the orchid lives is not harmed. Both mutualism and commensalism help one or more organisms survive by sharing resources.

When people intervene in these natural interactions by destroying habitats, killing off species, or polluting the natural environment, biodiversity often decreases. As organisms that perform specific roles in an ecosystem disappear, the natural systems that sustain life can break down, with serious consequences.

Figure 7.4 Oxpecker birds live in a mutualistic relationship with this kudu. As in the birds' relationship with rhinoceroses, they pick parasites off the kudu.

Ecosystems and Species of Concern

Plant and animal species often run into obstacles that make it difficult for them to survive. Some of these obstacles are natural, such as an unexpected storm or wildfire, but many of these problems stem from the actions of people.

When a species is in need of some type of conservation help, regardless of the reason, ecologists often call it a "species of concern." This term covers a wide range of conditions. Some species of concern have very minor problems. Those problems might require only that scientists monitor the species and its habitat to make sure that conditions do not become worse. On the other end of the scale, the term applies to species whose numbers have become so low, or whose habitats have become so degraded, that they need protection in order to survive. (See Lesson 7.3.)

A number of species of concern live in Pennsylvania. They include plants and animals that are a part of ecosystems all over the state. One animal species of concern is the bog turtle.

The bog turtle is native to many states on the east coast, from southwestern New England to Georgia. Scientists believe that the turtle exists in limited numbers in several states, including Connecticut, New Jersey, and New York. Its population is declining in Pennsylvania.

The small brown or black turtle is a reptile that lives in sphagnum bogs, marshy meadows, shrub swamps, and wet cow pastures. In times of summer inactivity, such as during very hot weather, the turtle burrows into the mud of wetland streams or crawls into empty muskrat burrows.

The female bog turtle lays between three and five eggs in May, June, July, or August—although not necessarily each year. The turtle nests in open ground areas of moss, grasses,

You Solve It! (continued)

and mud. It digs shallow holes for the eggs, usually among grasses and sedges.

The turtle eats a number of foods, depending on what is available. Its diet includes insects, worms, slugs, crayfish, and snails, as well as fruits and amphibian larvae. The turtles, as well as their eggs and young, are prey for several animals. These predators include wading birds, opossums, and raccoons. People walking through areas where bog turtles nest often trample the eggs as well. Many young bog turtles die or are killed before becoming adults.

Figure 7.5 The tiny bog turtle nests in grassy areas, where its eggs are often trampled by humans or eaten by other animals.

The loss of habitat from draining and filling of wetlands for suburban development is the major cause of the decrease in the population of bog turtles. The collection of bog turtles for sale as pets is another major threat.

To help ensure the survival of the bog turtle, the U.S. government listed it as a "threatened" species throughout most of its range in November 1997. However, the bog turtle is in such danger of extinction in Pennsylvania that it has been moved up from threatened to endangered on the Pennsylvania list. A threatened or endangered status allows the government to protect the turtle and its habitat.

Questions

1. Identify the habitat of the bog turtle.

2. Summarize the bog turtle's niche.

3. What caused the bog turtle to become endangered in Pennsylvania and threatened throughout the United States?

4. Describe how the loss of the bog turtle could affect other animals in the same ecosystem.

5. What could be the effect on ecosystems if other turtle species, such as the snapping turtle, box turtle, or wood turtle, declined in number or became extinct?

Lesson Review

1. Explain why the removal of a species from an ecosystem could be harmful to the ecosystem.

2. Define biodiversity, and explain its importance.

3. Describe a predator-prey relationship. Identify one predator-prey relationship.

4. Define symbiosis, and list its three forms.

5. Analyze the three types of symbiosis, and determine which one benefits the greatest number of organisms in an ecosystem. Explain your answer.

Lesson 7.2

Adaptations

Every organism has adaptations that allow it to survive in its particular environment. An *adaptation* is a special modification or characteristic that helps an organism better survive in its environment, and which typically develops over time or may be passed down from one generation to another.

Some adaptations are structural, or physical. Desert plants have leaves with thick, wax-coated surfaces that prevent moisture loss in the hot, dry climate. Large predator birds, such as bald eagles, have keen eyesight and are capable of flying at great speeds in order to catch prey.

Other adaptations are behavioral or concern the actions of animals or plants or the way they respond to stimuli. For example, an animal that cannot regulate its internal temperature, such as a lizard or snake, sits in the sun on cool days to warm itself. It retreats to its burrow to keep cool when the weather is hottest. Some birds migrate south at the end of summer to find their winter feeding grounds.

Structural Adaptations

A *structural adaptation* is a physical characteristic that helps an organism survive in its environment. The simplest structural adaptations help animals perform basic tasks, such as moving or eating. Most animals that move around on land have legs. Those that live in water have fins and flippers to move from place to place. Meat-eating animals have sharp incisors for killing and tearing apart prey. Animals that eat a diet of plants and seeds have large, flat teeth that allow them to grind plants into pieces that are easily swallowed.

Although species within similar biomes differ, the species within those biomes tend to have the same types of structural adaptations. For instance, plants in Australia's Great Simpson Desert and in North America's Sonoran Desert, although thousands of miles apart, would have the same types of adaptations.

Structural adaptations often evolve to overcome difficult environmental conditions. Plants that grow in the deep shade of tropical forests can have very large, dark green leaves that increase their ability to catch any light that reaches the forest floor. Some desert animals, such as the desert fox, have large ears through which they let off excess body heat.

Some animals and plants use the adaptation of camouflage to blend in with their surroundings and avoid predators. The white fur of the Arctic hare and the white winter coat of the rock ptarmigan help these animals blend in with their snowy surroundings. The chameleon is a lizard that changes its color to match whatever it happens to be crawling over or sitting on at the

Figure 7.6 Herbivores, such as this zebra, have large, flat teeth that grind plants and leaves. Carnivores, such as this tiger, have long sharp incisors that allow them to kill their prey and tear the meat from the bones.

Figure 7.7 The African stone plant (center) has the same coloring, shape, and texture as the stones around it to avoid detection.

time. The African stoneplant looks just like a pile of stones, which helps it avoid detection.

Mimicry is another adaptation, in which one species copies the appearance or behavior of another species. The viceroy butterfly protects itself by looking like the monarch butterfly, which birds avoid because of its bad taste.

Some structural adaptations decrease competition among species. If a group of different species lives in a certain habitat and eats almost the same type of food, small structural differences may ensure that the species' niches are different to prevent competition. A group of birds may develop beaks of slightly different sizes and shapes to allow them to feed on different insects, nuts, seeds, and fruits.

Some species have structural adaptations that help them avoid becoming prey. Speed can be a useful tool for both predator and prey. Antelopes can run fast to escape predators, but in contrast, the cheetah has speed that allows it to overtake its prey. Rosebushes protect themselves with thorns, and turtles have hard shells into which they can retreat for safety. The porcupine has sharp quills that protect it against enemies. Perhaps the strangest structural adaptation for avoiding predators involves actually losing a part of the body. When under attack, the glass lizard will break off its own tail. While the still-moving tail distracts the predator, the lizard has a chance to get away. The lizard usually grows another tail. Some animals have chemical defenses. The bombardier beetle squirts a hot, irritating chemical at predators. The skunk also sprays a smelly substance into the face of an approaching enemy.

Behavioral Adaptations

A *behavioral adaptation* is the way an organism acts or responds to its environment in order to survive. Some of these behaviors are reflexive and others are instinctive.

Reflexive Behaviors A *reflex* is a behavior that is triggered automatically by something outside an organism. The behavior (or action) happens without the organism's thinking about it, such as when you pull your hand back quickly after accidentally touching something that's too hot. Reflexes cause animals to blink or recoil when a bright light shines in their eyes or when an object moves toward their face. They might run when they suddenly hear a loud noise.

Instinctive Behaviors An *instinct* is a behavior that an organism carries out because it is genetically prone to do so. Instincts are not learned behaviors, but are natural reactions for members of a species.

Many behavioral adaptations help a species avoid predators. For example, some animals,

Figure 7.8 The viceroy (top) mimics the foul-tasting monarch (bottom) for protection.

Figure 7.9 The blowfish puffs itself up with air (top) to look larger and more threatening to predators than it does at its original size (bottom).

such as rabbits and rodents, hide in holes or burrows in the ground. Many animals, such as raccoons, rest during the day and come out to look for food at night, when they are less visible to predators. Some species—schools of fish, herds of antelopes and caribou, and flocks of birds—travel and live in groups because there is safety in numbers. Wolves are adapted to hunting in packs so that they can more easily trap and capture their prey. To look bigger and more frightening, a blowfish expands its body with air. Still other animals will play dead to escape predators. The opossum sometimes goes limp when it is under attack. The predator will often suspend the attack, giving the opossum the chance to escape.

Other behavioral adaptations help an animal survive shortages of food or intense heat or cold. To avoid the heat of summer, some frogs, lizards, and ground squirrels sleep through the summer in a dormant state called estivation. Other animals decrease their activity during winter months in a process called hibernation. After almost constant eating during the fall to build up body fat, some bears, bats, and other animals hide themselves away during the winter. Their bodily functions slow down and they sleep until spring, when they awaken and resume full activity in the warmer weather.

Some animals migrate yearly to find more favorable climates or feeding conditions when a drop in temperature, decreased rainfall, or a scarcity of food makes their home environment too harsh. Many birds, bats, and whales migrate north to south and back again each year. Some travel short distances, but others move thousands of miles. The Arctic tern, which migrates from the Arctic to the Antarctic each year, can make a round trip of 22,000 miles. Animals migrate up and down mountain slopes, too. For example, mule deer spend summers at higher elevations on mountains and then move in winter to lower elevations where it is generally warmer and there is more shelter.

Courtship rituals are important instinctive behaviors because they encourage animal reproduction. Male birds often attract females with special songs and calls as well as their bright colors. Male fence lizards bob their heads up and down to attract female attention, and in some species of fish, males perform an intricate and precise set of movements in the water. Sometimes animals will use certain structural adaptations in addition to their behavior to attract mates. The male peacock struts (behavior), using his colorful tail feathers (structural) to get females to notice him. Male fireflies flash the bioluminescent part of their bodies (structural) off and on in a certain pattern. Female fireflies recognize it as a mating call.

Other instinctive behaviors involve raising and protecting young. Many female animals will instinctively attack any other creature that comes near their young. Bears have attacked hikers when the hikers wandered too close to the cubs. Many animals build nests for their offspring in areas where they are safe from predators. Others protect their offspring by carrying them around. Some frogs carry young tadpoles on their backs as they look for a safe area of calm water in which to leave them. Female scorpions also carry their young on their backs and defend them from predators with their venomous stingers. The killdeer, a ground-nesting bird, may fake a wing injury to try to lure predators away from its nest.

Field Study

Adaptations in the Ecosystem

Every ecosystem has a variety of plants and animals that are adapted to that particular natural environment. In this activity, you will observe a local ecosystem to determine the adaptations that make organisms well suited to living there.

Materials
plant and animal identification books
pencil
table

Procedure

1. Choose a local ecosystem to observe. You might choose to observe a part of a forest; a meadow; a pond; or the edge of a lake, river, or stream.

2. Pick five plants and five animals to observe. Identify them. If necessary, use a guidebook to help with identification.

3. List the ten species in the table.

4. Identify structural adaptations of each plant and animal that help it survive in this ecosystem. For instance, one of the animals you observe might have coloring that helps it blend in with the natural environment. This camouflage would allow the animal to hide from predators. If you need help, research the plant or animal in an encyclopedia or other reference book. Then try to observe any adaptations you discover through your research.

5. Identify any behavioral adaptations you observe or learn about through your research.

6. List the adaptations you find in the table.

7. List in the table the way each adaptation helps the particular plant or animal.

Conclusions

1. What type of ecosystem did you observe?

2. List the most common adaptations you found among the plants and animals you observed.

For Discussion

1. Explain how the adaptations you observed in the plants and animals help them survive in this ecosystem.

2. Describe the niche of one of the organisms.

Extension

Observe plant and animal adaptations in a completely different type of local ecosystem. Compare and contrast the way organisms evolved to survive in the two different types of environments.

The Endangered Indiana Bat

The Indiana bat was once widespread throughout much of the East and the Midwest regions of the United States. However, the severe decline of the bat's population throughout its range, including Pennsylvania, led to its designation as "endangered" in March 1967.

The medium-sized brown bat lives in forested areas, often near rivers and creeks, where it feeds on insects. Most bats move to the southerly part of their range in August. The bats then feed from September through November, until it is time for hibernation. The bat spends winters in cool, damp limestone caves (primarily in West Virginia, Indiana, and Illinois) hanging upside down in clusters of several individuals. In March, most bats leave their winter caves and head for the northerly part of their range.

The Indiana bat usually mates during the first ten days of October. Females then bear their young in June. Each bat has just one offspring. The young bats are ready to fly and feed on their own after 25 to 37 days of development.

Several factors have contributed to the decline in the Indiana bat's population, including the disturbance of caves where they roost, their use in research, and increased insecticide poisoning.

Conservationists are now attempting to help the Indiana bat survive by creating management programs in certain areas. A major thrust of these programs is to keep people out of the caves where bats live, mate, and hibernate. Scientists have built special gates across the entrances of some caves in

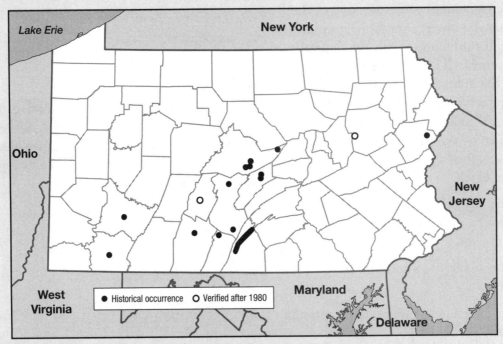

Figure 7.10 The habitat of the Indiana bat has been greatly reduced in Pennsylvania. Only two sites have been verified since 1980.

You Solve It! (continued)

an attempt to aid their survival. Government agencies also have attempted to purchase private land that contains caves where the bats hibernate. They hope that this will help increase the species' numbers.

Figure 7.11 The Indiana bat lives, mates, and hibernates in caves. To hibernate, the bats hang upside down in groups as shown in this photo.

Questions

1. List two behavioral adaptations that help the Indiana bat survive in winter.

2. Choose one adaptation from question 1. Infer how it helps increase the bat's chance of survival.

3. The Indiana bat travels in colonies between winter and summer homes. How does traveling in groups increase its chance of survival?

4. Explain why the Indiana bat would be more susceptible to harm from insecticides than would individuals of some other species.

5. Draw conclusions about why government agencies would prefer to purchase lands that contain critical bat caves rather than leave the caves in private hands.

6. The Indiana bat tends to congregate in large numbers in caves. How could this behavioral characteristic actually help *decrease* the bat's population?

Lesson Review

1. Define an adaptation.

2. Define the niche of a specific organism, and explain the structural and behavioral adaptations that help that organism live in its environment.

3. Contrast reflexive and instinctive behaviors.

4. Determine whether camouflage is a structural or behavioral adaptation. Explain your answer.

5. Infer what happens to animals that are not well adapted for their environment.

6. The anglerfish lives in the deepest part of the ocean, where it is always completely dark. The anglerfish uses a bioluminescent (light-producing) appendage that extends from its head to attract prey. Is this adaptation structural or behavioral? Explain your answer.

Lesson 7.3
Survival of the Fittest

Which is more likely to survive in the cold, snowy climate of northern Alaska: a gray rabbit with short fur, or a white rabbit with long, thick fur? The white rabbit with long, thick fur is obviously more likely to survive. This rabbit's color allows it to blend into its natural environment, and its thick fur helps it endure the cold. Species, or individuals within species, that are most fit for their natural environment have the best chance of survival.

English naturalist Charles Darwin observed this characteristic of the natural environment in the mid-1800s. Darwin said that populations of organisms change over time in response to the needs placed on them by the natural environments in which they live. In other words, individuals with the inherited characteristics that are most helpful for survival actually live and reproduce. This is adaptation, which often occurs through what Darwin called natural selection. *Natural selection* is the process that makes it more likely that organisms with the best characteristics for survival in a specific environment will survive, reproduce, and pass on their advantageous genetic traits to offspring. That's why, using the example above, most of the rabbits in a cold, snowy area of Alaska will probably have thick, white fur. Individuals with these characteristics survive, but most of those with short, gray fur are killed by predators or cannot endure the cold.

Populations evolve so that the most advantageous adaptations become common. For this to happen, however, three things must be true. First, the potential adaptation in question must be a trait that varies within a species. For example, there are variations in the color and length of fur among the population of rabbits mentioned above. Second, the adaptation—in this case, fur color and length—must be one that parents can pass to offspring genetically. Third, one version of the adaptation must benefit the members that have it in a way that lets them survive and reproduce more than individuals who do not have the adaptation. In this case, heavy, white, long fur is more of a benefit than short, dark fur. So individuals possessing the genes for white, long fur survive to reproduce more than individuals without these traits.

Remember that adaptations happen to a population over time. Some occur fairly quickly, but others develop only over millions of years.

Human Impact on Some Pennsylvania Species

Natural selection plays a large role in maintaining Earth's biodiversity by stocking populations with individuals that are most likely to survive in a particular environment. The activities of people can affect species, too, but some of those impacts are negative. For example, destroying habitat or polluting rivers and lakes can disrupt ecosystems. Species of plants and animals can be displaced or die. However, people also can have a positive impact on the survival of species. In many instances, scientists are working to undo some of the damage already done.

Scientists have come up with several methods to protect wildlife and maintain biodiversity. One method is to protect whole ecosystems, thereby conserving the plants and animals within them. The U.S. government has set aside more than 90 million acres of land in more than 450 wildlife refuges to protect species in their natural habitats. The nation's first national wildlife refuge was set up in Florida in 1903 to protect the dwindling population of the brown pelican.

Another method is to protect specific species that are endangered. The government protects habitat critical to the species' survival. In some cases, individuals may be bred in captivity (in zoos or research centers) and then returned into the wild. Captive breeding and reintroduction programs, goals of the Endangered Species Act, have been important in increasing the populations of endangered birds such as the bald eagle and the California condor.

Case Study

A Case of Adaptation to Pollution

In the mid-1800s, two varieties of peppered moths lived in the English midlands. One variety was light gray with brown speckles, and the other was dark gray.

In the early part of the century, before the Industrial Revolution brought coal-burning factories to the area, the light-colored moth was the most common variety. However, something peculiar began to happen as time passed. As factories spewed more dark soot into the air in and near cities in this part of England, dark gray moths became more common and light-colored moths became rarer. Scientists believe that the change in moth populations in response to pollution is a case of natural selection at work.

Research showed that before coal-burning factories became common in the area, tree trunks were normal in color—typically brown or gray, sometimes with a growth of green moss or lichens. When light-colored moths rested on these trunks, they blended in with their surroundings. Because they were harder to spot, more of these light-colored moths survived than the dark-colored moths, which were easy for predators to see. Because the genetic trait for light color was "selected" as advantageous in this environment, this genetic trait was passed on most often.

After the factories had been in operation for several years, the pollution from their smoke-stacks took its toll on the natural environment in the area. There were no laws in those days to monitor amounts of pollution, so black soot from the factories was heavy in the air of many cities, coating the outsides of buildings and the trunks of trees. As the coal soot blackened the trunks of trees near the factories, moths with dark coloring suddenly had a genetic trait that allowed them to be effectively camouflaged against the darker

Figure 7.12 The Industrial Revolution caused trees to become blackened, increasing the population of the dark-colored moth.

tree trunks. The dark-colored moth eventually became more common than the light-colored moth in these areas. Because of a change in the natural environment, the trait that ensured better survival changed. As a result, a different variety of the moth became more common.

Questions

1. Identify the type of moth that was more plentiful before the Industrial Revolution.

2. Identify the type of moth that became more plentiful after the Industrial Revolution.

3. Describe the environmental conditions that changed the more numerous type of moth near the factories.

4. Summarize the way the moth population adapted to the change in environmental conditions.

5. Predict how the population would have adapted had the factories all shut down for several years after they had been operating.

A third approach manages certain species that are hunted as game to ensure that their populations remain fairly stable. For example, laws restrict when hunters can kill the animals and how many they can kill. International treaties protect game species that cross national boundaries.

The bald eagle, which is native to Pennsylvania, is a well-known example of how people can almost wipe out a species but then work hard to undo the harm that was done.

When Europeans first settled in North America, bald eagles were common in every state but Hawaii. Six years after the Declaration of Independence was written, there were as many as 100,000 nesting bald eagles in what we now know as the lower 48 states. By the 1970s, there were fewer than 3,000.

Unregulated hunting and habitat destruction took a toll on bald eagle populations, but the major reason for the decline was the use of pesticides. The decline of the eagle became most serious in the mid-1900s because pesticides such as DDT were sprayed in wetland areas to kill mosquitoes. Eagles ate fish from the wetlands,

and these fish were contaminated with DDT. The pesticide caused the eagles to produce eggs with shells that were too thin to remain intact and allow young eagles to develop. So many bald eagles were unable to reproduce that the population decreased dramatically. In 1967, the U.S. government listed the bald eagle as endangered in most of the lower 48 states.

After declaring the bald eagle a population in need of protection, the government put several programs into effect to increase its population. New programs protected the eagle's nesting areas. Eagles were bred in zoos and other protected environments and then released into the wild to repopulate. The government also banned the use of DDT in 1972. This allowed for the start of reintroduction programs. Consequently, the eagle population began to recover. The government was able to move the eagle from the endangered list to the threatened list in 1995. The new listing meant that the bald eagle was in less serious trouble than it had been. By 1999, the population of eagles had increased to a level at which some government scientists believed that it no longer needed

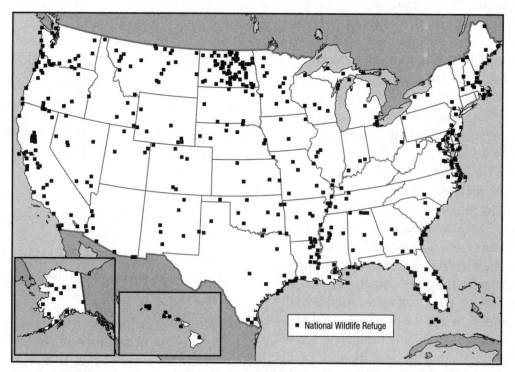

Figure 7.13 National wildlife refuges have been created across the United States to protect threatened and endangered species, as well as wildlife in general.

protection. In Pennsylvania, eagle populations are increasing, but it still remains listed as an endangered species.

The Pennsylvania Biological Survey (PABS) helps maintain the state's biodiversity by tracking and monitoring many plant and animal species, including species of concern. The organization—which is made up of scientists, representatives of state and federal agencies and major natural history museums, and private, interested citizens—began in 1979 to observe and report the status of as many of Pennsylvania's plants and animals as possible. This resulted in the 1985 publication of *Species of Special Concern in Pennsylvania*, a book with information on the well-being of 297 of Pennsylvania's species. Scientists realized that the work had to continue, and in 1988 the PABS was created as a nonprofit scientific organization to oversee the job.

The PABS coordinates a number of programs, including surveys and research on Pennsylvania wildlife as well as the production of publications for the public that explain how Pennsylvanians can best conserve the state's plant and animal life. Aside from its work on research and the monitoring of species, the PABS is now helping to develop a system of bioreserves throughout the state. These reserves will conserve Pennsylvania's many ecosystems for future enjoyment and study.

Threatened, Endangered, and Extinct Species

The Endangered Species Act (ESA) is the U.S. law that governs the protection of species whose populations are in decline and could be in danger of extinction. The current ESA, passed in 1973, forbids the hunting, killing, collecting, or harming of species listed as endangered or threatened. The law also forbids spending federal funds on any project that would threaten a species listed under the act or disturb or destroy habitat needed for that species to survive. The law protects the habitat of endangered species and develops recovery plans for listed species as well.

Under the ESA, scientists put species into several categories of concern, depending on the seriousness of their situation.

Threatened A *threatened species* is one that still has many individuals in the wild but whose numbers are dwindling to a point at which the species could become endangered. In Pennsylvania, the rough green snake is one of many threatened species.

Endangered An *endangered species* is one that has so few individuals remaining that extinction is a possibility in the near future. The Delmarva fox squirrel is endangered in Pennsylvania.

Extinct An *extinct species* is one that no longer exists. The passenger pigeon, once common in Pennsylvania and the eastern United States, is an extinct species.

Factors That Make Some Species More Prone to Extinction

Some species are more prone to becoming threatened or endangered because of factors such as their habits, their food and habitat requirements, and their rate of reproduction. Here are a few factors that can greatly affect species survival.

Specific food requirements Some animals eat very few foods. If habitat destruction or pollution destroys these food sources, these animals become vulnerable to population decline. For example, the Australian koala eats only eucalyptus leaves. As development and natural events such as wildfires destroy eucalyptus forests, the koala has nothing else to fall back on as a food supply.

Specific habitat or nesting requirements Just as some species require very specific foods, some species live in only one area or type of area. The Kirkland's warbler is a bird that nests only in jack pine trees that are between 6 and 15 years old. The green sea turtle lays its eggs only on a few specific beaches. If the habitat of such a species disappears, the animal has nowhere else to go. In the mid-Atlantic, the destruction of specific forest areas where the Delmarva fox squirrel lives has caused a decrease in the squirrel's population. It is endangered in Pennsylvania and several other eastern states.

High on food chains or food webs Species that are highest on food chains or webs are more vulnerable to some problems, such as chemical pollution in the natural environment. This was the case with the bald eagle, which was extremely sensitive to pesticides such as DDT that accumulated in the bodies of other animals it used as food. As the eagles ate these contaminated animals, the pesticides accumulated to an even greater extent in the eagles' bodies, causing population decline.

Migration Animals that migrate are more vulnerable to environmental changes than those that do not. Migratory animals depend on more than one habitat to survive. If just one of those habitats is destroyed or changed by human activity or natural events, the animal could suffer population decline.

Reproduces at a low rate Some animals, such as elephants, bats, blue whales, polar bears, and giant pandas, have very few offspring when they do reproduce. For example, the elephant has an average of just three offspring each decade. Populations of such species grow very slowly. When pollution, habitat destruction, or hunting kills these animals, it takes a long time for their populations to bounce back. Such populations can become endangered because they cannot easily recover.

Limited habitat range Certain animal species have a very small range of distribution. They may be found in just one forest area or on a specific island. If that area undergoes habitat destruction, is ravaged by a new disease, or becomes host to a new exotic species, the native species may have trouble surviving. Hawaii has many species that are native only to those islands. As populations dwindle there, species become vulnerable to extinction because they do not exist elsewhere.

Interference with human activities Some people hunt or poison animals because they attack people, kill livestock, or ruin farm crops.

Because these animals interfere with human activities, people may find it desirable to reduce these species' populations. Wolves were eliminated throughout most of the United States because they killed cattle and people feared them. Today, there is an attempt to reintroduce the gray wolf to areas of Yellowstone and Grand Teton National Parks.

Help for Threatened and Endangered Species

The National Marine Fisheries Service and the U.S. Fish and Wildlife Service are the lead agencies in charge of proposing species that the ESA will protect. These agencies can declare a species threatened or endangered. The agencies then must prepare a plan to help the species recover. If the species does recover, the government can propose to delist it, or remove it from the list of threatened or endangered species. Delisting means that the species is no longer in need of protection. That's what happened in 1999 when the government proposed delisting the bald eagle. Some people disagree with this move, so for now, the bald eagle is still listed as threatened. The peregrine falcon has been federally delisted, although it remains on some states' lists.

Some scientists estimate that human activities have accelerated the rate of species extinction to between 1,000 and 10,000 times the natural rate. We still don't know the ultimate consequences of this loss of biodiversity. However, the ESA has been helpful in halting the decline of many species, although not all of them. For instance, not all species in danger are protected under the ESA. What's more, the populations of some species that are listed have not yet bounced back. Improving conditions for many endangered species could take several decades. However, many scientists consider the act a success because the condition of about 40 percent of the species listed under the ESA has either stabilized or improved.

Help for the Vulnerable Barn Owl

Figure 7.14 The barn owl is a small owl with a white face and breast and light brown wings, back, and head.

Although it is not yet listed as threatened or endangered, the barn owl population in the northeastern United States has been declining. The primary reasons for the decline are the loss of dense grasslands where the barn owl hunts for food and the shortage of available nesting areas, such as abandoned farm silos and barns.

Barn owls usually eat small mammals such as meadow voles, shrews, mice, and rats. They are largely nocturnal and hunt for food in dense grassy environments such as meadows, lightly grazed pastures, hayfields, and marshes. The barn owl uses its keen hearing to locate prey moving through tall grass where it can't be easily seen.

Because of the shortage of nesting spaces for the owl, scientists in states such as Pennsylvania are helping the birds by providing nest boxes. Nest box programs have helped increase or

stabilize barn owl populations in many areas. The Pennsylvania Game Commission has placed nest boxes in some areas to ensure that the birds can find places to raise young. Nest boxes can be platforms placed inside silos and barns or enclosed boxes mounted on posts or utility poles.

Conservation of grassland habitats is also an important factor in stabilizing the population of barn owls. The ecosystems of dense grass are habitats for animals that the birds use for food. Development of the grasslands destroys the barn owl's food supply. This reduction in the habitats of the owl's prey is a major reason for the decline of the owl population.

Because the meadow vole is a major part of the barn owl's diet, conservation of this prey species will also help ensure the survival of the barn owl.

Figure 7.15 Nest boxes provide shelter in which young barn owls can be raised and may include a platform on which the young owls can exercise.

You Solve It! *(continued)*

Biologists suggest that in the future, increased monitoring of the population of barn owls and their nesting sites will be necessary. Scientists also believe that farmers would be more inclined to conserve the grasslands the owls need if they were educated about the owls' ability to catch rodents.

Questions

1. Describe the barn owl's habitat.

2. Explain why biologists are concerned about barn owl populations.

3. What has Pennsylvania done to help protect the barn owl and increase its population?

4. What would monitoring barn owl populations and nesting sites accomplish?

5. How might the ecosystem in which the barn owl lives be affected if the bird were to become extinct?

Lesson Review

1. Summarize the idea of natural selection. Who proposed the idea?

2. What three conditions must exist before natural selection can change a species population?

3. How does natural selection affect species adaptations?

4. Identify the law that governs the protection of species that are endangered or threatened in the United States.

5. Contrast the status of a threatened species with the status of an endangered species.

6. Is the case of the endangered bald eagle a success story? Explain your answer.

7. In your opinion, should the bald eagle be delisted? Why or why not?

8. What is the Pennsylvania Biological Survey, and why is it important?

9. Using one of the animals featured in this chapter as an example, explain how management practices are affecting the success of the species.

Chapter 8

Humans and the Environment

What's the fastest-growing city in the United States according to the 2000 census? New York? Los Angeles? Houston? Philadelphia? The answer is none of the above—it's Las Vegas, Nevada. Las Vegas grew 84 percent between 1990 and 2000, compared with a growth rate of 13 percent for the United States as a whole.

There's just one problem with that much growth in a place like Las Vegas: Las Vegas is in the middle of a desert. People like the climate because it's warm and the sun shines a lot, but it hardly ever rains in Las Vegas. The area gets only about 4 inches of rain each year.

However, even in dry places like Las Vegas, people need water to drink, cook, bathe, and wash clothing. Because water is always there when they turn on the tap, people in dry places such as Las Vegas have learned to live as if they were in a wet environment such as Pennsylvania. Two thirds of home water use in Las Vegas maintains green lawns in the middle of a desert.

Las Vegas gets its water from Lake Mead, a huge reservoir that was created when the Hoover Dam was built across the Colorado River several decades ago. Las Vegas is allowed a certain percentage of the water from the lake and the river, but that allotment is not enough to sustain the city's rapid growth. As Las Vegas continues to grow, the city will need to reach out to get more and more water from other places—places that one day might not want to or be able to share this precious resource.

Figure 8.1 Las Vegas is situated in the middle of the desert, yet many of its people want green lawns. Two thirds of the water used in Las Vegas is used to water lawns.

How long can a city like Las Vegas grow without the water resources to support the growth? Are there limits to the amount of water that the city can capture from other areas? Should we concentrate growth in areas that already have the natural resources to support that growth? Should growth be continued in areas that do not have the resources needed to sustain that growth? These are questions that must be considered as Earth's population continues to grow.

As you learned in Chapter 7, plants and animals must adapt to their natural environment or perish. People have the technology to adapt the environment to fit human needs. In many places around the world, human activities are changing ecosystems to suit human needs. The short-term effect is to make our lives more comfortable and give us the goods we want, such as cars, computers, and microwave ovens—not to mention green lawns in the desert. However, the long-term effect is something we don't yet know.

Lesson 8.1
Society and the Sustainability of Earth's Resources

When we turn on the tap, water pours out. When we flip a switch, the lights go on, the air conditioner starts to hum, or the furnace starts to burn fuel to keep us warm. Each of these processes that are designed to keep us comfortable depends on natural resources. As you learned in Chapter 2, some of these resources are renewable, which means that they will not run out. Renewable energy sources include wind, solar, and hydroelectric power. However, many other resources that we depend on are non-renewable. Nonrenewable resources exist in finite amounts in Earth's crust and will run out someday. Nonrenewable energy resources include coal, oil, natural gas, and uranium used for nuclear power. Many of the important mineral resources we use, such as iron, copper, and nickel, are also nonrenewable and will run out.

Worldwide energy reserves, the amount of usable energy resources such as coal and oil left in the ground, are especially critical to people today. Our way of life, especially in developed countries such as the United States, is based in part on the availability of fairly cheap energy and other natural resources. These resources allow us to drive cars, fly in airplanes, heat homes, and have enough electricity for all of our household needs. However, the majority (more than 85 percent) of the energy we use in the United States comes from burning fossil fuels such as coal, oil, and natural gas. Coal supplies

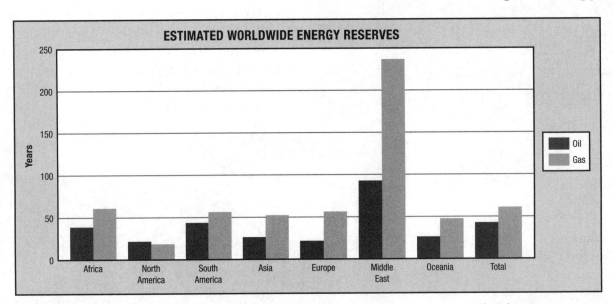

Figure 8.2 This graph shows how long worldwide energy reserves are expected to last based on present consumption levels. At the current rate of consumption, North America's reserves will be depleted more quickly than those on any other continent.

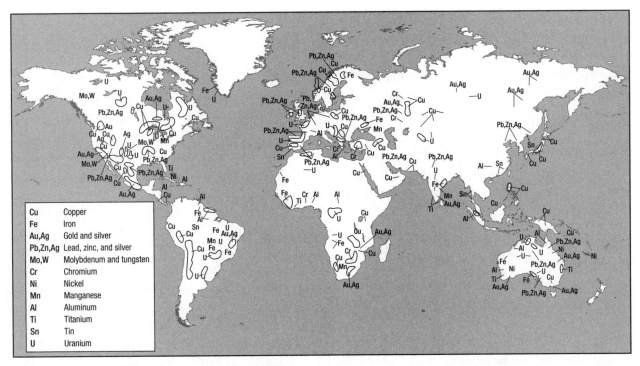

Cu	Copper
Fe	Iron
Au,Ag	Gold and silver
Pb,Zn,Ag	Lead, zinc, and silver
Mo,W	Molybdenum and tungsten
Cr	Chromium
Ni	Nickel
Mn	Manganese
Al	Aluminum
Ti	Titanium
Sn	Tin
U	Uranium

Figure 8.3 Natural resources are unevenly distributed throughout the world. Developed countries have the wealth and equipment to access these resources. Other countries—which may be less developed, poor, or war-torn—may not be able to access and benefit from their resources.

could last for hundreds of years at the present rates of consumption. But, as the graph on page 200 shows, oil and natural gas supplies could run out before the end of this century if consumption remains the same or increases. As our consumption of electric power and fuels for running motor vehicles increases, finding new natural resources that we can use to provide energy has become more important.

Distribution and Use of Natural Resources

If you look at the map above, which shows the location of major resources, it's easy to see that resources are very unevenly distributed over Earth's surface. Some countries, such as the United States, Canada, Brazil, and Australia, have many types of resources, but others, such as Colombia, Italy, Pakistan, and Sudan, have few if any major resource deposits of great value. The situation is the same with fossil fuels. One nation, Saudi Arabia, has 24 percent of the world's petroleum reserves, but many countries must import all of the oil they use.

There is also uneven consumption of resources. Developed countries such as the United States use a greater percentage of Earth's resources per person than do undeveloped countries. For example, with only about 5 percent of Earth's population, the United States uses about 24 percent of Earth's commercial energy resources. Contrast this with a developing country such as India. With 17 percent of Earth's population, India uses just 2 percent of Earth's supply of commercial energy.

Indians consume fewer resources and produce less waste per person than do people in the United States, at least at the moment. However, India is one of a number of rapidly developing countries. Others include China (with a population of more than one billion people) and Thailand. Impact on resource use is dependent not only on population but also on how much each person conserves.

As people in developing countries move forward economically and their personal wealth increases, their rates of resource consumption will increase as well. As millions of additional people purchase more TV sets, cars, cell phones, and computers and use more water and electricity, the impact of a country such as India on resources and ecosystems will increase. Its impact on the environment, through production of wastes and pollution, will increase as well.

Resources Without Wealth

Some countries have resources but still cannot meet their resource needs because of political and economic problems. This is the case in the West African countries of Angola and Guinea-Bissau and the Central Asian country of Uzbekistan.

Angola has rich deposits of oil, diamonds, and other valuable minerals, but Angola's people are very poor. Most of them will not live past the age of 47 because of malnutrition, unsafe drinking water, and lack of adequate health care. Because of the country's reserves of important resources, Angola should be able to raise the standard of living for its people. However, a civil war tore Angola apart for more than 25 years, forcing one third of the people of Angola to flee the fighting. They were unable to farm or live stable lives. While the people of Angola suffered, the diamond mines and oil wells kept operating. The country's leadership used much of the money received from selling these resources to buy weapons. Some of the money disappeared because of corruption.

Guinea-Bissau is also a poor nation, but it has mineral resources, such as petroleum and phosphates. Civil war has damaged Guinea-Bissau's economy as well, and the nation has no money to pay the high cost of getting the resources out of the ground. The nation may be able to tap into offshore oil reserves in the future, but today, Guinea-Bissau's economy depends on exporting small amounts of fish and agricultural products.

In Uzbekistan, there are substantial deposits of oil, natural gas, gold, and copper. The country does extract some of these resources, but much less than it could because the government does not have the money for more extensive projects. There is also a lack of foreign investment because of a tightly controlled economy and political repression.

Conservation of Resources

Worldwide demand for natural resources is high, especially in developed nations such as the United States. Because most resource supplies are finite, resource conservation is necessary. *Conservation* is the careful use of a resource so that its supply will last longer.

People in the United States in particular can contribute a great deal to sustaining Earth's resources by practicing conservation. As you just read, the United States has only about 5 percent of Earth's population, but people in the United States use about 24 percent of the Earth's commercial energy and 27 percent of the Earth's supply of wood. Per capita paper consumption in the United States is about 739 pounds per year, but China and India, with larger populations, consume about 60 pounds and less than 9 pounds per year, respectively. People in the United States use more water per capita than do people in other countries. Each person in the United States also uses more than 18,000 pounds of nonfuel minerals each year.

There are many conservation methods that can slow resource consumption; preserve crucial resources; and decrease the impact of resource extraction, processing, transportation, and manufacturing on the environment. These methods include source reduction, reuse of products, and recycling, as you learned in Chapter 2. Conservation methods also include the use of more energy-efficient appliances at home and more efficient machinery in manufacturing processes. Purchasing cars that get better gas mileage and using water more efficiently are also ways to conserve. Soil conservation is important for maintaining the topsoil fertility necessary to grow food. Forest conservation not only preserves trees as resources but also allows them to play other important roles, such as protecting watersheds, preventing soil erosion, and preserving wildlife habitat.

Making a Difference

Every individual has the power to conserve resources and decrease the negative effects of resource use on the environment. As an added bonus, conservation often saves money in the long term. For example, replacing the incandescent light bulbs most of us use in lamps and other light fixtures with more energy-efficient fluorescent bulbs costs more at the outset. However, as with many other appliances, spending a bit more for the energy-efficient product saves money in operating costs over the lifetime of the product. In other words, energy-efficient products may cost more to buy but less to use. For example, a fluorescent bulb lasts up to ten times as long as an incandescent bulb and uses 75 percent less energy. Replacing just one fourth of the lights you use most often with fluorescents can save about 50 percent of your household's lighting energy bill.

Here are some additional ways to conserve around the house.

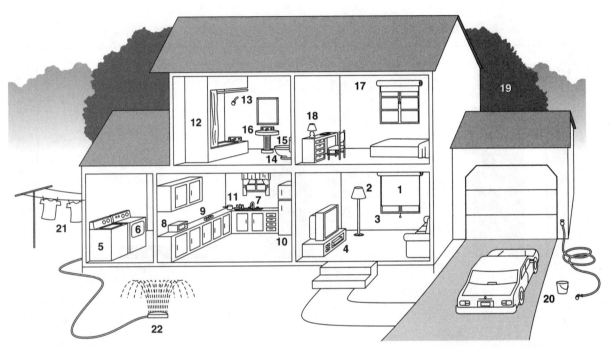

Living Room

1 **Curtains/pulled shades** Leave curtains or shades on south-facing walls open to let light and warmth in during the winter; keep them closed to keep heat out in the summer.

2 **Lamp** Replace incandescent bulbs with fluorescents.

3 **Sun/window** On bright days, let the sun light rooms instead of turning on lights.

4 **VCR in living room** Look for the Energy Star label when buying electrical appliances. These appliances exceed energy standards by 13 to 20 percent.

Laundry Room

5 **Washer** Wash clothes in cold water and wash only full loads to save water and energy.

6 **Dryer** Clean the dryer lint filter after each load to improve dryer efficiency.

7 **Faucet** Remind adults to repair leaky faucets, which can waste up to 20 gallons of water per day.

Kitchen

8 **Toaster oven** Use a toaster oven, which can use up to 50 percent less energy, for small items instead of the oven.

9 **Containers on kitchen counter** Bring lunch to school in reusable containers instead of foil and plastic wrap.

10 **Refrigerator** Keep cold water in the refrigerator instead of running tap water until it is cold.

11 **Kitchen sink** Hand-wash dishes in a tub filled with water. An open tap lets about 5 gallons of water go down the drain every two minutes.

Bathroom

12 **Shower** Take brief showers instead of baths to use less water and energy.

13 **Showerhead** A low-flow showerhead saves a couple of gallons of water every minute.

14 **Toilet** A displacement device (such as a brick) in the toilet tank can save 1 to 5 gallons of water per flush.

15 **Sink** Do not pour hazardous household chemicals down toilets or drains. Take them to hazardous waste collection centers.

16 **Bathroom sink** Shut the water off while brushing teeth or lathering your face with soap.

Bedroom

17 **Overhead light** Turn off lights in rooms you are not using.

18 **Small lamp** Use small lamps to light just the area you are using instead of an overhead fixture that lights the whole room.

Outside

19 **Trees** Leafy deciduous trees help save energy by sheltering a home from solar rays in summer and letting solar warmth through in winter when branches are bare.

20 **Bucket of water** Use a bucket of water to wash cars instead of running a hose.

21 **Clothesline** Dry clothing outside on a clothesline on warm days instead of using the clothes dryer.

22 **Sprinkler** If you must water lawns, do so early in the morning or late in the afternoon to reduce waste through evaporation.

Sustainable Energy Use in Pennsylvania?

Sustainable energy uses renewable energy sources in ways that minimize the damage to the environment or the depletion of the energy source. The bar graphs and text below show some recent facts and figures for energy use in Pennsylvania. Use them to answer the questions that follow.

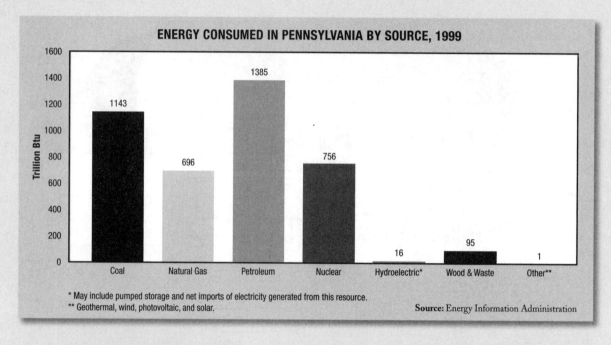

ENERGY CONSUMED IN PENNSYLVANIA BY SOURCE, 1999

Trillion Btu

Source	Value
Coal	1143
Natural Gas	696
Petroleum	1385
Nuclear	756
Hydroelectric*	16
Wood & Waste	95
Other**	1

* May include pumped storage and net imports of electricity generated from this resource.
** Geothermal, wind, photovoltaic, and solar.

Source: Energy Information Administration

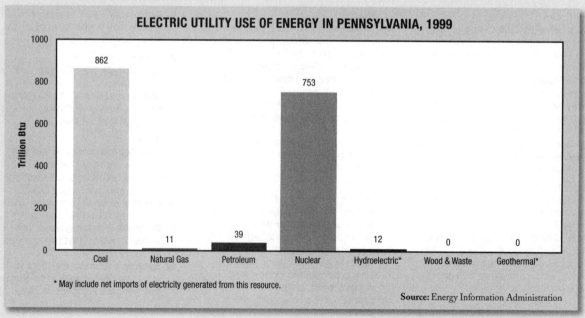

ELECTRIC UTILITY USE OF ENERGY IN PENNSYLVANIA, 1999

Trillion Btu

Source	Value
Coal	862
Natural Gas	11
Petroleum	39
Nuclear	753
Hydroelectric*	12
Wood & Waste	0
Geothermal*	0

* May include net imports of electricity generated from this resource.

Source: Energy Information Administration

You Solve It! *(continued)*

Questions

1. What three energy sources supply the most energy for the people of Pennsylvania? Place them in order, with the largest source first.

2. Which three energy sources are most important in generating electricity in Pennsylvania? Place them in order, with the largest source first.

3. Are the main energy sources in Pennsylvania renewable or nonrenewable sources?

4. Which renewable sources are used to generate electricity in Pennsylvania? What percentage of the state's total electricity does each source generate?

5. Is Pennsylvania's heavy reliance on fossil fuels a sustainable energy policy? Explain your answer.

Pennsylvania's per capita energy consumption is about 310 million Btu, compared with 351 million Btu for the nation as a whole. A Btu, or British thermal unit, is a unit used to measure heat. According to the 2000 U.S. Census, Pennsylvania's energy use by sector is as follows: commercial—583 trillion Btu; industrial—1,290 trillion Btu; residential—858 trillion Btu; transportation—984 trillion Btu.

6. Do Pennsylvanians, in general, consume more or less energy than the national average?

7. Explain why it is important for industry and transportation in Pennsylvania to use energy more sustainably. List some ways this could be accomplished.

Lesson Review

1. Evaluate the heavy worldwide dependence on fossil fuels. Is it a good long-term energy policy? Explain your answer.

2. How does resource consumption change for people in undeveloped countries as the countries develop?

3. Explain why a resource-rich nation such as Angola cannot use its resources to raise the standard of living of its people.

4. Define resource conservation.

5. List three ways to conserve energy around the house.

6. List three ways to conserve water around the house.

Lesson 8.2
Human Dependence on Natural Resources

Have you ever wondered why cities are located where they are? It's usually because there is some important resource nearby such as a transportation resource. In the 1600s and 1700s, boats were the main way to move people and goods. Therefore, many cities that grew up during those centuries were located on navigable rivers, at key junctures or points of several navigable rivers, or on bays that made good harbors.

Pennsylvania's two largest cities, Philadelphia and Pittsburgh, are good examples of this. Philadelphia's Center City, the oldest part of the city, is between the Delaware and Schuylkill Rivers, not far from the Atlantic Ocean. Its location helped make Philadelphia an important port. Pittsburgh is located where the Allegheny and Monongahela Rivers join to form the Ohio River. The rivers made Pittsburgh an important transportation center in western Pennsylvania.

In many other instances, the location of natural resources dictated where cities grew up. California grew tremendously during the mid-1800s when prospectors discovered gold in the foothills of the Sierra Nevadas (a mountain range) near Sacramento. Sacramento grew from a small town to an important city servicing the nearby mines. In Pennsylvania, the discovery and exploitation of resources such as iron, coal, and oil helped shape the development of the state.

Pennsylvania's Reliance on Natural Resources

Pennsylvania has been an industrial leader in the United States since colonial days, at least in part because of the location of its abundant natural resources. Two of the first important resources in the Commonwealth were iron ore and trees. Both were needed to make pig iron in the iron forges of eastern Pennsylvania during the 1700s.

Figure 8.4 Downtown Pittsburgh and Three Points Park overlook the junction of the Monongahela, Allegheny, and Ohio Rivers. This junction made Pittsburgh an ideal shipping port and contributed to the growth of the city.

Producing iron takes iron ore and a substance containing carbon that, in the presence of high heat, removes oxygen impurities from the iron. In the earliest days of iron production in Pennsylvania, the source of carbon was charcoal, obtained by cutting and burning trees from the colony's extensive forests. Eastern Pennsylvania towns such as Reading grew initially because of nearby iron deposits.

Coal veins lie under most of Pennsylvania. When lumber for making charcoal started to become scarce in some areas, Pennsylvania's iron forges were able to shift to coal. Two major beds of anthracite coal were discovered in eastern Pennsylvania. The northern field helped build cities such as Scranton and Wilkes-Barre. The southern field helped spur development in many communities in and around Carbon and Schuylkill Counties. For instance, many towns in Schuylkill County, such as Minersville, Shenandoah, and Pottsville, grew where they are because of nearby coal mines. In many cases, coal companies created settlements by building housing for immigrants from countries such as Wales or Poland who came to work the coal mines. Look at a map of Pennsylvania, and you can see that the names of towns—Carbondale, Minersville, Factoryville—tell you something about the town's origins.

Beginning in the 1800s, Pennsylvania's coal was an important element in the growth of the local steel industry, helping to spur the growth of the state's steel towns, such as Allentown, Bethlehem, and of course, Pittsburgh. But by the mid-1800s, Pennsylvanians were starting to use coke for iron and steel making. Coke is an almost pure carbon substance made from bituminous coal—the soft coal deposits of western Pennsylvania.

In the mid-1800s, Pennsylvania's iron and steel industry was still concentrated in the east, in towns of the Lehigh Valley, as well as around Harrisburg and Philadelphia—but that was about to shift. With the high demand for quality iron for the building of new railroads starting in the mid-1800s, larger coke-fueled furnaces were becoming more and more common in the western part of the state, near the huge deposits of bituminous coal.

By the late 1800s, the seams of bituminous coal were mined increasingly for coke production. In many valleys of southwestern Pennsylvania, thousands of coke ovens were built to supply the steel industry centered in an area stretching from Pittsburgh to Cleveland. With all the main ingredients for steel nearby or within easy reach, the western Pennsylvania city of Pittsburgh became a steel center in the 19th century. The city's steel mills played an important part in the growth of the United States, providing steel for the nation's bridges, railroads, and factories. Pittsburgh's steel mills made two thirds of the steel produced in the United States by 1900 and worked at maximum capacity all through World War II. During the war, Pittsburgh alone turned out more steel than Germany and Japan put together.

Coal from Pennsylvania's mines also helped fuel many factories in the late 1800s and early 1900s. Today, western Pennsylvania provides bituminous coal for the electric power industry and coke for making iron and steel. Pennsylvania still has large deposits of hard, anthracite coal in eastern counties such as Lackawanna, Luzerne, and Schuylkill.

Although Pennsylvania is no longer a major producer of oil, commercial oil production in the United States began in Pennsylvania in 1859, as you read in Chapter 2. For hundreds of years people had gathered oil in areas in western Pennsylvania called seeps, where it oozed from the ground. People in colonial America used that oil as fuel for lamps.

Edwin Drake was one of a group of investors who thought the area around Titusville would be a good spot to drill for oil. Drake's group began to drill in the Titusville area during the summer of 1859 and hit oil in August. Oil derricks and boom settlements quickly sprang up in the area.

Pennsylvania's oil region produced half of the world's oil until 1901, when oil production in eastern Texas surpassed it. Spindletop, the huge gusher that began the East Texas oil boom, produced more than 75,000 barrels of oil per day. By contrast, a large well in Pennsylvania's oil-producing region produced just 3,000 barrels per day during peak production.

Manufacturing is still an important part of Pennsylvania's economy, but it does not lead the state's economy. Pennsylvania does remain among the nation's leading producers of steel, ranking third behind Indiana and Ohio. Pennsylvania also has fields that produce coal that is made into coke for the iron and steel industry. Pennsylvania's top industries include electrical equipment plants in suburbs of Philadelphia and Pittsburgh, as well as pharmaceutical and other chemical plants.

The major money-making sector of the Pennsylvania economy today is the service industry rather than manufacturing. Health care, hotels, and law and engineering firms are leaders in the service sector. Most are in Philadelphia and Pittsburgh. Agriculture, which you learned about in Chapter 4, is another important sector of Pennsylvania's economy.

Resource Shortages and Population

The state with the largest population is California, with more than 35 million people—almost 13 percent of the nation's population. During the ten years between 1990 and the last census in 2000, Pennsylvania grew just 3.4 percent, but California's population grew 13.6 percent.

Which state is more fortunate, Pennsylvania or California? If the measure is the availability of resources, Pennsylvanians might be pleased that it is not growing quite as fast. California's high rate of growth has caused many environmental problems.

With a skyrocketing population, how can California find room for the hundreds of thousands of new people who come to the state each year? The answer for California has been rapid development. California must add new homes, roads, schools, parking lots, gas stations, and office buildings for its growing population. Increasingly, the new development gobbles up open space that was once grassland, forest, wetland, desert, or farmland. For

Figure 8.5 Traffic is heavy during rush hour on Interstate 405 in Costa Mesa, California. California's large population consumes many resources, but it also abides by some of the strictest environmental regulations in the country.

You Solve It! *(continued)*

example, California loses about 122,000 acres of farmland to development each year, or about 1.5 percent of the present total. Half of the state's farmland could be gone in just a few decades, according to some estimates.

The explosive growth in California's population has also affected the availability of energy and water resources. California's officials have been successful in educating many people in the state about energy conservation. The amount of energy used by each Californian dropped during the 1980s and 1990s. However, the total electric power demand for the state still grew during the last few years of the 1990s because of the population increase.

The demand for water has also increased with the number of people in the state. Because much of southern and central California is very dry, it takes a complex system of tunnels,

aqueducts, and canals to bring water to the state, sometimes from hundreds of miles away. Some resource experts predict that, if population continues to grow, California's water supply could fall short of demand in just a couple of decades.

Questions

1. Contrast the rate of growth of California with that of Pennsylvania during the decade from 1990 to 2000.

2. How does growth affect wildlife habitat?

3. Explain how a state's per-person energy use can decrease while the state's electricity demand increases.

4. In your opinion, should California limit its growth? Explain your answer.

Lesson Review

1. Why were many cities located on water when they were founded?

2. List three major resources that contributed to Pennsylvania's industrial development.

3. Which Pennsylvania city once led the nation in the production of steel?

4. Describe the uses of Pennsylvania coal.

5. What is the location of the first successful oil well in Pennsylvania?

Lab Study

Solar Power in Pennsylvania

Solar power is a renewable energy source that does not create pollution and uses a fuel—the sun—that's free. In places where there is an abundance of sunshine, it is possible to use the sun to produce electricity in solar power plants. Nationwide, the sun provides a very small percentage of electric power. In Pennsylvania, the sun is also not a major factor in the production of electric power, but a number of buildings use roof-mounted solar collectors to heat homes and make hot water.

In this activity, you will observe the ability of solar energy to heat a substance and evaluate how the use of certain materials affects its efficiency. Then you will draw conclusions about how practical it would be to depend on solar power as a main energy source in Pennsylvania.

Materials

8 rectangular metal pans (must be identical)	6 large rubber bands or string	white paper or fabric
water	clear plastic wrap	black paper or fabric

Procedure

1. Fill the metal pans with the same amount of water. The pans should be one-half to two-thirds full.

2. Place the pans in a freezer until the water is completely frozen.

3. Cover six of the pans with each of the following: two with plastic wrap, two with white paper or fabric, and two with black paper or fabric. Attach the covers with a rubber band or string.

4. On the next sunny day, beginning at about 10:00 A.M., place one pan covered with clear wrap, one pan covered with white paper or fabric, one pan covered with black paper or fabric, and one uncovered pan outside. Tilt each pan the same amount so that it is facing north. Place the other four pans in a similar position facing south.

5. Let the pans sit in the sun while the water melts. Every 15 minutes, lift the individual coverings of each pan, and note the relative rates at which the water melts in each pan. Record your observations.

Data Table

Time	Clear Plastic		White		Black		Uncovered	
	Tray 1	Tray 2	Tray 1	Tray 2	Tray 1	Tray 2	Tray 1	Tray 2
15 min.								
30 min.								
45 min.								
60 min.								
75 min.								
90 min.								

Conclusions

1. Which setup was best at collecting solar energy? Could you have predicted this before running the experiment? Explain.

2. Why did that particular design produce the best collector?

For Discussion

1. What would be the best design for the solar water heater? Which materials might you use?

2. You have experimented with passive solar design. Describe some ways that the movement and location of the sun can be used to keep a home comfortable without using a lot of electricity. Think about materials, location of windows, types of shades, and so on.

3. Would solar energy be a good renewable energy source for heating in Pennsylvania? Explain your answer.

4. Given your results, what would you do to improve the design of the system?

Lesson 8.3

Human Impact on the Environment

The natural resources used to keep us warm or cool, light our homes and schools, speed us down highways in cars or through the sky in planes, and make products such as DVDs and books like the one you're reading have a price. Removing resources such as oil, coal, iron, and copper from the ground changes the surface of the land and disrupts ecosystems. The transportation and processing of raw materials, as well as the manufacturing and processing of finished goods, create pollution that enters air, water, and soil. Scientists are now only starting to understand the impact that these pollutants have on the natural environment.

Human Impact on Earth's Atmosphere

Air pollution isn't new. The fires lit by the earliest humans sent smoke and soot into the air. Today, everyday human activities such as driving a car, using a lawn mower, or turning on electrical equipment (electric power is often produced by burning fossil fuels in a power plant) all produce air pollution. There are also natural sources of air pollution. These natural sources include volcanic ash, soot from forest fires, and fine soil particles from dust storms, but they don't tend to be as harmful as human-made pollutants.

Air pollution is a serious problem because air is such an important resource. All living organisms need it to live. If the air becomes polluted with high levels of certain harmful substances, it can endanger the health of people, wildlife, and plants.

In the United States, the first deadly air pollution incident occurred back in 1948 when a deadly cloud of sulfur dioxide and soot hung over Donora, Pennsylvania, for five days. The cloud formed when hazardous pollutants emitted by the city's steel mills, an area zinc smelter, and a local factory producing sulfuric acid were trapped over Donora by the surrounding mountains and weather patterns that caused the air to stall over the area. Twenty people died, and

about 7,000 became ill. Today, however, the huge volume and toxicity of substances we release into the air from factories, power plants, homes, and offices is greater than at any other time in history.

There are two major classes of air pollutants. Primary pollutants are those that factory smokestacks and motor vehicle tailpipes release into the air. Primary pollutants can also be natural substances such as volcanic ash, dust, or sea salt. The air captures these pollutants and circulates them through the atmosphere. Secondary pollutants are new substances that form as primary pollutants react with each other and with what is already in the atmosphere. Soot (also known as particulates) is a primary pollutant, and smog is a secondary pollutant.

In general, air pollutants come in three forms: aerosols, gases, and particulates. Aerosols are particles so tiny that they remain suspended in the air. Gases are compounds that form the basic substance of air. Particulates are particles in the air. Some are as small as aerosols, and some are larger. Larger particles settle out of air eventually—like the sooty grime or dust that forms a layer on cars or windowsills.

Acid Deposition Rain is naturally slightly acidic, but in northeastern states such as Pennsylvania, the rain can be ten times more acidic than natural rainfall. In some places, droplets and solid particles with 1,000 times the acidity of normal rain can fall on forests, lakes, and buildings. This is acid deposition, often called acid rain. *Acid deposition* consists of acids or acid-forming substances that fall from the atmosphere to the ground.

Acid deposition occurs when electric power plants and factories, especially those that burn coal and petroleum, release sulfur dioxide and nitrogen dioxide into the air. They form secondary pollutants, such as nitric and sulfuric acid, as well as particles of sulfate and nitrate salts that form acids. These chemicals fall to earth as acidic precipitation or as tiny solid acidic particles.

Northeastern states such as Pennsylvania have some of the most severe problems with acid deposition because they are downwind of power

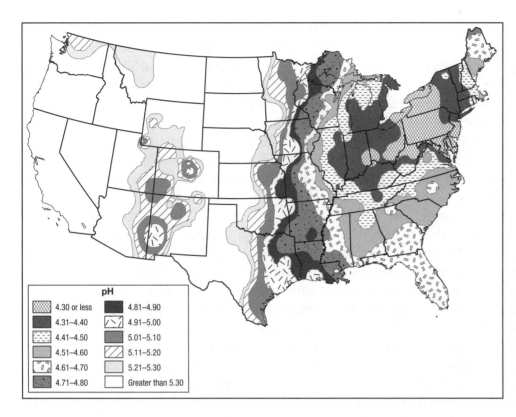

Figure 8.6 The pH of rainfall in the United States is lower, or more acidic, in areas of higher elevation or areas that are underlain by shale, sandstone, or carbon-rich rock.

pH

4.30 or less	4.81–4.90
4.31–4.40	4.91–5.00
4.41–4.50	5.01–5.10
4.51–4.60	5.11–5.20
4.61–4.70	5.21–5.30
4.71–4.80	Greater than 5.30

plants and factories in the Midwest that are fueled by high-sulfur coal and petroleum. These plants often have very tall smokestacks that release their pollutants high in the air. Years ago when these plants were designed, engineers thought that injecting the pollutants high into the air would get rid of them. Upper-level winds would supposedly just blow them away. We now know that the high stacks just allow the pollution to travel long distances in the upper atmosphere. As a result, acid rain often causes problems hundreds of miles away from where the pollution that forms it was generated.

Acid rain can harm people, wildlife, and property. It irritates the human respiratory system and corrodes the surfaces of cars and buildings. Acid deposition also damages forest ecosystems, primarily by weakening trees. The excess acid changes the chemistry of soil. For example, the acidity can cause the release from soil of aluminum ions that damage the roots of trees. The trees then become more likely to suffer damage or to be killed by disease, weather extremes, or storms. The aluminum ions also wash into lakes, causing the death of fish. Many lakes and streams in the Northeast can no longer support certain species of aquatic life because of acid rain.

Global Warming Earth's atmosphere does more than provide oxygen for animals and people to breathe and carbon dioxide for plants to make food. It also keeps Earth warm enough for life to exist. The fact that Earth is not a permanently cold and hostile environment is because of greenhouse gases. They hold heat energy from the sun near Earth's surface—like the glass of a greenhouse holds in heat. The most important greenhouse gas in terms of global warming is carbon dioxide, but methane, water vapor, ozone, nitrogen oxides, and a group of chemicals called chlorofluorocarbons are also greenhouse gases. These gases make the greenhouse effect possible. The *greenhouse effect* is the natural process in which heat is trapped near Earth's surface by the atmosphere. If you've ever gotten into a closed car that's been sitting in the sun on a hot summer day, you have experienced the greenhouse effect on a small scale. Like the car's windows, earth's atmosphere allows certain wavelengths of the sun's radiation to pass through. The waves heat objects, which reradiate heat at a different wavelength that greenhouse gases block and keep near Earth's surface.

Although many processes tend to warm the atmosphere, other processes tend to cool it. Particulate pollution reflects solar radiation back into space, so volcanic eruptions that send large amounts of particulates (ash) into the air tend to have a cooling effect. After the eruption of Mount Pinatubo in 1992, there was a temporary global cooling of at least 9°F.

A global rise in average temperature would occur when the processes that warm the atmosphere have a greater effect than those that cool it. The injection of excess amounts of carbon dioxide into the atmosphere is one of the main reasons that warming processes seem to be having a greater effect right now than cooling processes. People began to upset the balance of greenhouse gases in the atmosphere in the mid to late 19th century. At that time, which was the start of the Industrial Revolution in the United States, large amounts of coal were burned to power factories. The burning of fossil fuels such as coal, petroleum, gasoline, and natural gas produces carbon dioxide as a by-product of combustion. As industrialization increased, so did the concentration of carbon dioxide in the air. Because trees absorb carbon dioxide during photosynthesis, the massive cutting and burning of forests during the twentieth and twenty-first centuries has also increased carbon dioxide concentration in the air.

The concentration of carbon dioxide in the atmosphere has risen 30 percent during the last century. Before worldwide industrialization, the concentration of carbon dioxide was a bit less than 300 parts per million (ppm). It is now at least 362 ppm. Scientists have determined that this concentration is higher than any level during the past 420,000 years.

Most scientists agree that the result of this increase in atmospheric carbon dioxide is global warming. *Global warming* is the unnatural warming of the average temperature of the atmosphere near Earth's surface as a result of the increase in atmospheric greenhouse gases such as carbon dioxide. Earth's mean surface temperature has gradually risen since the 1860s, with some of the hottest years on record occurring in the last two decades.

Many scientists predict serious consequences for the natural environment because of global warming. For example, many scientists project a melting of polar ice caps that would contribute to sea level rise. Low-lying islands and coastal areas would be flooded or disappear. Warmer temperatures would also affect Earth's biomes, causing warmer climate zones to move toward the poles. Plants and animals would have to adjust or die as conditions in many ecosystems would change.

Smog *Smog* is a word that comes from the combination of the words "smoke" and "fog," probably because that was the way it appeared to those who named it during the early part of the 1900s. Most large cities with lots of motor vehicles and warm, dry, sunny climates have photochemical smog. In summer, smog can be a problem in any city with warm weather, sunshine, and lots of pollution from motor vehicles.

Smog is a brown, hazy cloud that forms when primary pollutants, such as nitrogen oxides from vehicle exhaust and hydrocarbons from motor vehicles and other sources, combine in the presence of sunlight to form a stew of secondary pollutants such as ground-level ozone, formaldehyde, and nitric acid.

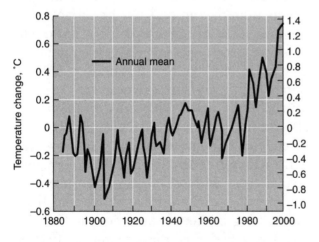

Figure 8.7 This line graph shows the average temperature over the past 120 years, with the most drastic increase happening in the past two decades. The effect of the eruption of Mount Pinatubo is shown in the last valley on the graph.

On very sunny days, photochemical smog reaches its highest concentration in the early afternoon, when it can trigger health alerts. The mix of chemicals can cause eye and throat irritation and breathing difficulty, especially in people with respiratory illnesses such as asthma. Smog also harms plants and can corrode certain materials.

Ozone Depletion We owe the existence of life on Earth, in part, to ozone. Ozone is a molecule composed of three atoms of oxygen (O_3). Recall that on the ground, ozone is a secondary pollutant that is part of smog. But in the stratosphere (between 9 and 34 miles above Earth's surface), ozone forms a protective layer around the planet that stops 99 percent of the sun's harmful ultraviolet radiation from reaching Earth's surface.

Our use of chlorine-containing chemicals such as chlorofluorocarbons (CFCs) releases chlorine atoms into the atmosphere. CFCs have been used for decades as coolants in refrigerators and air conditioners and as an ingredient in making plastic foam packaging. CFCs were also used as a propellant in aerosol spray cans before the EPA banned their use in 1976. Although there are substitutes for CFCs for some uses, many manufacturers still use them in refrigerator systems. If the CFCs are released from these systems or other sources, they rise into the stratosphere where ultraviolet radiation breaks them down, releasing chlorine oxide molecules. These molecules then break down ozone into oxygen molecules.

Studies have shown that the average ozone level in the atmosphere dropped in the 1980s and 1990s. In addition, since the early 1970s, scientists have observed a huge area over Antarctica where the ozone thins to at least half its normal concentration during each Antarctic spring. This area, often called an ozone "hole," forms as the result of a huge vortex of wind that swirls around the South Pole during the Antarctic winter. This wind system is isolated from the rest of the planet and contains extremely cold air. Water-containing compounds crystallize within the vortex, allowing chemical reactions, such as the production of ozone-destroying chlorine oxide, to take place on the surfaces of the crystals. As spring and the sun return, the chlorine oxide in the vortex reacts with ozone in the presence of sunlight, destroying the ozone. This is why the ozone "hole" appears each spring. An area of thinning ozone appears during the Arctic spring over the North Pole at times as well, but the Arctic vortex is not as strong and cold as the Antarctic vortex. This creates conditions that are not as favorable for the chemical reactions that destroy ozone.

Reductions in ozone have been recorded elsewhere as well, such as in the mid-latitudes of the northern hemisphere. Since the late 1970s, the increase in exposure to ultraviolet radiation in North America has increased about 4 percent per decade as a result.

Ozone depletion could have several effects. For people, less ozone protection from solar ultraviolet would mean more severe sunburns and a greater incidence of cataracts and skin cancers. Greater penetration of harmful ultraviolet radiation would also cause damage to phytoplankton, the producers that form the foundation of aquatic food webs. It could also decrease yields of some crops and damage forests.

Human Impact on Earth's Hydrosphere

For many years, releasing waste into Earth's surface waters was common and not considered much of a problem. After all, if you poured waste into a river or stream, the river or stream would just carry it away. Then, eventually, it would go into the ocean—a body of water so vast that no amount of pollution could possibly hurt it—or so people thought.

Of course, we now know that line of thinking was wrong. Rivers, streams, lakes, and even the ocean all have a limit to the amount of pollution they can absorb before they become unusable for drinking or before aquatic wildlife sickens and dies and aquatic ecosystems break down.

There are many types of water pollution. As you learned in Chapter 3, they include pathogens such as bacteria and viruses from sewage and untreated human and animal waste.

Organic wastes that decompose and deplete dissolved oxygen can cause the death of many aquatic organisms. Nutrients that flow into surface waters from farmland as well as chemicals produced by mining and industrial activity also seep into water or are dumped into it. Sediment washing into surface waters also pollutes that water, clogging streams, filling lake bottoms, and disrupting aquatic ecosystems by making it more difficult for aquatic plants to make food.

Sewage Discharge In most places in the United States, when you flush the toilet or pour something down the drain, the waste (sewage) travels through a system of pipes to a sewage treatment plant. There, the waste is treated, or cleaned at least partially, before the plant releases it to surface waters such as a river, lake, or bay. In some places, however, the sewage pipes and stormwater pipes are the same system. Stormwater pipes carry excess rainwater that hits the ground and runs off streets, parking lots, driveways, sidewalks, and lawns (runoff) into sewers after heavy rainfall. Runoff eventually enters streams, rivers, and bays, carrying pollution—grease, animal waste, lawn chemicals, sediment—it has picked up along the way. At times of heavy rainfall, the combination of sewage and stormwater systems can carry untreated sewage into nearby surface waters. The release of this contaminated stormwater can cause the growth of bacteria, viruses, and other microorganisms that cause disease in waterways. For this reason, many public health experts warn people to avoid swimming on beaches that are near stormwater outflow pipes after a heavy rainfall.

Nutrient Runoff An important component of farm runoff is fertilizer, which you learned about in Chapter 4. Much of the fertilizer applied to farm fields leaves the fields in runoff that flows into nearby surface waters. In the central United States, the nitrates in fertilizer have contaminated many bodies of water in the Mississippi River watershed. They then flow with the river into the Gulf of Mexico. The fertilizer spurs the growth of *algae blooms,* which are huge clumps of algae that are

Figure 8.8 These workers on the Yaquina River in Oregon are cleaning up an oil spill, which threatens the salmon and steelhead populations.

eaten by oxygen-using bacteria when they die. The decomposers suck all the oxygen out of these areas, causing the death of fish and other aquatic wildlife that need dissolved oxygen to survive. As a result, a "dead zone" the size of New Jersey forms in the Gulf of Mexico near the U.S. coast each year as excess nutrients contained in runoff create seasonal algae blooms.

There are a number of sources of nutrient runoff. Sewage contains nitrates and phosphates, which normal wastewater treatment cannot easily remove. As a result, water released back into surface waters from wastewater treatment plants still contains these substances. Laundry detergents that contain phosphates are a major source of nutrients in sewage. Phosphate-containing detergents are banned by some municipalities because of the damage they can do. Soil can also release nutrients to nearby waters when plows on farm fields or bulldozers at construction sites dig up soil.

Nutrient overload in lakes can lead to a problem called eutrophication. In eutrophication, nitrates and phosphates also stimulate the excessive growth of algae and other aquatic plants. Again, this process creates a lack of oxygen in the lake as oxygen-using decomposers devour dead plant matter. Over thousands of years, sediment and organic matter gradually fill in lakes, giving them the characteristics of shallow ponds with limited ability to support life. Eutrophication speeds this process, giving a lake the characteristics of a shallow pond within just a few years. As a result, the process is often referred to as the premature aging of a lake.

Petroleum Spills Much of the oil that moves around the world every day does so in huge oil tankers. In some cases, the tankers have run aground on rocks or have developed mechanical or structural problems that caused them to release huge amounts of oil. Offshore oil wells are also a source of oil spills. A spill can occur when equipment breaks, allowing oil to shoot up from underwater wells directly into the ocean above it. Oil contains toxic substances that kill tiny marine organisms as soon as the oil spills into the water. Some poisonous volatile chemicals in oil evaporate within a few days. More damaging are the substances that form a sticky slick that coats the fur of marine mammals such as seals and the feathers of birds. The oily coating destroys the ability of fur or feathers to insulate animals from cold or help them stay afloat, causing many animals to freeze or drown. Some fish also die of suffocation when globs of oil block their gills.

The effects of oil spills can be very long-lasting, especially in cold climates or waters that are calm. Beaches and other shorelines with calm waters can remain coated with oil for many years. In areas where strong wave action helps scour the shoreline, the oil could be gone in a year or so. In either case, an oil spill can greatly damage the local economy as tourist areas are forced to close temporarily. Animals such as crabs, clams, and mussels can accumulate high levels of toxic chemicals from the oil in their bodies, making them unsafe for people to eat.

In 1989, the *Exxon Valdez* oil tanker ran aground on rocks in Alaska's Prince William Sound. The tanker spilled 11 million gallons of oil into the clear, cold waters of the sound. The oil coated more than 3,000 miles of shoreline and killed thousands of animals, including birds, sea otters, fish, whales, and seals.

Industrial Waste Manufacturing processes produce waste chemicals, many of which are toxic to living organisms. Some of these chemicals are legally discharged into surface waters such as streams, rivers, lakes, and bays. Some are illegally discharged, or discharged in amounts that exceed government limits. These chemicals can contaminate drinking water supplies, harm aquatic life, and make waters unfit for swimming and other types of recreation.

Thermal Pollution When coal-burning power plants and nuclear plants produce electricity, they also produce a great deal of heat. Power plants and factories often draw water from nearby rivers, lakes, and bays and use it as a coolant for machinery. They then release the hot water back into the waterway. This process causes *thermal pollution*, the excessive heating of surface waters such as lakes, rivers, and streams.

Thermal pollution raises the temperature of adjacent waters, throwing off the balance of the ecosystems of these water bodies. Fish and other

Figure 8.9 The Berkeley Pit, an open-pit copper mine in Butte, Montana, is approximately 1.5 miles by 1 mile across and contains approximately 30 billion gallons of acidic water. This water is constantly monitored so that it does not contaminate local aquifers and other groundwater.

aquatic life live within a certain range of water temperature. If the temperature goes too far above or below that range, the aquatic life can be harmed. Warmer temperatures also lower the concentration of dissolved oxygen in the water, causing stress on fish by making them breathe faster to take in enough oxygen. Many fish also die on intake screens that filter large objects out of water as it is sucked into plant cooling systems.

Human Impact on Earth's Lithosphere

Extracting natural resources from the land has impacts as well. For example, more than 200 years of mining has left its mark on Pennsylvania's streams, rivers, and land. Farms also can have harmful impacts on soil and water supplies.

Mine Damage As rain falls and seeps through abandoned mines and mine waste, it can send toxic substances into surface and underground waters. These substances include acid mine drainage from coal mines, radioactive waste from uranium mines, and toxic metals such as mercury from gold and silver mines.

Strip mining to remove coal or other resources near Earth's surface also scars the landscape. It removes topsoil and vegetation, disrupting whole ecosystems. Surface mining often goes one step further, using explosives and giant mechanical shovels to level the whole tops of mountains to reach the deposits inside. The waste dirt and rock is then left in nearby valleys

Major Minerals and Their Common Uses	
Mineral	**Some Major Uses**
bauxite (aluminum ore)	cans, foil, light bulbs, cookware, license plates, airplane and auto parts
cassiterite (tin ore)	coatings for food cans, staples, and paper clips; solders; cast iron; dental fillings
calcite	steel production, cement, building stone, conditioning soil
chalcopyrite (copper ore)	electrical wire, household water pipes
diamond	gemstones, cutting tools
gold	jewelry, coins, electronic and computer circuitry
graphite	pencil "lead," lubricant
gypsum	plaster of Paris, wallboard
halite	table salt, road ice removal and control, water softener
hematite (iron ore)	steel production, cookware, tools, automobiles
limestone	agricultural lime; building stone, cement; steel production
quartz	glass production
silver	electrical equipment, photographic chemicals, jewelry
sulfur	chemical fertilizer production, sulfuric acid for industry
talc	talcum powder, cosmetic and paint production, insulation, crayons, paper, soap
wolframite (tungsten ore)	filaments in light bulbs, paints, tips of high-speed cutting tools

Figure 8.10 Minerals are used in all types of products that we use every day.

Environmental Effects of Mining and Metal Processing

Location	Environmental Effects
Copper Basin, TN	Sulfur dioxide emissions from a copper smelter in operation for more than 100 years have killed all vegetation over a 50-square-mile area.
Palmerton, PA	Emissions from a zinc smelter that operated between 1898 and 1980 have totally destroyed vegetation in a 3-square-mile area and affected plants and animals in a wider radius around the plant.
Torch Lake, MI	Disposal of waste from copper mining between the 1860s and 1960s was responsible for an outbreak of liver cancer in some fish species.
Leadville, CO	Acid mine drainage and toxic metal pollution from mining in the headwaters of the Arkansas River system have adversely affected aquatic communities up to 50 miles downstream.
Blackbird Mine, ID	Releases of copper, cobalt, and other metals from mining have contaminated almost 25 miles of Panther Creek, decimating the local fish population.
Iron Mountain Mine, Reading, CA	Periodic fish kills have occurred in local waters, caused by metals released from mines and mine wastes.

Figure 8.11 Mining and metal processing pollution has had many serious negative environmental effects across the country.

and streams. External mine damage is often reversed, reclaiming and reconstructing the land on the basis of its original form.

Farmland Agriculture can also have negative effects on ecosystems, especially where grasslands and forests are removed to create farm fields. As you learned in Chapter 4, soil is an important resource that takes a long time to form. Farm practices that leave soil exposed to erosion can make an area unable to support crops.

Much of the most productive farmland in the United States requires irrigation to supplement natural precipitation. Irrigation systems bring water from rivers and reservoirs, often many miles away, through pipes, channels, and ditches to farm fields. Although irrigation can boost an area's crop production, it can also lead to a serious problem called salinization, the accumulation of salt in soil. Salinization occurs when the heat from the sun evaporates water from the soil, leaving salt behind. The salt accumulation damages plants by preventing them from absorbing enough water through their roots. Over time, the soil can become so full of salt that growing crops on it can become extremely difficult.

Human Impact on Earth's Biosphere

As you have already learned, the mining, processing, transportation, and use of natural resources in manufacturing can tear up Earth's surface, cause soil erosion, and produce pollution that fouls air, water, and soil. Of course, these problems also affect communities of plants and animals that live in the ecosystems impacted by these activities.

Mining for important resources such as coal, iron, copper, lead, and uranium means tearing up Earth's surface and then separating the coal or ore recovered from waste rock around it. This process leaves large piles of mine waste from which toxic chemicals can leach. The United States has more than 500,000 abandoned mines. It is estimated that these mines have contaminated 452 square miles of lakes and reservoirs and 11,806 miles of streams and rivers. Smelting operations that refine ore to produce metals create a great deal of air pollution as well, much of which is toxic to life. The chart on this page shows some of the effects on plants and animals of toxic releases from mining and smelting.

The effects of acid deposition on species in the northeast have been serious in some areas. The biological effects of acid rain were first discovered several decades ago when more than 100 lakes in New York's Adirondack Mountains were found to no longer have fish. About 300 kilometers of trout streams in Pennsylvania have also suffered the effects of acid rain. As a result of acid deposition, some streams in the state are too acidic for fish species such as brook trout during spring runoff. The disappearance of fish and other aquatic life from lakes and streams has had a domino effect, also reducing the populations of fish-eating bird species such as ospreys, loons, and ducks.

The Dangers of DDT

DDT is now banned in the United States and many other countries around the world, in part because of the work of Rachel Carson. Because the dangers of DDT are now so well known, it is hard to imagine how highly it was regarded when it was first widely used in the 1940s.

DDT is one of a group of pesticides called the organochlorines. In 1939, an entomologist named Paul Mueller discovered that the chemical, which had been around for decades, could kill a number of different types of insects. DDT became well known when the U.S. Army used it during World War II to kill body lice that carry typhus. It also became an effective tool for killing mosquitoes that carry malaria. The use of DDT as an insecticide for disease-carrying pests and those that ruin crops expanded greatly during the 1940s and 1950s. The chemical was so highly praised that Mueller won the Nobel Prize in 1948.

At first, few people suspected that DDT was dangerous. It was sprayed throughout the United States to eradicate mosquitoes.

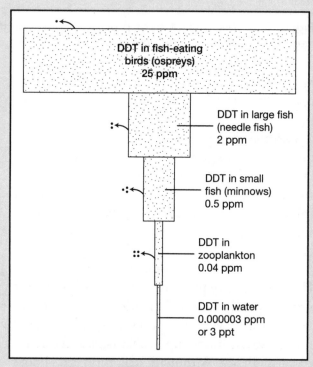

Figure 8.12 The effects of DDT are cumulative, increasing each time a contaminated organism is used as a food source. The dots shown represent units of DDT and the arrows show where small concentrations of DDT are lost through respiration and waste excretion.

You Solve It! *(continued)*

Trucks rode down suburban streets spraying the chemical as children played nearby. But Rachel Carson's research in *Silent Spring* brought the problems connected with DDT to light for the first time. During the 1950s and 1960s, populations of birds of prey, such as ospreys, peregrine falcons, and bald eagles, took a nosedive. Research showed that a chemical by-product of DDT had become stored in the fatty tissues of many members of the affected species. The chemical had caused the birds' eggshells to thin so much that the eggs broke and the birds were unable to produce offspring.

As a result of evidence of the toxic nature of DDT for wildlife and people, the United States banned the use of DDT in 1972. Although several other countries have banned it as well, DDT is still used in many other nations. Banning DDT was a crucial step in allowing for the recovery of these affected birds.

Questions

1. How did the work of Rachel Carson affect the use of DDT as a pesticide in the United States?

2. How was DDT used in the 1940s through the early 1970s?

3. Explain why people thought at first that DDT was not dangerous.

4. How did DDT affect the populations of birds of prey?

5. In your opinion, was the banning of DDT necessary? Explain your answer.

Lesson Review

1. List the two major classes of air pollutants, and define each one.

2. Summarize how acid rain forms.

3. Compare and contrast the greenhouse effect and global warming.

4. Why is the depletion of ozone a serious problem?

5. How does sewage in runoff affect surface waters?

6. Explain how algae blooms form and why they are a problem for some species of aquatic life.

7. Explain how energy conservation could decrease the chance of oil spills.

8. Describe the biological effects of acid deposition.

Case Study

Rachel Carson's Legacy

In 1962, a book by Rachel Carson titled *Silent Spring* was published. Its subject was the danger to the environment caused by the use of pesticides such as DDT. The book was a bestseller for more than one year and is now known as one of the most important books on the environment ever written. Many people believe the environment movement that began in the 1960s and 1970s grew out of the concerns about the effects of pesticides on the environment raised by Carson's research for *Silent Spring*.

Carson had long been interested in taking an independent look at the effects of pesticides on ecosystems. She proposed articles to magazines at least twice but was turned down. Then in 1958, a friend in Massachusetts contacted Carson to tell her about the deaths of several birds after DDT was sprayed near her home to kill mosquitoes. Carson decided that it was time to put everything else aside and find out whether DDT was actually as safe as most people seemed to believe. Her research became the book *Silent Spring*.

In *Silent Spring*, Carson presented evidence that pesticides such as DDT were toxic to wildlife and that contamination of plants and animals that might be eaten in some form by people would eventually harm people as well. The popular book alarmed the public and began the first intense discussion about whether the abundant use of pesticides has negative effects.

The pesticide industry attacked Carson and the book, but her research held up. As a result of Carson's work, the use of some classes of pesticides was restricted. Eventually DDT was banned in many countries, including the United States.

Rachel Carson was a Pennsylvanian, born in Springdale in 1907. Carson, who was a marine biologist and science writer, earned her bachelor's degree from Pennsylvania College for Women and a master's degree from Johns Hopkins University in Maryland. For most of her life, Carson worked as a marine biologist for the U.S. Fish and Wildlife Service. She wrote another well-known, bestselling book, *The Sea Around Us* (1951), that discussed ocean life and the harm people were doing to it. Rachel Carson died in 1964, only two years after the publication of *Silent Spring*.

Figure 8.13 Rachel Carson's work spurred the environmental movement that continues to this day.

Questions

1. Why do you think two magazines turned down Rachel Carson when she wanted to write an article about the possible harmful effects of pesticides?

2. Summarize two of the points Carson made in *Silent Spring*.

3. Infer why the pesticide industry reacted negatively to Carson's book.

4. Describe the lasting effects of *Silent Spring*.

5. In your opinion, why was it so important to Rachel Carson to write a book on the subject of pesticides, even after more than one editor had rejected the idea?

Lesson 8.4

Supply and Demand

In Chapter 6, you learned that each ecosystem has a certain carrying capacity, a population that its resources can sustain. Earth as a whole also has a carrying capacity. Although there are places on Earth that have reached their carrying capacity, the planet has not. As a result, Earth's population continues to grow. At some point, however, even Earth will reach its carrying capacity and will contain the greatest population that it can support. When will that occur? No one really knows, but as Earth's population rises, we are moving closer to that point.

Increasing Demand for Nonbiological Resources

Earth's population is 6 billion and counting. The population of the United States is rising as well. Census 2000 showed that there are now more than 280 million people in the United States—a 13 percent increase in just the ten years between 1990 and 2000. Demographers, people who study population, believe that Earth's population could reach 9 billion within approximately 50 years.

With increases in population come increased demands for natural resources and increased impacts on the natural environment. As developing countries develop, their people consume more per person, further increasing the demand for resources.

Land When the United States was young, citizens were primarily rural people. Today, most people in the United States live in cities or in the suburbs and other areas around them. This process of movement from rural areas to cities is not unique to the United States. Between 1950 and 1998, Earth's urban population increased from 200 million to 2.5 billion—about half of Earth's people. By 2025, more than 65 percent of Earth's people will live in cities.

Figure 8.14 The Florida Everglades is a unique ecosystem that is being encroached upon by urban and agricultural development. Led by a guide, these people tour the Everglades to learn more about this important and threatened ecosystem.

Cities have been attracting increasing numbers of people for many reasons. Many people, especially in developing countries, migrate from rural areas to cities to find jobs and ensure better lives for their families. Some leave rural areas because of poverty or landlessness. Many are also pushed into cities by military conflicts in the countryside where they live. Life in cities may seem safer by comparison.

The Florida Everglades is a good example of what can happen when urban areas sprawl out into previously wild lands nearby. As growing agricultural and urban areas nearby pinch off more of this marshland ecosystem, the Everglades suffers harm through pollution from agriculture, loss of water needed to maintain its marshes, and loss of species habitat. Many Everglades species, such as the Florida panther and the American crocodile, are now endangered as a result. Efforts to restore the Everglades and protect its endangered species are underway, but those efforts will be in conflict with the continued growth of the area surrounding the Everglades.

Field Study

Calculating Population Density

Calculating population density establishes the number of organisms living in a specified area. To make these calculations, scientists determine the number of organisms in a specified population and divide by the area in which the population lives. In this activity you will use the actual count or the estimation method to determine the population size of an organism in an area near your school. Then you will calculate the population density of the organism.

Materials

meter sticks	notebook
string	pencil
stakes	

Procedure

1. Your teacher will assign your team an organism found in your schoolyard and show you how to identify it.

2. Before you begin, get the area of your schoolyard in square meters or square kilometers from your teacher.

3. Decide whether to use the actual count or the estimation method to determine the size of your population.

4. If you select the estimation method, measure a square area in the schoolyard in which your organism is found. Use stakes and string to mark off your square.

5. Count the number of organisms in the marked area.

6. Use the count from step 5 to estimate the entire population in the schoolyard.

7. Determine the size of your population. Record it in the table.

8. Calculate the population density of your organism. To do this, divide the population size by the area of the schoolyard.

Conclusions

1. Did you use the actual count or estimation method to determine the size of your population? Explain.

2. Summarize the procedure you used to determine the size of your population.

Data Table

Team	Organism	Method of Determination	Size	Population Density
1				
2				
3				
4				
5				
6				
7				
8				
9				
10				

3. Was it easy or hard for you to determine the size of your population? Explain.

4. How reliable do you think your figures are? What factors affect their reliability?

For Discussion

1. Would the figures you obtained be different if you repeated the measurements tonight? How about tomorrow or next year? Explain your answer.

2. Review the class results. Is there any relationship between the population density and physical features of the various organisms? Explain your answer.

Extension

Repeat this activity at different times of year, and compare the results. Draw conclusions about the reasons for any differences you observe.

Water As you have already learned, less than 1 percent of Earth's supply of water is fresh water that people use for drinking and growing food. However, water is unevenly distributed and not always where it is needed. Today, 28 percent of Earth's population does not have access to safe drinking water. With Earth's population growing while water supplies are not, the quantity of water available to each person worldwide has been decreasing. In the future, experts believe that billions of people could live in areas with water supplies that are inadequate to their needs.

Energy Today, developed countries are heavily dependent on fossil fuels, especially oil, for producing electricity, fueling motor vehicles and airplanes, and producing materials such as plastics from oil-based petrochemicals. The United States, which uses more energy than any other country, gets more than 90 percent of that energy from nonrenewable fossil fuels and nuclear energy. At present rates of consumption, U.S. oil reserves could be used up in about 24 years. Earth's reserves could last at least 44 years. But as population increases, consumption rates could also increase, unless conservation and use of renewable fuels become more common.

Increasing Demand for Biological Natural Resources

The increase in human population has placed greater demands on biological resources such as food supplies and forests. It has also helped increase the rate of habitat destruction that has been a major factor in species decline.

Food Crops As you learned in Chapter 4, modern agriculture has given farmers the ability to grow more food per acre than in the past. Since 1940, crop production in the United States has doubled. However, although the United States and other developed nations can feed their populations, people in many poor nations suffer malnutrition. In Africa, for example, food production has increased since 1961, but the increase has not been large enough to offset Africa's increase in population during that time. More than 100 countries are so short of food

that they have to import staple grains (corn, wheat, rice) from countries such as the United States, Canada, and Australia, which have a surplus. To feed the world's growing population, farm production of staple crops such as grains will have to increase yearly.

Fisheries A rise in population and an emphasis on fish as a healthy food in developed countries has caused a rise in fish consumption in recent years. The rise in the consumption of fish worldwide has led to overfishing (a situation in which commercial fisheries take more fish than the population can naturally replace) of a large number of the world's fisheries. Today, at least 70 percent of the world's marine stocks are overfished, depleted, or fished to capacity. Marine fish species such as the Atlantic cod, Atlantic swordfish, sharks, and bluefin tuna have become much less plentiful and could become even more rare if commercial fisheries do not take fewer fish and allow the populations to replenish themselves. In addition, the decline in many fish species will have an effect on ocean food webs and ecosystems that is still not fully known. Some fish populations are now under management plans that will protect them until their populations can bounce back.

Forests Forests play an important role in Earth's natural environment, offering watershed protection, maintaining the atmosphere's carbon balance, and sustaining biodiversity. They also provide us with paper, cardboard, and wood for homes and furniture as well as wood that many people in the developing world use for cooking and heating fuel. Forests are being cut to fulfill these human needs at an increasing rate. Earth's forest cover is now between 20 and 50 percent less than it was in preagricultural times. By some estimates, an area of forest the size of Mexico was lost between 1980 and 1995, along with the forest ecosystems and the plant and animal communities that were a part of them. The loss of tropical forests is especially serious because they shelter some of the most diverse of Earth's ecosystems. Efforts are now underway to slow the loss of forests through conservation and habitat protection.

The Serpentine Aster: A Plant in Danger in Pennsylvania

There are still serpentine aster plants in southeastern Pennsylvania, mostly in Chester, Delaware, and Lancaster Counties. However, without federal protection under the Endangered Species Act, the serpentine aster may disappear from Pennsylvania.

The plant is found in a very unusual habitat. It grows in soils that are rich in the mineral serpentine. Because serpentine contains toxic amounts of heavy metals such as nickel and chromium, which would likely kill other plants, scientists are not sure just how the serpentine aster manages to survive. Nevertheless, the plant is well adapted to its environment.

Habitat loss is the main reason for the plant's scarcity in Pennsylvania. The serpentine barrens where the plant grows were first mined in the 1800s for the mineral magnesite. Serpentine itself has been mined since that time for use in road building. Surface mining operations naturally disturb or kill the plants. Today, suburban and industrial development of the areas where the plant grows also threatens it.

The U.S. Fish and Wildlife Service now has the serpentine aster under consideration for listing as either threatened or endangered at the federal level. However, the serpentine aster is already listed as a threatened species in Pennsylvania. Some sites where the plant grows are already protected, one by a private organization and the state government, one by a county government, and another by an arboretum. The state of Pennsylvania is attempting to protect other sites by reaching

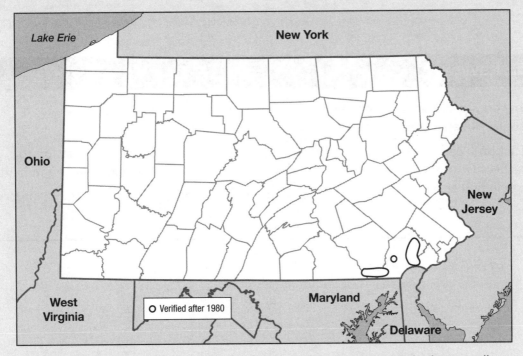

Figure 8.15 Very little habitat remains for the serpentine aster. Only three small areas in southeastern Pennsylvania remain as a natural habitat of the plant.

You Solve It! *(continued)*

agreements with landowners and halting further disturbance of the plant's habitat while the application for protection of the plant is under review.

Questions

1. Where in Pennsylvania is the serpentine aster found?

2. Why is the environment where the plant grows unusual for a plant?

3. Explain the reason for the decline in the plant's population.

4. What is being done to help preserve the serpentine aster?

Figure 8.16 The serpentine aster lives in soils that contain large amounts of nickel and chromium, heavy metals that would kill other plants.

Lesson Review

1. How does population growth make resource conservation harder?

2. What problems does the Everglades face because of the growth of surrounding areas?

3. What is overfishing, and why is it a problem?

4. List three things that forests do to maintain Earth's natural environment.

5. Infer why habitat loss is the main factor in species decline.

Chapter 9

Environmental Laws and Regulations

Today, the gasoline that pours from pumps into car gas tanks is always unleaded, but that was not always the case. Before the late 1980s, much of the gasoline sold in the United States contained the additive tetraethyl lead. Lead doesn't occur naturally in gasoline. Starting in the 1920s, gasoline producers put lead in gasoline because the additive eliminated an annoying engine noise called knock.

However, lead is poisonous to living organisms. In adults, elevated blood lead levels are associated with high blood pressure, heart disease, and stroke, and children are four to five times more susceptible to the harmful effects of lead than adults are. Elevated blood lead levels in children have led to problems such as increased hyperactivity, reduced attention span, interference with growth and neural transmission, and reading and learning disabilities. Over the many decades in which leaded gasoline was used, motor vehicle tailpipes spewed 7 million tons of lead dust into the environment and into people's systems.

As early as the 1920s, there was evidence that tetraethyl lead could become a public health problem. Several workers involved in testing the additive died suddenly from lead poisoning. Some

Figure 9.1 Most vehicles today use unleaded gasoline.

public health officials started to raise questions about the danger of adding the toxic substance to gasoline. However, these concerns did not prompt action to remove lead from gasoline until the 1960s, when new evidence of lead's harmful effects on people appeared.

In the 1970s, there was an explosion of new environmental laws, enacted to protect the public from the worst effects of environmental pollution. Lead in gasoline became a target of the newly created U.S. Environmental Protection Agency (EPA). With the legal clout to do so, the EPA used its power to begin a phaseout of lead in gasoline, starting in 1972. Although there was opposition, the evidence of lead's harmful effects on human health was too overwhelming to ignore. In addition, the catalytic converter (a pollution control device that carmakers adopted to meet lower auto exhaust emissions standards) was being used more. Lead ruined catalytic converters, giving automakers another reason to allow leaded gasoline to fade away. The phaseout continued until 1986, when lead was banned as an additive for gasoline in cars in the United States. Although lead has been gone from gasoline in the United States and several other developed countries for years, laws in many countries in Asia, Africa, Latin America, and Eastern Europe still allow the widespread use of leaded gasoline.

Lesson 9.1
Protecting Our Planet

Pollution isn't new. Back in 1273, an ordinance was passed in England to limit the burning of coal because of the soot it created. What *is* new is the high volume and great toxicity of pollution produced in modern times. People have a great ability to extract and use natural resources and change Earth's surface. In the process, people have caused incredible environmental damage.

By the 1960s, the evidence of serious environmental damage in the United States seemed to be everywhere. Pollutants such as smog and soot regularly enveloped many urban areas. Sites where hazardous waste had been dumped for years were endangering local communities and groundwater supplies. Years of mining with few if any restrictions had left huge, ugly gashes in Earth's surface. Piles of mine wastes dotted these landscapes, leaching toxic chemicals into nearby streams, rivers, and lakes. The waters of many rivers and lakes had been used as sewers for years and contained a toxic mix of chemicals and sewage. Probably the most memorable symbol of the terrible state of the environment at the time was the Cuyahoga River, near Cleveland, Ohio. Loaded with industrial waste, the river actually caught fire in 1969. Many people made jokes about the river, but it had become clear that the nation's environmental problems were serious and had to be addressed.

Figure 9.2 Firefighters work to control the fire on the Cuyahoga River as it engulfs a tugboat.

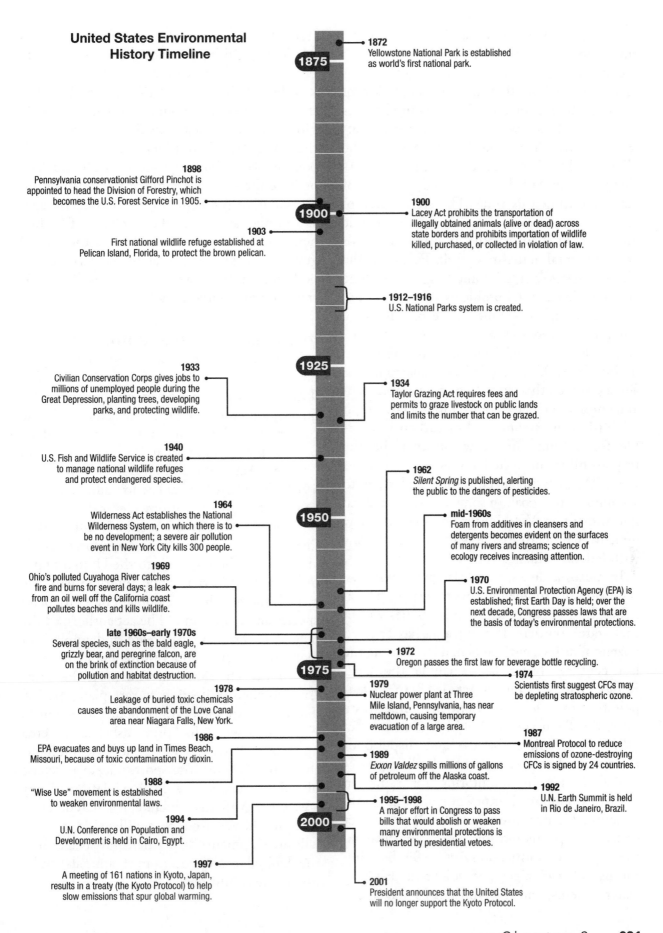

United States Environmental History Timeline

1872
Yellowstone National Park is established as world's first national park.

1875

1898
Pennsylvania conservationist Gifford Pinchot is appointed to head the Division of Forestry, which becomes the U.S. Forest Service in 1905.

1900

1900
Lacey Act prohibits the transportation of illegally obtained animals (alive or dead) across state borders and prohibits importation of wildlife killed, purchased, or collected in violation of law.

1903
First national wildlife refuge established at Pelican Island, Florida, to protect the brown pelican.

1912–1916
U.S. National Parks system is created.

1925

1933
Civilian Conservation Corps gives jobs to millions of unemployed people during the Great Depression, planting trees, developing parks, and protecting wildlife.

1934
Taylor Grazing Act requires fees and permits to graze livestock on public lands and limits the number that can be grazed.

1940
U.S. Fish and Wildlife Service is created to manage national wildlife refuges and protect endangered species.

1962
Silent Spring is published, alerting the public to the dangers of pesticides.

1950

1964
Wilderness Act establishes the National Wilderness System, on which there is to be no development; a severe air pollution event in New York City kills 300 people.

mid-1960s
Foam from additives in cleansers and detergents becomes evident on the surfaces of many rivers and streams; science of ecology receives increasing attention.

1969
Ohio's polluted Cuyahoga River catches fire and burns for several days; a leak from an oil well off the California coast pollutes beaches and kills wildlife.

1970
U.S. Environmental Protection Agency (EPA) is established; first Earth Day is held; over the next decade, Congress passes laws that are the basis of today's environmental protections.

late 1960s–early 1970s
Several species, such as the bald eagle, grizzly bear, and peregrine falcon, are on the brink of extinction because of pollution and habitat destruction.

1972
Oregon passes the first law for beverage bottle recycling.

1975

1974
Scientists first suggest CFCs may be depleting stratospheric ozone.

1978
Leakage of buried toxic chemicals causes the abandonment of the Love Canal area near Niagara Falls, New York.

1979
Nuclear power plant at Three Mile Island, Pennsylvania, has near meltdown, causing temporary evacuation of a large area.

1986
EPA evacuates and buys up land in Times Beach, Missouri, because of toxic contamination by dioxin.

1987
Montreal Protocol to reduce emissions of ozone-destroying CFCs is signed by 24 countries.

1989
Exxon Valdez spills millions of gallons of petroleum off the Alaska coast.

1988
"Wise Use" movement is established to weaken environmental laws.

1992
U.N. Earth Summit is held in Rio de Janeiro, Brazil.

1995–1998
A major effort in Congress to pass bills that would abolish or weaken many environmental protections is thwarted by presidential vetoes.

1994
U.N. Conference on Population and Development is held in Cairo, Egypt.

2000

1997
A meeting of 161 nations in Kyoto, Japan, results in a treaty (the Kyoto Protocol) to help slow emissions that spur global warming.

2001
President announces that the United States will no longer support the Kyoto Protocol.

Although there were laws related to the environment before then, the 1970s marked the beginning of the enactment of dozens of important laws that are the foundation of environmental protection in the United States today. The 1960s were a time of tremendous citizen activism in the United States. The Civil Rights Movement and the women's rights movement both reached a peak of activity during this time. The seriousness of environmental problems and a growing public awareness of them created an atmosphere for environmental activism as well. People in the United States wanted something to be done about environmental problems.

Responding to public concerns, the U.S. Congress passed a number of federal environmental laws. Federal laws apply to the whole nation. In each case, a federal department or agency writes the regulations that implement and enforce each law. For example, a law might establish a maximum level of carbon monoxide for outdoor air. It would then be the responsibility of a federal agency, such as the EPA, to write specific rules and steps to accomplish this goal. In some cases, the federal government in Washington enforces the law directly. In other cases, the states enforce the law with federal guidance.

In most instances, states also pass their own statewide environmental laws to deal with local issues. In that case, the law only applies within that state's borders. Pennsylvania has enacted dozens of its own environmental laws during the last century. These laws include the Coal Refuse Disposal Control Act (1968) to prevent pollution from leaching from coal mine waste piles, the Pennsylvania Pesticide Control Act (1974) to regulate the use and disposal of pesticides, the Environmental Radiation Act (1979) to require monitoring for radiation releases around nuclear power plants, the Wild Resource Conservation Act (1982) to protect endangered plants and animals in Pennsylvania, the Lead Ban Notification Act (1989) banning the use of lead pipes and solder in drinking water systems, and the Nutrient Management Act (1993) to establish a program to control nutrient (fertilizer) runoff from farms into Pennsylvania's surface waters.

Where federal standards are established, a state cannot establish standards that are weaker. However, it can enact a law that is stronger than the federal law. California has enacted many air pollution laws that are stronger than federal laws because the state has some of the most serious air pollution problems in the nation. Because California has been at the forefront of finding new ways to reduce air pollution, the federal government and several states have copied air pollution control laws that began as California state environmental laws.

Important Environmental Laws

The U.S. Congress has passed many important environment laws during the last few decades. These laws cover air quality, water quality, solid waste and toxic substances, wildlife conservation, land use, and workplace safety. Some of the most important laws are listed below.

Lacey Act (1900, amended 1935, 1945, 1981) The first federal law to address wildlife conservation on a nationwide scale, this act prohibited interstate shipment of wildlife killed illegally according to state or territorial law. It also banned the import into the United States of exotic species that could interfere with the growth and healthy development of native plant species and crop plants. The act authorized the federal government to create and implement plans to preserve and restore populations of game birds. The 1981 amendments to the Lacey Act extended protection to rare plant species. They also extended government protection to fish species, which had previously been covered under other laws. Today, the Lacey Act prohibits the import, export, transport, sale, or purchase of wildlife taken or sold in violation of any law, whether that law is state, tribal, federal, or foreign. The act also makes it illegal to mislabel wildlife shipments, bring harmful species into the United States, or import animals under inhumane conditions.

Wilderness Act (1964) This law established the National Wilderness System to protect undeveloped public land from mining, oil drilling, logging, grazing, and other similar activities. Today, about 4 percent of U.S. land is contained in national wilderness areas. An overwhelming majority of this acreage is in Alaska. A huge area of the United States (by some estimates, about 150,000 square miles) that could be included in the wilderness system is not part of it because of pressure from mining, lumber, ranching, and other interests that want these areas to stay open for development.

National Environmental Policy Act (1969) The NEPA is considered one of the most important of all environmental laws. It requires federal agencies to consider the environmental effects of any of their actions when they undertake, finance, or issue permits for a project. The list of possible environmental effects of a project must be written up in an Environmental Impact Statement (EIS). The EIS includes details of the specific project and its probable impact on air, water, soil, and living organisms. If the project is expected to have an adverse ecological impact, the EIS must

How Laws Are Made

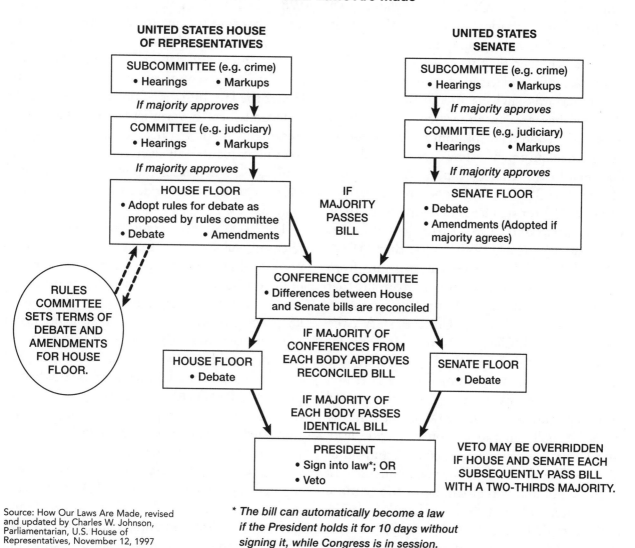

Source: How Our Laws Are Made, revised and updated by Charles W. Johnson, Parliamentarian, U.S. House of Representatives, November 12, 1997

* *The bill can automatically become a law if the President holds it for 10 days without signing it, while Congress is in session.*

Figure 9.3 Environmental laws follow the same research, revision, and approval process as do other laws.

also include alternatives that would have less negative environmental impacts. For example, engineers may plan to build a federal highway over a section of wetland. The EIS must show alternative routes and designs that may have less of an environmental impact. In this case, the EIS would include routes that would not disturb the wetland. The NEPA does not apply to the actions of state or local governments or private parties, but many states have passed their own versions of the NEPA, often called "baby NEPAs." Some of these state laws are stricter than the federal law, requiring an EIS for any project, regardless of its source.

Occupational Safety and Health Act (1970) This act created the Occupational Safety and Health Administration (OSHA). OSHA is concerned with making sure that people are safe at work, whether they work in an office or a factory. The act protects workers from safety and health hazards such as excess heat or cold, chemical hazards, unsanitary conditions, high noise levels, and dangers from faulty or poorly designed equipment. The act created the National Institute for Occupational Safety and Health (NIOSH), which does research that helps OSHA set standards for workplace safety. OSHA is part of the U.S. Department of Labor.

Clean Air Act (1970, amended 1977, 1990) The CAA regulates air emissions from a number of sources in an attempt to ensure that people in the United States breathe air that is not harmful to their health. Under the CAA, the EPA has established "national ambient air quality standards," or NAAQS, for several atmospheric pollutants known to be potential health hazards. Six of these pollutants, called criteria pollutants, are in the table on the facing page. The pollutants are carbon monoxide, lead, nitrogen oxides, ozone, particulates, and sulfur dioxide. The NAAQS set the maximum amount of these pollutants that can be in the outdoor air. If areas of a state have levels of these pollutants that exceed the NAAQS, the state must come up with a State Implementation Plan (SIP) specifying air pollution control measures that will be followed to bring the air

pollution levels down so that they comply with the CAA standards.

The CAA also establishes emissions standards that specify the maximum amount of certain harmful pollutants that sources such as factories, cars, and buses can release into the air. As a result of the Clean Air Act standards, for example, automakers have produced cars that produce less pollution, and many industrial facilities have installed pollution control devices on their smokestacks. The 1990 CAA amendments require the sale of "cleaner burning gasoline or other fuels" in several cities with serious ozone problems, including Philadelphia.

Clean Water Act (1972, amended 1977, 1981, 1987) The goal of the Clean Water Act was to improve the quality of the nation's rivers, streams, lakes, and bays, making them suitable for swimming and fishing. Two main targets of the CWA were sewage and industrial pollutants. Under the law, billions of dollars were given to state and local governments to build sewage treatment plants (also called wastewater treatment plants) all over the country. These plants greatly decreased the amount of untreated waste pouring into surface waters from sewer systems.

The CWA also required each facility releasing substances into U.S. waters to get a permit that would set limits for specific pollutants, depending on the industry involved. The facilities were required for the first time to keep strict records of all releases of pollution into surface waters. The law specified that these records would be open to the public and that citizens could sue facilities that violated their permits. The CWA's citizen suit provision has often been used to stop the release of pollution into surface waters and to punish violators responsible for such releases.

Endangered Species Act (1973) As you learned in Chapter 7, the ESA authorized the government to identify endangered and threatened plant and animal species and place them under protection to prevent their extinction. It also required the government's lead agencies in this area, the U.S. Fish and Wildlife Service

Major Human-Made Air Pollutants

Pollutant	Description	Sources	Effects
Carbon monoxide (CO)	Colorless, odorless gas	• Vehicles burning gasoline • Kerosene- or wood-burning stoves	• Causes headaches • Reduces mental alertness • Causes heart damage • Causes death
Lead (Pb)	Metallic element	• Vehicles burning leaded gasoline • Metal refineries	• Causes brain and kidney damage • Contaminates crops and livestock
Nitrogen oxides (NO_x)	Several gaseous compounds made up of nitrogen and oxygen	• Vehicles • Power plants burning fossil fuels • Coal-burning stoves	• Damages lungs • Reacts in atmosphere to form acid rain • Deteriorates buildings and statues • Damages forests • Forms ozone and other pollutants (smog)
Ozone (O_3)	Gaseous pollutant	• Vehicle exhaust and certain other fumes • Other air pollutants in the presence of sunlight	• Damages lungs • Irritates eyes • Causes respiratory tract problems • Damages vegetation • Creates smog
Particulate matter	Very small particles of soot, dust, or other matter, including tiny droplets of liquids	• Diesel engines • Power plants • Industries • Windblown dust • Wood stoves	• Damages lungs • Irritates eyes • Damages crops • Reduces visibility • Discolors buildings and statues
Sulfur dioxide (SO_2)	Gaseous compound made up of sulfur and oxygen	• Coal-burning power plants and industries • Coal-burning stoves • Refineries	• Irritates eyes • Damages lungs • Kills aquatic life • Reacts in atmosphere to form acid rain • Damages forests • Deteriorates buildings and statues

Figure 9.4 The criteria pollutants listed in this chart are monitored by the Clean Air Act.

and the National Marine Fisheries Service, to create plans to protect the habitats of threatened or endangered species and to devise plans to help species recover.

Federal Insecticide, Fungicide, and Rodenticide Act (1972) Under this law the federal government was granted the authority to control the distribution, sale, and use of pesticides. The FIFRA requires farmers, utility companies, and other large-scale users of hazardous pesticides to register when purchasing these chemicals. The law also requires people who handle and apply these pesticides to take tests and receive certification stating that they know how to handle the pesticides safely. The FIFRA requires companies that make pesticides to register them with the EPA. The EPA then monitors the products to make sure that they are properly labeled when sold and will not cause excessive harm to the environment, wildlife, or people.

Safe Drinking Water Act (1974, amended 1977, 1986) The SDWA protects drinking water supplies by requiring public drinking water systems to test regularly for several dozen contaminants that can harm human health. The U.S. government has set what are called "maximum contaminant levels" for these pollutants. Drinking water is not considered safe if pollutants exceed these levels. If testing reveals contamination, the water utility must notify the public of the problem, and steps must be taken to correct it.

Resource Conservation and Recovery Act (1976, amended 1984, 1986) The RCRA deals primarily with the production, transportation, treatment, storage, and disposal of any waste considered hazardous. Under the RCRA, generators of hazardous waste must keep strict track of how much they produce, where it is shipped, and where it is sent for disposal. Hazardous waste can only be disposed of in specially designated hazardous waste facilities that are constructed to prevent release of the waste into the environment. The RCRA also strictly regulates the transportation of hazardous wastes, requiring specially permitted trucks to operate along specific routes.

Toxic Substance Control Act (1976) The TSCA regulates toxic substances. Under it, the EPA can track the approximately 75,000 industrial chemicals currently produced in or

Figure 9.5 Farmer preparing to insecticide field. Wearing a protective mask, a farmer opens a bag of insecticide to be used on the fields.

imported into the United States. Periodically, the EPA reviews the composition and effects of these chemicals. The EPA can require manufacturers to conduct further tests on substances it considers potentially dangerous. It can also require companies producing substances it considers potentially harmful to the natural environment or human health to file regular reports on those chemicals.

Manufacturers must also list and report any new substances they produce and must report to the EPA on their toxicity. Although the EPA rarely uses this power, it can stop the production of any substance it considers too dangerous or for which there is not enough information to determine its effects. Under the TSCA, the EPA can also ban a substance already in use if it considers the substance a threat to human health and the environment.

Surface Mining Control and Reclamation Act (1977) This law attempts to minimize the negative effects of mining, such as scarring of Earth's surface and leaching of pollution from abandoned mines or mine wastes. Because mining has been an important activity in Pennsylvania for hundreds of years, the state has a number of mining laws that predate this act.

Comprehensive Environmental Response, Compensation, and Liability (Superfund) Act (1980, amended 1986, 1990) While the RCRA deals with hazardous waste produced now, the CERCLA deals with hazardous waste that was produced and disposed of in the past—often illegally and always unsafely. Sites that come under the CERCLA jurisdiction are those that threaten the natural environment or the health of the public. The sites that pose the greatest risk are placed on the National Priorities List (NPL). The federal government usually begins cleanup of these sites and then tries to locate the party responsible to "make the polluter pay." Pennsylvania has about 93 NPL sites, but that number changes as old sites are cleaned up and new ones are added. The law also created a tax on the chemical and petroleum industries. The money became part of a trust fund—the Superfund—that is used to clean

Figure 9.6 This Superfund site was once the location of a uranium refinement plant. Workers are removing 70,000 tons of radioactive soil.

up hazardous waste sites when the site is abandoned or the party responsible for the damage cannot be determined.

Food Security Act (1985) This legislation, also called the "Farm Bill," includes provisions that deal with preserving the natural environment on farmlands. Among other provisions, the act provides increased protection for wetlands and encourages soil conservation on soils subject to high levels of erosion.

Water Quality Act (1987) This amendment to the Clean Water Act establishes additional controls on toxic pollutant discharges in "hot spot" areas where pollution problems are especially severe. The act requires states to develop measures to control nonpoint water pollution sources, such as runoff from farm fields and mine and construction sites, as well as developed urban areas. The legislation also continues assistance to local and state government for the building of wastewater treatment plants.

Environmental Laws at Work

Environmental lawyers have used the nation's environmental laws to fight air pollution, clean up rivers and lakes, preserve forests and wetlands, rid the environment of toxic substances, force polluters to pay for cleanups, and ensure compliance with government regulations by industry and government itself.

Before 1970, environmental lawyers had few laws to use to help them bring cases to court to protect the environment. However, they are now armed with many laws they can use as legal weapons. Here are a few examples of U.S. environmental law at work.

Chesapeake Bay Rescue In this case, plaintiffs (those bringing the suit) used the citizen suit provision of the Clean Water Act to stop an industrial facility from discharging illegal levels of pollutants into the Chesapeake Bay. Under the provisions of the Clean Water Act, factories and other facilities are allowed to discharge a certain amount of pollutants into nearby surface waters, but they cannot exceed this limit. The factories must also keep records of their discharges. In the mid-1980s, a Bethlehem Steel wastewater treatment plant was found to be discharging pollutants such as oil, zinc, and chromium into the Chesapeake Bay above the limits set by its permits under the Clean Water Act. Concerned about the large amount of pollutants entering the bay from the plant, two environmental organizations, the Chesapeake Bay Foundation and the Natural Resources Defense Council, sued Bethlehem Steel to force the company to stop violating its discharge permits. The company settled the suit out of court for $1.5 million and agreed to increase treatment levels to ensure that less pollution from the plant would enter the bay.

Stopping Delaware River Pollution In the late 1980s, a group of citizens living along the Delaware River and an environmental group used the provisions of the Clean Water Act to

Figure 9.7 Toxic pollution released into waterways damages ecosystems, pollutes drinking water, kills organisms, and causes illness.

sue Texaco for environmental damage it had caused to the Delaware River. The suit claimed that a Texaco facility along the river had, over a period of several years, released tons of oil, grease, and other toxic pollutants into the river at levels that violated its discharge permits. As a result, water quality downriver from the plant had suffered. After several years of litigation, the oil company lost its case and was forced to pay more than $1.5 million in fines for its Clean Water Act violations. The court also forced Texaco to undertake a comprehensive environmental study of the river to determine the environmental damage its pollution had done to both water quality and the river's aquatic ecosystem. The company was then required to repair the damage.

Nuclear Waste Safety A group of environmental organizations and local Native American tribes sued the U.S. Department of Energy (DOE) in early 2000 for violation of the Nuclear Waste Policy Act. The act requires the DOE to bury all high-level radioactive waste deep underground in a secure waste depository.

The suit charged that the DOE illegally reclassified high-level waste into a less dangerous category so that it could be disposed of more quickly and cheaply. Groups in Washington and Idaho with members living near the sites where the government proposed to keep the waste were plaintiffs in the suit. They feared that leaving the waste in underground tanks (some of which were already leaking) under concrete caps, rather than moving it to a more secure site, could endanger local groundwater and surface water supplies. The case is now going forward after a federal judge turned down the DOE's attempt to have it dismissed.

Drinking Water Protection The state of Nevada and several environmental groups sued the EPA in 2001 for actions that, among other things, violated standards of the Safe Drinking Water Act. The U.S. government plans to locate a permanent depository for high-level nuclear waste at Yucca Mountain, Nevada, against the wishes of the state's government. The state of Nevada insists that the waste could leak into groundwater supplies that are used locally for drinking water and irrigation, violating Safe Drinking Water Act health standards. The suit contends that the EPA manipulated data to minimize the possible negative health impact of the waste on drinking water supplies and thus ensure that the site could be used for waste disposal. The case has not yet been decided.

Cleaning Up Mercury Pollution In early 2002, a trial began in Maine in which an environmental group and local citizens sued a chemical plant for polluting the Penobscot River with mercury, a toxic metal known to be harmful to human health and to wildlife. The suit was brought under the provisions of the Resource Conservation and Recovery Act. As a result of the lawsuit, the plaintiffs hope to force the former and present owners of the factory (now closed) that released the pollution to pay for a study that will determine the effects that the mercury pollution has had downriver of the plant. The polluters will then be forced to clean up the contamination they left behind.

Figure 9.8 Despite protests from local residents and the state government, the nuclear waste repository at Yucca Mountain continues construction and is expected to open in 2010.

Clearing the Air Environmental groups went to court in 2001 to force the EPA to comply with the Clean Air Act and come up with a plan to reduce ground-level ozone concentrations in both Houston and Galveston, Texas. These two cities have severe smog problems and ground-level ozone levels that have exceeded the CAA's ozone health standards more than any other region in the nation. Under the CAA rules, the state of Texas was forced to come up with a State Implementation Plan to bring down ground-level ozone levels. The environmental groups sued when the EPA accepted a Texas plan that would not have brought ozone levels down far enough to be in compliance with the CAA's health standards. The suit would force the EPA to devise a new plan to decrease ozone concentrations to a point at which the air in Houston and Galveston does not violate health standards for ozone.

Saving a Swamp At times, environmental groups and others sue the government for failure to enforce environmental laws. At other times, environmental groups will join a lawsuit on the side of the government to defend the government's position. This gives the government position added weight and support. This happened in a case in Massachusetts several years ago. A company wanted to build a shopping mall on an area of wetlands called Sweedens Swamp. The EPA denied the permit because it said that the company could have used another site nearby that would not have required destroying wetlands. The company sued the EPA to overturn the agency's denial of

its permit. Several environmental groups joined the lawsuit on the side of the EPA, supporting the EPA's denial of the permit and protection of the wetlands. The shopping mall builder lost the suit, and the wetland was saved.

Protecting Endangered Species Two environmental laws, the NEPA and the Endangered Species Act, temporarily stopped construction of a dam in the 1960s. The Tennessee Valley Authority (TVA) decided to build the Tellico Dam across the Little Tennessee River. The dam, which would have flooded farms and homes in the Little Tennessee's valley, would have provided some hydroelectric power, but it was not crucial to the area. TVA started construction in the late 1960s. Opponents of the dam first took the TVA to court to force it to comply with the NEPA and prepare an EIS that would both detail the environmental effects of the dam and propose alternatives.

The environmental law that made the greatest impact in this case, however, was the Endangered Species Act. In 1973, a zoologist from the University of Tennessee discovered a small fish, the snail darter, which appeared to live in only a small portion of the Little Tennessee River—the same portion slated to be flooded by Tellico Dam. Because there were only a few thousand of these fish living in this small stretch of river, the fish was classified as an endangered species. With that designation, its habitat had to be protected. The TVA speeded up work on the dam, hoping to get it finished before opponents could act to stop it, but an environmental group sued. Initially, the environmentalists lost their

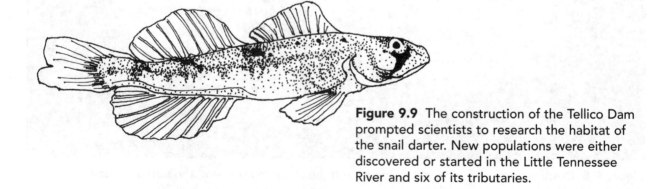

Figure 9.9 The construction of the Tellico Dam prompted scientists to research the habitat of the snail darter. New populations were either discovered or started in the Little Tennessee River and six of its tributaries.

bid to have the dam stopped because most of it had already been completed, but they prevailed on appeal. The building of the dam was stopped with the structure about 80 percent complete. Newspaper headlines had a great time making fun of the ruling, stating that a tiny fish had stopped a huge dam. Nonetheless, the Endangered Species Act had worked as a wildlife preservation tool—at least for a while.

The TVA did not give up the fight to save the dam. In 1979, it won an exemption from the Endangered Species Act in court. The dam was completed, and some of the snail darters were removed from the Little Tennessee and placed in a nearby river to help ensure their survival.

Figure 9.10 When full, landfills are covered and grass and trees are planted to restore the land.

Impacts of Environmental Laws: Preserving Land, Protecting Wildlife and Human Health

When environmental laws were enacted, some of them decades ago, they had very ambitious goals. For example, some legislators thought the Clean Water Act could eliminate the discharge of all toxic materials into surface waters within a few years of its passage. These types of ambitious goals have generally not been met, but environmental laws have achieved many positive results. For example:

- As a result of the Clean Air Act, levels of carbon monoxide, sulfur dioxide, small particulates, nitrogen oxides, and ground-level ozone have all decreased. In 1990 alone, CAA regulations limiting emissions from smokestacks and vehicles saved an estimated 79,000 lives and prevented 15 million respiratory illnesses.
- Since the early years of the phaseout of lead in gasoline ordered by the EPA in the 1970s, the average level of toxic lead in the blood of people in the United States has dropped more than 75 percent.

- The Clean Water Act has increased the number of U.S. lakes and rivers that are now categorized as "fishable and swimmable." Between 1972 and 1997, that percentage rose from 36 percent to more than 60 percent.

Environmental laws have made our air and water cleaner. They have protected our homes, workplaces, and food supplies from many hazardous chemicals. They have preserved some of the most spectacular wild places in our country from destruction and maintained biodiversity by protecting species. Environmental laws have given us safer drinking water and protected us from the health threats of toxic substances such as lead and mercury.

Although the United States has many useful laws to protect the environment, these laws are often under attack. Some members of Congress and some U.S. presidents who believe that environmental laws are too restrictive for businesses have tried to weaken them. In some cases, they have succeeded. Keeping environmental laws strong involves a constant struggle between competing interests.

Case Study

Chesapeake 2000 Agreement

People have lived along the Chesapeake Bay, the nation's largest and most productive estuary, for hundreds of years. They have taken fish and drinking water from it. They have used it for recreation and transportation. However, they have also allowed sewage, factory waste, and chemical-filled farm runoff to pour into it. They have destroyed wetlands and forests along its shores. In addition, people have taken so many fish from the bay's waters and harmed so many species with pollution that the bay's natural ecosystem is in trouble.

In 1987, a coalition of people in several states, including Pennsylvania, agreed to work together to restore the water quality and aquatic ecosystem of the Chesapeake Bay. So much work remains to be done that in 2000, they rededicated themselves to the task and established new goals for improving the environmental quality of the bay.

The states of Maryland and Virginia were participants in this new agreement, called the Chesapeake 2000 Agreement. These states surround the bay. Pennsylvania is also a participant because the bay's major tributary, the Susquehanna River, flows through Pennsylvania. Any attempt to improve water quality in the bay will involve its entire watershed, including the Susquehanna. The Susquehanna splits the eastern half of Pennsylvania. Its watershed includes large metropolitan areas such as Lancaster, Harrisburg, Scranton, and Wilkes-Barre. What happens in Pennsylvania along the Susquehanna River and its many tributaries will ultimately affect the Chesapeake Bay.

The Chesapeake 2000 Agreement has five main goals: 1) restoring and protecting the Chesapeake Bay ecosystem; 2) restoring habitats and other natural areas that are crucial to supporting plant and animal species of the bay; 3) improving the bay's water quality; 4) promoting the type of land use along the shores of the bay and its tributaries that will prevent deterioration of the natural environment; and 5) involving communities around the bay and its tributaries in restoring and protecting it.

Although Pennsylvanians won't have a hand in implementing the parts of the plan that deal directly with the bay's waters and living species, the Chesapeake 2000

Figure 9.11 The Chesapeake Bay watershed covers parts of six states: New York, Pennsylvania, Maryland, Delaware, West Virginia, and Virginia.

Agreement gives Pennsylvanians plenty of goals to meet in the Susquehanna watershed. For example, some fish that live in the upper reaches of the bay also migrate up rivers such as the Susquehanna. One goal is to remove blockages that prevent the movement of migratory fish upstream. This action can help increase the populations of these species. To meet the goal of habitat protection, Pennsylvania hopes to develop a watershed management plan for the Susquehanna and its tributaries that includes the restoration and preservation of buffer corridors of forest and wetland along the watershed's rivers and streams. These forest and wetland buffer areas help maintain water quality, serve as habitat and breeding grounds for waterfowl and other aquatic organisms, and prevent erosion of sediment. Sediment makes waters cloudy, reducing the ability of aquatic plants to undergo photosynthesis. Too much sediment can disrupt aquatic food webs.

Pollution is a huge problem in the Chesapeake that affects both plants and animals in this ecosystem. Pennsylvania and the other participants in the agreement have pledged to reduce the amount of fertilizer runoff coming from farms and entering tributary rivers and streams. Another goal is to make the bay free of toxins by eliminating all sources of toxic pollution discharges into the bay. The elimination of toxins would prevent the bioaccumulation of these harmful chemicals in the bay's living organisms, especially those organisms at the top of the bay's food web. Pennsylvania will also attempt to reduce the release of pesticides into waters that will eventually enter the bay and decrease the discharge of sewage from boats on the Susquehanna and other rivers.

Because population is increasing in the Chesapeake Bay and Susquehanna River watershed—an additional 3 million people are projected by 2020—all improvements must take into account the increased environmental pressures created by millions of new people in the area. Because this increase in people will mean the need to use more resources, the Chesapeake 2000 partners also have the goal of finding ways to use resources sustainably. That means reducing the sprawling development that chews up forests and wetlands that border the bay and its tributaries. It also means tightening controls on sewage treatment, abandoned waste sites, and discharges into the bay.

Finally, the Chesapeake 2000 Agreement hopes to involve people in communities throughout the watershed in the bay's revival. There will be attempts to educate the public about the problems of the Chesapeake watershed and to involve as many people as possible in local projects. With their input and assistance, the hope is that the people and local communities in Pennsylvania, Maryland, Virginia, and Washington, DC, will help make the program work.

Questions

1. List the main goals of the Chesapeake 2000 Agreement.

2. Summarize the problems faced by the Chesapeake Bay ecosystem.

3. Why is Pennsylvania involved in the agreement, even though it does not border the Chesapeake?

4. List three specific actions Pennsylvania will have to take in order to meet the goals of the agreement.

5. Infer why the participants in the agreement want to get local communities and local people involved in implementing the plan.

Impacts of Environmental Laws: Economic Problems and Conflicting Rights of Property Owners

Everyone wants a clean and healthy environment, but not everyone agrees on how to achieve it. Some people believe that many of the federal environmental laws discussed in this chapter are too strict and unnecessarily costly.

Pollution control equipment costs factories and power plants a lot of money. Companies that make motor vehicles, for example, had to spend a great deal of money over the last few decades to redesign cars so that they would emit less pollution and get better gas mileage. Many companies resent the need to spend this money because it eats into their profits. In some cases, they believe that environmental laws and regulations place unnecessary and costly restrictions on their operations. Some companies have moved their businesses to rural areas or even other countries to take advantage of less strict environmental controls, cheaper labor, and lower taxes.

Some people believe that some environmental laws restrict their right to use their land as they please. For example, a homeowner might have a house that sits on three acres of land, one acre of which is wetland. Perhaps the owner wants to fill part of the wetland with soil and build a toolshed or garage on it. He or she probably can't fill the area with soil because federal regulations will not allow destruction of a wetland. This is called a regulatory taking. A *regulatory taking* is when government regulations take away, without compensation, the right of a property owner to do certain things with the property. Takings have been an area of conflict between people who support strong environmental laws and those who believe that the laws should be relaxed.

Opposition to environmental laws also comes from people who think the laws cost jobs. This was the conflict in the spotted owl controversy in the Pacific Northwest in the early 1990s.

The northern spotted owl lives in old-growth forests in western Washington and Oregon and northern California. Old-growth forests are complex and diverse ecosystems with towering conifers hundreds and sometimes more than a thousand years old. Just one tree in such a forest can shelter hundreds of species of invertebrates and plants. With fewer than 4,000 pairs of owls remaining in this habitat, the U.S. Fish and Wildlife Service listed the northern spotted owl as "threatened" in 1990 under the provisions of the Endangered Species Act.

When the owl was listed, its habitat immediately became federally protected. Biologists and environmental groups saw protecting the owl as an opportunity to preserve the old-growth forests by stopping the extensive logging in the area.

Charging that the logging allowed by the U.S. government was not protecting the forest ecosystem that sheltered the owls, a federal judge in Seattle ordered a ban on logging on 24 million acres of national forests in the Pacific Northwest in 1994. Most logging was restricted to forest areas that had previously been cut.

Figure 9.12 Automakers are now redesigning vehicles to meet new federal standards for low emissions. Many low-emission vehicles already display a sticker such as the one shown above. Low-emission regulations will become standard in 2004.

Figure 9.13 Many loggers protested the ban on logging to save the spotted owl and its old-growth forest habitat.

A great deal of tension followed the decision to halt logging in these areas. Biologists who wanted to preserve the forest were pleased that clear-cutting of the old-growth forest had stopped, but timber corporations saw the moratorium on logging in the national forest areas as an unreasonable and unnecessary intrusion on their business. Loggers joined protests, carrying signs with slogans such as "Loggers are an endangered species, too." The loggers had a right to be fearful.

Because of the restrictions and several other factors, the amount of timber cut from national forests in Washington and Oregon dropped from 6.4 billion board feet to less than 1 billion board feet between 1988 and 1997. More than 20 percent of timber employees lost their jobs during that time, although less than half of the job losses were due to protection of the spotted owl and the old-growth forests. Since that time, the economy in the area has rebounded.

The owl population has been helped by preserving some areas of old-growth forest. The population is still dwindling, but at a slightly slower rate. According to scientists, it could take 40 years before the owl population stabilizes and stops decreasing.

In many cases, huge conflicts have developed between those who want to uphold environmental laws and regulations and those who are willing to break them because they find them unreasonable. In the mid-1980s, the U.S. Fish and Wildlife Service decided to reintroduce the gray wolf into the area around Yellowstone National Park. Biologists thought that this predator would strengthen the Yellowstone area ecosystem. The gray wolf is natural to the area but was wiped out in the early 20th century by hunters and ranchers who didn't like the wolf's tendency to eat cattle and game animals. Local ranchers, loggers, and hunters did not like the idea of bringing the wolf back, so some of them vowed to destroy the program by killing the wolves. Opponents took the case to court and were able to halt the project for a while. Environmental groups that supported the reintroduction of this species, now very rare in the United States, appealed the decision, and the wolves remain.

Enforcing the Endangered Species Act

The house looked fairly normal from the outside, but officers with Pennsylvania's Fish and Boat Commission Nongame and Endangered Species Unit had gotten a tip that there was illegal activity going on inside. After months of investigation, they were ready to make their move. With a search warrant in hand, Pennsylvania and federal wildlife agents entered the house in Bedford County.

In the basement, the officers found what they were looking for—dozens of illegally captured reptiles and amphibians, many of them endangered. There were pens along the walls, holding several types of snakes and even an American alligator. Aquariums and a child's wading pool held many other animals, including several rare turtles.

Poaching, the illegal capture of wildlife, is a multi-million-dollar business in the United States today. Animals that are listed as "threatened" or "endangered" under the provisions of the Endangered Species Act cannot be collected, traded, or sold, but it still often happens.

Reptiles and amphibians are particularly popular with poachers. Many of the animals end up as pets in people's homes because they don't need constant attention. Unfortunately, many also end up dead within a short period of time because people often do not know how to care for them properly. Collectors, many in other countries, are also willing to pay large sums of money for animals caught in the United States.

Some people do not understand or want to understand the harm of poaching these animals. However, removing animals from the wild, especially those that are threatened or endangered, can do incredible harm to the population of a species in a particular ecosystem. Many reptiles, such as turtles, reproduce slowly. It takes them a long time to reach the age when they can have offspring. When they do reproduce, they often have very few offspring at a time. Healthy adults are the first individuals poachers seek out. When many healthy adults are removed from a species population that reproduces slowly, the population can easily be wiped out in an area.

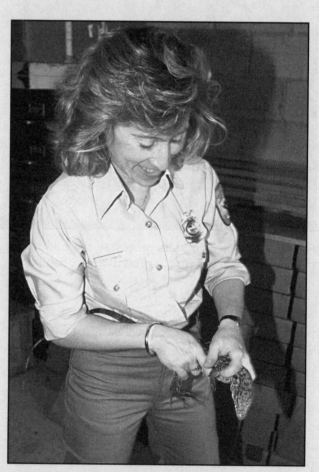

Figure 9.14 This Fish and Wildlife Services officer inspects an incoming shipment of wildlife to make sure that it does not violate any U.S. laws protecting threatened or endangered species.

You Solve It! *(continued)*

It is difficult to catch poachers, who are very secretive about their activities. Wildlife officers don't usually catch them in the act of poaching, and often agents actually have to see a person collecting a threatened or endangered animal to make a case against him or her. It can take months to build a case against a poacher, and often agents rely on tips from the public for leads.

Pennsylvania authorities did punish the Bedford County poacher. He was arrested and paid a $5,000 fine for his illegal activities. The U.S. Fish and Wildlife Service could also bring additional federal charges against the man for violation of the Endangered Species Act. That violation carries even more severe penalties.

Many members of the public are unknowing accomplices in poaching. They buy illegally collected animals without knowing where they came from. Wildlife officers believe that most people would not buy endangered animals if they were aware of the situation. The key is to know the species you are buying, deal with reputable pet shops, and ask the right questions. For example, if you buy a turtle from a pet shop, make sure that it is "captive-bred." That ensures that the animal was not born in the wild and captured illegally.

Questions

1. Define poaching.

2. Describe the market for poached reptiles and amphibians.

3. Explain why poaching animals such as turtles can be especially harmful to their populations in the wild.

4. How can members of the public avoid purchasing poached animals?

5. In your opinion, is poaching of threatened and endangered species an important problem? Explain your answer.

Lesson Review

1. Explain why a number of environmental laws were passed starting in the 1970s.

2. What are National Ambient Air Quality Standards, and how do they relate to the function of the Clean Air Act?

3. What was the goal of the Clean Water Act? What main tools did the act use to deal with the problems?

4. Discuss the positive and negative aspects of the Endangered Species Act.

5. Compare and contrast the Resource Conservation and Recovery Act and the Superfund Act.

6. Identify the law that protects drinking water supplies in the United States.

7. Explain how the National Environmental Policy Act protects the environment.

Glossary

A

abiotic factors nonliving physical and chemical parts of an ecosystem

acid deposition acid rain; droplets and solid particles with up to 1,000 times the acidity of normal rain

acid mine drainage exposure of pyrite to air and water during mining, causing sulfuric acid and iron hydroxide to form

adaptation special, inherited characteristic that helps an organism better survive in its environment and which is developed over time

algal blooms large masses of algae that are eaten by oxygen-using bacteria when they die

allergy reaction by the body to a foreign substance that, in similar amounts and circumstances, is harmless to most other people

asthma disorder of the lungs in which airways tend to constrict, resulting in episodes of breath-lessness, wheezing, coughing, and tightness of the chest

autotrophs algae that make their own food; producers

B

bed load sediment carried along the bottom of the channel of a stream or river

behavioral adaptation way in which an organism acts or responds to its environment in order to survive

biodiversity variety of living organisms on Earth

biological control using other living things that are enemies of a pest in order to control it

biomass fuels organic matter that contains stored solar energy

biome geographic region of Earth that is inhabited by a community of distinct types of plant and associated animal species

biomonitoring biological approach to moni-toring an ecosystem's health

biorational pesticide naturally occurring compound or a chemical such as a toxin or growth regulator derived from a living organism

biosphere layer of soil, water, and air that sustains life

biotechnology management or manipulation of living organisms for the benefit of people

biotic factors living components of an ecosystem

bog wetland in which soils consist predominantly of decom-posed plant material called peat or muck

C

carnivores animals that consume other animals

carrying capacity number of individuals of a species that an ecosystem can support

climax community community that keeps a fairly constant number and variety of organisms for a long period of time; forms in the last stage of succession

commensalism relationship in which one organism benefits while the other is not affected

community populations of living organisms that interact with one another in an ecosystem

composting biological method of waste disposal in which worms, bacteria, fungi, and other organisms decompose piles of fruit and vegetable food scraps, wood, and lawn clippings

condensation return of water vapor to a liquid state by cooling

condenser part of a turbine in which steam passes over pipes filled with cool water

coniferous forest forest in which coniferous, or cone-bearing, trees dominate

conservation careful use of a resource so that its supply will last longer

conservation tillage planting method in which farmers disturb surface topsoil and vegetation as little as possible

consumer organism that gets its energy and nutrients by feeding on other organisms

contour farming farming method in which farmers plow their fields and plant crops across the slope of the land instead of up and down the slope in order to help prevent water from running downhill and taking valuable soil with it

crop rotation changing of the crops planted in a field from year to year

cryptosporidium pathogen whose eggs can enter surface water when heavy rains increase the amount of animal wastes in runoff

D

deciduous describes a tree that survives during a cold or dry season by dropping its leaves

decomposer type of bacteria or fungus that breaks down dead organisms and wastes

desert area, either hot or cold, that typically gets less than 10 inches of rain each year

detritivores organisms that feed by either shredding sediments that enter a stream or river or by filtering their food directly from sediments in the water

divide any ridge between two streams along which precipitation runs off

drought period during which the amount of precipitation that falls in an area is lower than normal

drought emergency period during which agencies, suppliers, and users, including the general public, are asked or required to take measures to reduce water consumption by at least 15 percent

drought warning period during which measures are taken to avoid or reduce shortages, relieve stressed sources of water, and find new sources of fresh water

drought watch period during which governmental agencies, public water suppliers, water users, and the public are alerted to the possibility of drought

E

ecosystem group of living organisms that interact with one another and the nonliving physical environment as one unit

ecological succession process in which the communities of an ecosystem change over time

ecology scientific study of interactions between organisms and their environments

effluent wastewater from factories and refineries that is released directly into urban water supplies

emergent wetlands marshy areas where plants are rooted in soil but emerge above water

endangered species species that has so few individuals remaining that extinction is a possibility in the near future

energy pyramid shows the trophic levels in a food web and the amount of energy that moves from one level up to the next

evaporation process whereby the heat of the sun changes water on Earth's surface from a liquid to a gas

exotic pest insect or other organism that is not native to an area and is introduced to that area by some means

extinct species species that no longer exists

F

food and fiber system system that produces enough food to feed the more than 280 million people of the United States

food chain transfer of energy from one organism to another

food processing transformation of raw foodstuffs from the farm into the food that humans can consume

food web network that shows many connected food chains

forested wetlands areas where the dominant plant types include mature woody trees

fossil fuels fuels such as wood, charcoal, peat, coal, oil, and natural gas that release energy when burned

G

gene part of a cell that determines the characteristics that living things inherit from their parents

genetic engineering alteration of the physical characteristics of plants and animals by transferring genes

geothermal energy heat that is transferred by water, which can be brought to the surface and used to drive electric generators as well as to heat homes and other buildings

global warming unnatural warming of the average temperature of the atmosphere near Earth's surface as a result of the increase in atmospheric greenhouse gases such as carbon dioxide

gradient slope of a river channel

greenhouse effect natural process in which heat is trapped near Earth's surface by the atmosphere

green revolution modern farming method that uses scientifically produced varieties of grain (rice, wheat, corn) and fertilizers, pesticides, and water to increase crop yields

groundwater water from rain and melting snow that seeps into the ground and is stored beneath Earth's surface

H

habitat place where a particular species lives and from which it obtains what it needs for survival

herbivores animals that eat only plants; primary consumers in a food chain

heterotrophs animals and fungi that eat plant and animal matter in an ecosystem

homeostasis natural stability in an ecosystem that keeps it from undergoing radical change and helps it recover when stresses are so great that they cause serious problems

host plant resistance natural defense mechanisms of a plant, including physical adaptations, natural chemical resistance, and a tolerance to pest damage and defoliation, that ward off pests

humus mixture of decomposed organic matter in topsoil that supplies nutrients to plants and helps retain soil moisture

I

instinct behavior that an organism carries out because it is genetically prone to do so

integrated pest management (IPM) important pest management tool that uses a mix of methods such as traps, disease-resistant plants, and natural pest-killing substances, as well as the introduction of predators to control pests

L

landfill regulated area where wastes are placed in the land

limiting factor conditions of the environment that limit the growth of a species

longwall method procedure in mining in which a cutting head moves back and forth across a coal seam, causing pieces of coal to fall onto a flexible conveyor for removal from the mine

M

marsh wetland that generally forms at the mouth of a river or in areas where there is poor drainage

microbes very tiny pathogens, or organisms such as protists, bacteria, or viruses, that cause disease

mimicry adaptation in which one species copies the appearance or behavior of another species

mouth place where a stream or river ends by flowing into another body of water

multicropping practice of growing many crops together in the same field

municipal solid waste waste that consists of paper, yard waste, food, and plastics

mutualism symbiotic relationship in which both species benefit

N

natural pesticide pesticide that is made of natural (not synthesized) ingredients such as minerals mined from the earth (kaolin clay, diatomaceous earth), bacterial extracts, or plant extracts

natural selection process that makes it more likely that organisms with the best characteristics for survival in a specific environment will survive, reproduce, and pass on their advantageous genetic traits to offspring

niche role an organism plays within an ecosystem including the food it eats and how it obtains that food

nonpoint source (NPS) pollutants pollutants that are carried far from their sources by rain and melting snow and are eventually deposited in soil or into freshwater and groundwater systems

nonrenewable resource material or energy source that cannot be replaced during the time of a human life span

no-till cultivation process in which a machine drills holes in the topsoil for planting seeds without turning the soil over at all

O

omnivores animals that eat both plants and other animals and can be primary or secondary (or higher) consumers

ores mineral deposits from which valuable metals and nonmetals can be recovered at a profit

organism any form of life

P

pandemic outbreak of a disease that affects an exceptionally high portion of a population and occurs over a very large geographic area

parasitism relationship in which one species, the parasite, feeds on a second organism, the host

parasitoid insect that develops on or within an insect host, ultimately killing the host

pathogen disease-causing organisms that infect insects, plants, humans, and other animals

pest any organism that spreads disease, destroys property, competes with people for resources such as food, or is just a nuisance

pioneer species hardy species, including mosses and lichens, that is one of the first to establish itself at the start of the process of succession

point source (PS) pollutants contaminants that are discharged or emitted from an identifiable source

population group of individuals of the same species found in a given area or located in the same area at a given time

precipitation liquid or solid water that falls from clouds to Earth

predator natural enemy that feeds on an insect or pest

primary consumer herbivore or omnivore that feeds on plants

primary succession process of emergence of an ecosystem where it has never previously existed

producer organism that uses elements from the environment to make its own food

Q

quarry excavation pit in Earth's crust from which rock resources are removed

R

raptors protists in streams and rivers that eat other protists

reclamation restoration of mined land to its original condition by reconstructing the land's topography and replanting vegetation

recycling series of activities that reuse a product's raw materials to manufacture new products

reflex behavior that is triggered automatically by something outside an organism

regulatory taking situation in which government regulations take away, without compensation, the right of a property owner to do certain things with the property

renewable resource any material or energy source that cycles or can be replaced within the period of a human life span

room and pillar method mining method in which rooms are cut into a coal bed, leaving a series of pillars, or columns of coal, to help support the mine roof and control the flow of air

runoff precipitation that runs off the ground

S

saprotrophs protists that feed on decayed organic material

scavenger organism that feeds on dead organisms

scrub-shrub wetlands wetlands whose dominant plants are scrub and shrubs as well as trees that are less than 20 feet tall, such as alders and willows

secondary consumer carnivore or omnivore that feeds on primary consumers in an ecosystem

secondary succession process that begins in an ecosystem when something has disturbed or destroyed the natural community

sewage polluted water that contains human waste, garbage, and other household wastewater

shifting cultivation farming method in which farmers clear a plot of land in the forest, plant crops on it for a few years until the soil is depleted, and then move on to clear a different field

shredders organisms that eat the tissue of other organisms, organic matter, and wood

slash-and-burn agriculture farming method in which farmers clear fields by cutting the trees and burning the vegetation where it lies on the ground

smog brown, hazy cloud that forms when primary pollutants such as nitrogen oxides and hydrocarbons from vehicles and other sources combine in the presence of sunlight to form secondary pollutants such as ground-level ozone, formaldehyde, and nitric acid

soil upper layer of land surface that all growing things use for physical support, water, and nutrients

soil horizon arrangement of different soil layers composed of several types of soil

solar energy energy from the sun

source place where a stream or river begins

source reduction alteration of the design, manufacture, or use of materials to reduce the amount and toxicity of the waste generated

species group of organisms that are alike in several ways, including appearance and genetic makeup, and that can breed with one another to produce healthy offspring

strip cropping planting method in which wide rows or strips of crops such as corn are planted alternately with rows of a grass or legume crop

structural adaptation physical characteristic that helps an organism survive in its environment

subsistence farming farming method that just meets a farmer's survival needs

substrate material that organisms live in, on, or around

swamp forested wetland in which trees and bushes are the dominant plants

symbiosis relationship in which organisms live closely together over a long period of time

T

terracing farming method in which farmers build a series of broad, flat ridges that run down a hillside like stairs

tertiary consumer organism that eats secondary and primary consumers

thermal pollution excessive heating of surface waters such as lakes, rivers, and streams

threatened species species whose numbers are dwindling to a point at which the species could become endangered

topography physical characteristics of the land

transpiration release of water vapor from plants' leaves into the air

tributaries feeder streams

trophic level all organisms in a feeding level that are the same number of steps away from the sun

turbidity amount of suspended matter in water

V

velocity distance water flows during some period of time, such as meters per second or feet per second

W

watershed drainage basin; region drained by, or one that contributes water to, a stream, lake, or other body of water

weathering slow wearing away of rock by wind, water, and temperature fluctuations

weed feeder arthropod (such as an insect), other animal, or pathogen that feeds on weed pests

wetland area that contains unique types of soil, is home to plants adapted to a wet environment, and contains water all year or at certain times during the year

Resource Directory

The following private and government organizations do research, compile data, educate the public, take legal action, and act as advocates to protect the natural environment, wildlife, and public health. Each organization also maintains a Web site (listed below) at which you can find useful information on a number of environmental topics.

Agriculture and Food

Center for Science in the Public Interest
1875 Connecticut Ave. NW, Suite 300
Washington, D.C. 20009
202-332-9110
www.cspinet.org
Advocates for nutrition, health, and food safety. Publishes Nutrition Action Healthletter.

The Land Institute
2440 East Water Well Rd.
Salina, KS 67401
785-823-5376
www.landinstitute.org
Supports the practice of environmentally sustainable agriculture by sponsoring research and educational programs.

Air Quality

Center for Clean Air Policy
940 First St. NE., Suite 1140
Washington, D.C. 20002
202-408-8896
www.ccap.org
Promotes solutions to environmental and energy problems that balance environmental and economic interests.

Center for Environmental Information
55 St. Paul St.
Rochester, NY 14604
585-262-2870
www.rochesterenvironment.org
Provides information to the public and to educational institutions about air and water pollution, especially in western and central New York State.

Ecosystems and Land

American Forests
P.O. Box 2000
Washington, D.C. 20013
202-955-4500
www.americanforests.org
A special research and education program of the American Forestry Association that sponsors research on forest ecosystems and urban forestry and plants trees for environmental restoration.

American Wildlands
40 East Main #2
Bozeman, MT 59715
406-586-8175
www.wildlands.org
Supports the protection of biodiversity in the West, with special attention to the northern Rocky Mountains.

The Nature Conservancy
4245 North Fairfax Dr., Suite 100
Arlington, VA 22203-1606
800-628-6860
www.nature.org
Purchases land to protect it from development. Works to preserve the plants, animals, and natural communities on Earth by protecting the lands and waters they need to survive.

Chesapeake Bay Foundation
Philip Merrill Environmental Center
6 Hemdon Ave.
Annapolis, MD 21403
410-268-8816
www.cbf.org
Pennsylvania State Office (CBF)
The Old Water Works Building
614 North Front St., Suite G
Harrisburg, PA 17101
717-234-5550
Protects and restores Chesapeake Bay ecosystem through programs as well as public education.

Coast Alliance
600 Pennsylvania Ave. SE, Suite 340
Washington, D.C. 20003
202-546-9554
www.coastalliance.org
Informs the public about the value of coastal ecosystems and works to protect coastal resources, ecosystems, and habitat.

National Parks Conservation Association
1300 19th St. NW, Suite 300
Washington, D.C. 20036
800-628-7275
www.npca.org
Dedicated to the protection and proper management of the national parks.

The Sierra Club
85 Second St., 2nd floor
San Francisco, CA 94105
415-977-5500
www.sierraclub.org
Explores and protects wild places, promotes the responsible use of Earth's ecosystems and resources, and educates the public to protect and restore the environment. Publishes Sierra.

**Pocono Environmental
Education Center**
R.D. 2, P.O. Box 1010
Dingman's Ferry, PA 18328
570-828-2319
www.peec.org
*Provides on-site environmental
programs for visitors to its campus
located within the Delaware
Water Gap National Recreation
Area.*

Energy and Mineral Resources

Alliance to Save Energy
1200 18th St. NW, Suite 900
Washington, D.C. 20036
202-857-0666
www.ase.org
*Supports research projects and
educational programs that
promote energy efficiency.*

**American Society of Mining
and Reclamation**
3134 Montavesta Rd.
Lexington, KY 40502
877-701-2086
http://ces.ca.uky.edu/asmr
*Promotes efforts to protect and
restore land disturbed by mining.
Also provides information to the
public.*

**Clean Fuels Development
Coalition**
4641 Montgomery Ave.
Bethesda, MD 20814
301-718-0077
www.cleanfuels.org
*Supports development and
production of fuels that reduce air
pollution and lessen the United
States' dependence on imported oil.*

Government Agencies

Federal

**National Marine Fisheries
Service**
Office of Science and
Technology
1315 East West Highway
Silver Spring, MD 20910
301-713-2367
www.nmfs.noaa.gov
*Federal agency responsible for
listing most threatened and
endangered marine species.
Maintains a list on its Web site.*

National Parks Service
Northeast Region
U.S. Customs House
200 Chestnut St., 5th floor
Philadelphia, PA 19106
215-597-7013
www.nps.gov
*Caretakers of 83.3 million acres
of national parks, monuments,
lakeshores, seashores, and other
lands where wildlife and natural
habitat are generally protected
by law. Web site has links to
information on the major parks.*

**U.S. Department of
Agriculture (USDA)**
Washington, D.C. 20250
**Natural Resources
    Conservation Service**
Pennsylvania State
    Conservationist
One Credit Union Place,
    Suite 340
Harrisburg, PA 17110-2993
717-237-2238
www.usda.gov
*Provides technical, economic, and
marketing assistance to United
States farms and ranchers.
Responsible for safety of meat,
poultry, and eggs. Steward of
nation's 192 million acres of
national forest and rangelands.*

U.S. Department of Energy
Philadelphia Regional Office
1880 John F. Kennedy Blvd.,
    Suite 501
Philadelphia, PA 19103-7483
215-656-6950
www.doe.gov
*Promotes energy efficiency and
development of renewable and
alternative energy sources. Web
site has background on all energy
sources, energy conservation, and
energy efficiency.*

**U.S. Environmental
Protection Agency**
Ariel Rios Building
1200 Pennsylvania Ave. NW
Washington, D.C. 20460
www.epa.gov
U.S. EPA Region 3
2650 Arch St. (3CG00)
Philadelphia, PA 19103-2474
800-438-2474 or 215-814-5000
*Does research, monitors pollutants,
and writes and enforces regulations that seek to protect the
natural environment and public
health. Web site is a good source
of information on major environmental issues, pollutants,
ecosystems, health, and laws and
regulations.*

U.S. Fish and Wildlife Service
Pennsylvania Ecological
    Services (Field Office)
315 South Allen St., Suite 322
State College, PA 16801-4850
**US Fish and Wildlife Service
    Region 5** (includes PA)
300 Westgate Center Drive
Hadley, MA 01035
413-253-8300
www.fws.gov
*Conserves, protects, and enhances
fish, wildlife, and plants and their
habitats. Lead agency in listing
most threatened and endangered
plants and animals in the United
States. Maintains a list on its
Web site.*

State of Pennsylvania

Pennsylvania Department of Agriculture

2301 North Cameron St.
Harrisburg, PA 17110-9408
717-787-4737
www.pda.state.pa.us
Works on behalf of agriculture, food safety, and animal health in Pennsylvania.

Pennsylvania Department of Conservation and Natural Resources

Rachel Carson State Office
  Building, 7th floor
P.O. Box 8767
Harrisburg, PA 17105-8767
717-787-2869
www.dcnr.state.pa.us
Maintains and preserves Pennsylvania's state parks and state forests. Provides information on the state's ecological and geological resources.

Pennsylvania Department of Environmental Protection

Rachel Carson State Office
  Building, 16th floor
P.O. Box 2063
Harrisburg, PA 17105-2063
717-772-0801 (chief
  information officer)
www.dep.state.pa.us.
Protects Pennsylvania's air, land, and water from pollution and provides for the health and safety of its citizens through a cleaner environment.

Integrated Pest Management and Pesticides

Beyond Pesticides

701 E St., Suite 200
Washington, D.C. 20003
202-543-5450
www.beyondpesticides.org/main.htm.
Committed to pesticide safety and the adoption of alternative pest management strategies that reduce or eliminate dependence on toxic chemicals.

Pennsylvania Integrated Pest Management Program

Department of Entomology
Penn State University
501 ASI Building
University Park, PA 16802
814-863-4641
Pennsylvania Department of Agriculture IPM Coordinator
Bureau of Plant Industry
2301 North Cameron St.
Harrisburg, PA 17110-9408
717-772-5204
paipm.cas.psu.edu
Collaboration between Pennsylvania State University and the Pennsylvania Department of Agriculture that seeks to promote effective and safe pest control alternatives.

Pesticide Action Network North America

49 Powell St., Suite 500
San Francisco, CA 94102
415-981-1991
www.pesticideinfo.org
Maintains a database that provides information on the toxicity of pesticides and their health effects.

Laws and Regulations

Earth Justice

426 17th St., 6th floor
Oakland, CA 94612
510-550-6700
www.earthjustice.org
Dedicated to protecting natural resources, wildlife, and public health through activity as a nonprofit public interest law firm.

Environmental Defense

257 Park Avenue South
New York, NY 10010
212-505-2100
www.edf.org
Links science, economics, and law to protect clean air and water and to help maintain a healthy and nourishing food system and flourishing ecosystems.

Environmental Law Foundation

1736 Franklin St., 9th floor
Oakland, CA 94612
510-208-4555
www.envirolaw.org
Works for preservation and enhancement of human health and the environment by enforcing environmental law on behalf of ordinary citizens.

Natural Resources Defense Council

40 West 20th St.
New York, NY 10011
212-727-2700
www.nrdc.org
Uses law and science to protect the planet's wildlife and wild places and to ensure a safe and healthy environment. Publishes On Earth.

Population

**Population Association
of America**
8630 Fenton St., Suite 722
Silver Spring, MD 20910-3812
301-505-6710
www.popassoc.org
*Studies the social and scientific
aspects of changes in human populations. Publishes Demography.*

**Population Reference
Bureau**
1875 Connecticut Ave. NW,
    Suite 520
Washington, D.C. 20009-5728
800-877-9881 or 202-483-1100
www.prb.org
*Compiles information and
publishes materials on population
trends worldwide.*

Solid Waste and Recycling

Earth's 911
5110 N. 44th St., Suite L120
Phoenix, AZ 85018
602-224-5444
www.earth911.org
*Provides the public with
community-specific resources such
as the names of local recycling
centers and household hazardous
waste disposal sites.*

Water Resources

Clean Water Action
4455 Connecticut Ave. NW,
    Suite A300
Washington, D.C. 20008-2328
202-895-0420
www.cleanwateraction.org
*Lobbies for clean, safe, and
affordable drinking water.*

WaterWiser
6666 West Quincy Ave.
Denver, CO 80236
800-926-7337
www.waterwiser.org
*Site organized by the American
Water Works Association and the
U.S. Bureau of Reclamation
that supplies information on
water efficiency
and conservation.*

Wildlife and Endangered Species

**Center for Plant
Conservation**
P.O. Box 299
St. Louis, MO 63166
314-577-9450
www.mobot.org/CPC
*Dedicated to the conservation of
rare plants.*

Defenders of Wildlife
1101 14th St. NW, #1400
Washington, D.C. 20005
202-682-9400
www.defenders.org
*Promotes the preservation and
protection of all native wild
animals and plants, with special
focus on prevention of extinction
and loss of biodiversity.*

**Endangered Species
Coalition**
1101 14th St. NW, #1400
Washington, D.C. 20005
202-772-3231
www.stopextinction.org
*Opposes attempts to weaken the
Endangered Species Act.*

National Audubon Society
700 Broadway
New York, NY 10003
212-979-3000
www.audubon.org
*Dedicated to conserving and
restoring natural ecosystems to
maintain biological diversity.
Focuses on birds as well as other
wildlife. Publishes Audubon.*

National Wildlife Federation
11100 Wildlife Center Dr.
Reston, VA 20190-5362
703-438-6000
www.nwf.org
*Protects wildlife, wild places, and
the environment.*

Ocean Conservancy
1725 DeSales St., Suite 500
Washington, D.C. 20036
202-429-5609
www.cmc-ocean.org
*Provides educational and public
information to build support for
preserving the health, diversity,
and beauty of ocean ecosystems.*

The Wilderness Society
1615 M St. NW
Washington, D.C. 20036
800-843-9453
www.wilderness.org
*Works to protect U.S. wilderness
and develop a nationwide
network of wild lands.*

**The Wildlife Conservation
Society**
2300 Southern Boulevard
Bronx, NY 10460
718-220-5100
www.wcs.org
*Works from Bronx Zoo
headquarters to save wildlife and
wild lands throughout the world.*

World Wildlife Fund
1250 24th St. NW
Washington, D.C. 20037
202-293-4800
www.worldwildlife.org
*Provides programs and services to
promote the protection of
endangered species worldwide.
Purchases natural areas to
preserve particular species.*

Index

Page numbers followed by *ls* indicates a lab study; *cs* indicates a case study; *fs* indicates a field study; *ys* indicates a You Solve It! feature.

A

Abiotic factors
  of aquatic ecosystems, 15–18, 20–21*fs*, 158
  as defining factors in biomes, 157–158
  definition of, 148
  population limitation by, 152
Acid mine drainage
  aquatic ecosystems and, 18, 53*cs*, 54–55, 178*ys*
  detection of, 84
  formation of, 218
  laws/regulations concerning, 239
  soil pollution by, 74
Acid rain
  formation of, 55, 76–77*ls*, 212–213
  human health and, 213
  impact on forests, 149, 213
  impact on streams, 18, 213, 220
  nitrogen in environment and, 168
  in Pennsylvania, 53*cs*, 212–213
Adaptations, 186–188, 189*fs*, 192, 193*cs*
Aerosols, 212, 215
Agricultural Revolution, 100–101*ys*
Agriculture, 218–219
  destruction of habitats for, 160
  drought relief for, 79*ys*
  effect on wetlands/watersheds, 27–28, 215–218
  effects of volcanic eruptions on, 85
  energy costs for, 118*ys*
  erosion and, 219
  history of, 99–101*ys*
  IPM and, 138–139
  laws/regulations concerning, 103, 239
  markets of, 95, 98
  methods of, 82*cs*, 94–95, 98, 109–111
  organic farming, 124–125*ys*
  pest control methods of, 129–131, 134–135
  pollution by, 2, 74, 81, 219
  price of products from, 108*ys*
  processing of products, 102
  production of, 93–95, 98, 102, 116
  regions of in United States, 103–105
  renewable resources of, 38
  research and development in, 103
  technology used in, 48–49, 94–95, 100*ys*, 101*ys*, 116–117

transportation/distribution of products, 102, 112*fs*
Air pollution
  acid/basic rain and, 76–77*ls*
  adaptations to, 193*cs*
  characteristics of pollutants, 212
  in Chesapeake Bay area, 83*cs*
  detection of, 84
  from human activities, 212–215
  illness associated with, 71–73
  impact on ecosystems, 149
  laws/regulations concerning, 234–235, 241, 244
  from manufacturing, 59, 75
  pollutants, 71–73, 234, 241
  from smelting, 219–220
  solid waste disposal and, 60–61
  sources of, 71, 212
  use of alternate energy sources and, 56
  use of fossil fuels and, 42, 55, 56, 71–72
  wetlands as preventative, 24
Algae
  in aquatic ecosystems, 14–18
  dissolved solids and, 17
  iron deposits and, 40
  symbiotic relationships of, 181
Algal bloom, 17, 29, 86*ys*, 110, 168, 216–217
Allegheny National Forest, 150, 170–171*cs*
Allergies, 73
Alternate Fuels Incentive Grant Program, 74
Altitude, 158, 161
Amphibians
  in aquatic ecosystems, 14, 23–24
  effect of droughts on, 33
  poachers of, 246–247*ys*
Animals
  adaptations of, 186–188
  of aquatic biomes, 162
  biotechnology and, 117
  as biotic factors, 147
  as consumers, 150–151
  control of habitats by, 156
  of desert biomes, 161
  domestication of, 95, 99*ys*
  effect on wetlands/watersheds, 27, 215
  factors determining location of, 103
  of forested biomes, 159
  of grasslands, 160, 161
  human impact on, 219–220
  improvement of species, 101*ys*
  as livestock in United States, 104, 105
  pollution and, 74, 217
  processing of meats, 102

role in nitrogen cycle, 167
role in water cycle, 165
symbiotic relationships of, 181, 184
Aquatic ecosystems
  abiotic limiting factors in, 148
  acid mine drainage and, 18, 53*cs*, 54–55, 178*ys*
  acid rain and, 55
  biology of, 14
  biomonitoring of, 87
  El Niño and, 84–85, 86*ys*
  factors affecting, 15–18
  global warming and, 53*cs*
  human impact on, 215–218
  introduction of exotic species to, 145–146
  of Lake Erie, 92*ys*
  types of, 146
Aquifers, 165
Atmosphere, human impact on, 212–215
  See also Air pollution; Global warming
Autotrophs
  in aquatic ecosystems, 14, 24
  role in carbon cycle, 166
  role in food web, 150
  use of sunlight, 39
  See also Producers

B

Bacillus thuringiensis (Bt), 123, 130, 135
Bacteria
  as biotic factors, 147
  decomposition by, 16, 18, 23, 45, 151, 167
  nitrogen cycle and, 167–168
  as parasites, 181
  as pathogens, 27, 50, 69, 113, 131, 184, 215, 216
  pest control with, 123, 130, 135
Barbed wire, 117
Base level of rivers, 7*ys*
Bed load of streams, 3
Biodiversity
  ecological succession and, 173
  environmental health and, 87–89
  factors affecting, 15–18
  of forested biomes, 159
  as foundation of ecosystems, 181, 184
  homeostasis and, 181
  investigation of, 90–91*fs*
  natural selection and, 192
  of Perkiomen Creek, 19*ys*
  protection of, 243
  types of, 180
Biological infestations, 50, 52*cs*, 86*ys*

by chemical fertilizers, 110
diseases from, 68–71
human activities affecting, 2, 29
laws/regulations concerning, 79*ys*, 234, 236, 237, 239, 241, 243
monitoring of, 39
natural events affecting, 2, 50
nonpoint source pollutants, 81
by pathogens, 50
by pesticides, 139
sources of, 68–70, 135
See also Water pollution
Drive Clean Pennsylvania program, 74
Drought
effect on resource availability, 50
effect on wetlands/watersheds, 32–33
El Niño and, 84–85
human health and, 86*ys*
impact on forests, 52*cs*
laws providing relief for, 79*ys*
in Pennsylvania in 1999, 34–35*cs*
Dysentery, 69

E

East Side Project, 170–171*cs*
E. coli, 113, 114*ys*
Ecological succession, 172–175, 176–177*fs*
Ecology, principles of, 80
Ecosystems
abiotic factors affecting, 15–18, 20–21*fs*, 148–149
adaptations in, 186–188, 189*fs*
agricultural destruction of, 111
alterations by IPM, 139
aquatic, 14–18, 29–30, 92*ys*, 146
balance in, 119
biodiversity of, 87–89, 90–91*fs*, 180–181, 184
biology of, 14
biomes of, 157–162
biomonitoring of, 87
biotic factors affecting, 14, 20–21*fs*, 147
carrying capacity of, 152–153
definition of, 146–147
earth as, 80
El Niño and, 84–85, 86*ys*
fire's role in, 33, 50, 160, 161, 175
food webs within, 149–151
forests, 52–53*cs*, 98, 121–124, 146, 170–171*cs*
freshwater, 19*ys*, 20–21*fs*
global warming and, 33, 53*cs*
homeostasis of, 145–146, 157
human activities affecting, 27–29, 55, 78*ys*, 145–146
impact of mining on, 218

introduction of exotic species in, 122–124, 145–146, 156
laws/regulations concerning, 231–247
monitoring of, 29–30, 87
natural events affecting, 32–33, 50, 84–85, 86*ys*, 157, 173, 174–175
of ponds, 163–164*ys*
protection of, 192
restoration of, 242–243*cs*
in soil, 109
species extinction and, 88–89, 92*ys*
stages of succession in, 172–175
symbiosis in, 181, 184
wetlands, 22–25, 27–29
Educational programs
Chesapeake 2000 Agreement, 243–244*cs*
of Conservation International, 57
for integrated pest management, 120
on streamside buffer zones, 31
Watershed Educational Program, 32
Effluent, 29, 68
Electricity generation
alternative sources for, 44–45, 60–61
coal-burning power plants and, 55–56
distribution, 56
in hydroelectric plants, 56
in nuclear power plants, 56
in Pennsylvania, 46, 47*ys*, 55–56
El Niño, 84–85, 86*ys*
Endangered species, 179–197
American crocodile, 223
bald eagle, 194–195
bog turtle, 126–127*cs*, 184–185*ys*
definition of, 195
factors affecting, 195–196
Florida panther, 223
gray wolf, 245
Indiana bat, 190–191*ys*
laws/regulations concerning, 195, 232, 238, 241, 244, 246–247*ys*
protection of, 184–185*ys*, 190–191*ys*, 192, 196
serpentine asters, 227–228*ys*
spotted owl controversy, 244–245
urbanization and, 223
as vulnerability indicator, 29
wetland habitats for, 23
Endangered Species Act (ESA, 1972)
agencies of, 196
establishment of, 238
goals of, 192
provisions of, 195
reptiles/amphibian poaching and, 246–247*ys*
spotted owl controversy and, 244–245
Energy
alternative resources, 44, 60–61, 210–211*ls*
conservation of, 57, 202, 204–205*ys*

consumption/production of, 42, 51*ys*
costs of, 118*ys*
distribution of, 56
from fossil fuels, 41–42, 55–56
increasing demand for, 226
renewable sources of, 39
transfer of in ecosystems, 149–151
worldwide reserves, 200–201
Environmental Impact Statement (EIS), 233–234
Environmental Protection Agency (EPA)
ambient air standards of, 234
chlorofluorocarbons ban, 215
food processing and, 113
lawsuits against, 239, 240
lead in gasoline and, 229, 241
pesticide regulation by, 134, 137, 236
resource conservation by, 57
toxic substance monitoring by, 236–237
on wetland impairment, 28
Erosion
effect of, 151
factors affecting, 8–9*ls*, 33, 109, 111
impact on watersheds/wetlands, 32
laws/regulations concerning, 237
prevention of, 81
role in carbon cycle, 166
stream turbidity and, 17
Estivation, 188
Eutrophication, 216–217
Evaporation, 1–2
Exotic species
laws/regulations concerning, 232
niches of, 156
as pests, 122–124, 145–146
Extinction
of blue pike, 92*ys*
definition of, 195
of dinosaurs, 179
factors affecting, 88–89, 195–196
impact on ecosystems, 179–180
laws/regulations on endangered species, 232
of passenger pigeon, 89, 195
as vulnerability indicator, 29
Exxon Valdez oil spill, 78*ys*, 217

F

Farming. *See* Agriculture
Fault lines, 5
Federal Insecticide, Fungicide, and Rodenticide Act (FIFRA, 1972), 236
Fertilization, 120–121, 181
Fertilizers
farm production and, 94, 111, 116–117
laws/regulations concerning, 236
restoration of soils by, 110

Art Acknowledgements

All Illustrations by ElectraGraphics except; **197:** Joe Sohn/Visions of America
All Maps by Ortelius Design except; **27:** ElectraGraphics

Photo Acknowledgements

1: NASA Johnson Space Center; **4:** Hal S. Korber; **10:** Jeff Greenberg/PhotoEdit; **14:** Hal S. Korber; **16:** Hal S. Korber; **22:** Hal S. Korber; **23:** Hal S. Korber; **24:** Hal S. Korber; **28:** Bob Nichols, USDA Natural Resource Conservation Service; **29:** Hal S. Korber; **31:** Edward Dix/DCNR Bureau of Forestry; **32:** Michelle D Bridwell/PhotoEdit; **33:** Hal S. Korber; **37:** Michelle D. Bridwell/PhotoEdit; **38:** Larry Lefever/Grant Heilman Photography, Inc.; **39:** Michael P. Gadomski; **40:** Michael P. Gadomski; **44:** Steve Mulligan; **48:** Michael P. Gadomski; **50:** Mark E Gibson/Visuals Unlimited; **52:** Steve Mulligan; **53:** Bernd Wittich/Visuals Unlimited; **54:** Hal S. Korber; **55:** Roger Ressmeyer/Corbis; **57:** Howie Garber/Getty Images; **59:** AISI/Visuals Unlimitied; **61:** M. Yamashita/Woodfin Camp/PictureQuest; **66:** Jeff Greenberg/Visuals Unlimited; **67:** Larry Lefever/Grant Heilman Photography, Inc.; **71:** Steve Dunwell/Getty Images; **72:** C P George/Visuals Unlimited; **73:** William Taufic/Corbis; **75:** Runk/Schoenberger/Grant Heilman Photography, Inc.; **78:** Susan Ban Etten/PhotoEdit; **80:** NASA; **81:** Dana White/PhotoEdit; **83:** Cathy Melloan /PhotoEdit; **87:** Gary Meslaros/Visuals Unlimited, Inc.; **88:** David Frazier/Getty Images; **93:** Larry Lefever/Grant Heilman Photography, Inc.; **95:** Grant Heilman/Grant Heilman Photography, Inc.; **98:** Greg Neise/Visuals Unlimited; **104:** Arthur C. Smith III/Grant Heilman Photography, Inc.; **105:** Alan Pitcairn/Grant Heilman Photography, Inc.; **106:** Holt Confer/Grant Heilman Photography, Inc.; **110:** Tim McCabe, USDA Natural Resources Conservation Service.; **110:** Tim McCabe, USDA Natural Resources Conservation Service.; **110:** Tim McCabe, USDA Natural Resources Conservation Service.; **113:** Peter Dean/Grant Heilman Photography, Inc.; **116:** Science Photo Library/Photo Researchers; **117:** Michael Newman/PhotoEdit; **119:** Barry L. Runk/Grant Heilman Photography, Inc.; **119:** Penn State University/IPM Extension; **119:** Runk/Schoenberger/Grant Heilman Photography, Inc.; **120:** Runk/Schoenberger/Grant Heilman Photography, Inc.; **121:** Robert L. Anderson/USDA Forest Service; **124:** Ken Hammond/USDA; **127:** Brad Mogen/Visuals Unlimited; **129:** Penn State University/IPM Extension; **130:** Inga Spence/Visuals Unlimited; **134:** Larry Lefever/Grant Heilman Photography, Inc.; **137:** David Young Wolff/PhotoEdit; **138:** Penn State University/IPM Extension; **139:** AP Photo/Ed Betz; **139:** Johann Schumacher Design; **140:** Runk/Schroenberger/Grant Heilman Photography, Inc.; **145:** Barry Runk/STAN/Grant Heilman Photography, Inc.; **156:** Mark E. Gibson; **160:** Arthur C. Smith III/Grant Heilman Photography, Inc.; **174:** Renee Skelton; **179:** Paul A. Souders/Corbis; **180:** Frank Siteman/PhotoEdit; **184:** A. Wolfe/Photo Researchers; **185:** Fred Habegger/Grant HeilmanPhotography, Inc.; **186:** Ruth Cole/Animals, Animals/Earth Scenes; **186:** Ingrid Van Den Berg/Animals, Animals/Earth Scenes; **187:** Runk/Schoenberger/Grant Heilman Photography, Inc.; **187:** Runk/Schoenberger/Grant Heilman Photography, Inc.; **188:** Runk/Schoenberger/Grant Heilman Photography, Inc.; **191:** Richard Thom/Visuals Unlimited, Inc.; **193:** Breck P Kent/Animals, Animals/Earth Scenes; **193:** Breck P Kent/Animals, Animals/Earth Scenes; **197:** Lynn Stone/Animals, Animals/Earth Scenes; **199:** Mark E Gibon/Visuals Unlimited; **206:** Jeff Greenberg/Visuals Unlimited; **208:** A. Ramey/PhotoEdit; **216:** Peter K. Ziminski/Visuals Unlimited; **217:** William J. Weber/Visuals Unlimited; **222:** Photo by Brooks Studio. Courtesy of the Lear/Carson Collection, Connecticut College.; **223:** Robin Karpan/Visuals Unlimited; **228:** Dr. Ann F. Rhoads; **229:** Jeff Greenberg/PhotoEdit; **230:** Bettmann/Corbis; **236:** Frank M. Hanna/Visuals Unlimited; **237:** Jeff Greenberg/Visuals Unlimited; **238:** S. Maslowski/Visuals Unlimited; **239:** The Yucca Mountain Project; **241:** Beth Davidow/Visuals Unlimited; **245:** Dan Lamont/Corbis; **246:** Hollingsworth, John and Karen/U.S. Fish and Wildlife Service